AN INTRODUCTION TO

PROBABILITY AND MATHEMATICAL STATISTICS

GEORGE BACHMAN and LAWRENCE NARICI. Functional Analysis

P. R. MASANI, R. C. PATEL, and D. J. PATIL. Elementary Calculus

WILLIAM PERVIN. Foundations of General Topology

ALBERT L. RABENSTEIN. Introduction to Ordinary Differential Equations

JAMES SINGER. Elements of Numerical Analysis

EDUARD L. STIEFEL. An Introduction to Numerical Mathematics

HOWARD G. TUCKER. An Introduction to Probability and Mathematical Statistics

CHIH-HAN SAH. Abstract Algebra

DONALD W. BLACKETT. Elementary Topology: A Combinatorial and Algebraic Approach

LEOPOLDO V. TORALBALLA. Calculus with Analytic Geometry and Linear Algebra

AN INTRODUCTION TO

PROBABILITY AND MATHEMATICAL STATISTICS

Howard G. Tucker

Department of Mathematics
University of California, Riverside

NEW YORK **ACADEMIC PRESS** LONDON

ACADEMIC PRESS INC.
111 FIFTH AVENUE
NEW YORK, NEW YORK 10003

United Kingdom Edition
Published by
ACADEMIC PRESS INC. (LONDON) LTD.
Berkeley Square House
London W.1

Library of Congress Catalog Card Number 62-13131

Fourth Printing, 1967

PRINTED IN THE UNITED STATES OF AMERICA

To My Mother and Father

Preface

This text in probability and mathematical statistics is designed for a one-year course meeting three hours per week. It is designed for undergraduate university students who are majoring in mathematics, who are juniors or seniors, and who have already completed the standard freshman-sophomore sequence of calculus courses. It is assumed that they are taking at least one other undergraduate mathematics course concurrently; for example, this course might be advanced calculus, linear algebra, modern algebra, differential equations, set theory, or undergraduate topology. It is not that any knowledge in any of these courses is a prerequisite to the study of this book, but simply that at the time the student is using this book he should be immersed in mathematics. Students who are majoring in physics and who are favorably inclined toward abstract mathematics are included in the class of students for whom this book is intended.

This book is not intended for anyone who is primarily interested in results and recipes. It should not be used as a text for service courses offered for assorted majors in departments other than the mathematics and statistics departments. This book is designed *only* for those students who love mathematics and *not* for those who regard mathematics only as a tool.

As for the book itself, the student and instructor are hereby forewarned that this is not a recipe book of statistical procedures. It is not a compendium of statistical lore and is not even to be treated as a reference book. Many topics usually found in junior-senior level statistics texts are purposely omitted, e.g., sufficient statistics, the chi-square test, moment generating functions, sequential analysis, and nonparametric inference. In addition, it is not an applied problem workbook. There are no long lists of problems which require finding out whether one chewing gum chews longer than another or whether a human being is less likely to get lung cancer from one brand of cigarettes than another, i.e., this book is not saturated with a repetitive list of numerical problems. Above all, this is intended to be a mathematics book. Its title accurately reflects the original desire of giving "an introduction" to probability theory and mathematical statistics. The quoted pair of words found in the title of this book should be considered in their exact meaning. The principal aim is to present the student with a solid foundation of probability theory from the mathematical point of view and to use this to introduce the essential ideas *in depth* of three fields of statistical inference: point estimation, tests of hypotheses, and confidence intervals. The entire presentation is decidedly from the point of view of giving a sound mathematics course and of providing a meeting place for other junior-senior level mathematics courses that the student is now studying. Although the applications are not stressed and are not of paramount interest, they are certainly not ignored. Indeed, the exciting thing about probability and statistics brought out in the text is that here is where purely abstract mathematics and physical reality do come very close together.

The exercises found at the end of each section constitute a very important part of this book. All of them should be assigned to the student as he proceeds through the course. In keeping with the intended spirit of this book, most exercises are of a theoretical nature. In solving the exercises at the end of a section the student will often have to prove corollaries to the theorems proved in that section. Also, he will frequently have to supply missing steps to theorems proved in that section. Thus, the exercises are not merely applications of results just proved; rather, they involve the student in the entire mathematical development of that section and force him to go over the details many times. Some of the exercises are rather trivial, but some are quite difficult and will prove to be a definite challenge to the better students. As was said before, these exercises are a very important part of the book, and as each section of the text is completed, *all of the exercises* should be assigned to the student.

A few specific features of this book are the following:

1. Random variables are treated as measurable functions.
2. Sampling is treated in terms of product spaces.
3. Distributions are derived by the transformation method.
4. Probability is given an axiomatic treatment.
5. A chapter on the matrix theory needed is inserted in the middle of the book.
6. The Neyman theory of confidence intervals is given a systematic treatment.
7. A more natural definition of the multivariate normal distribution is given.
8. Expectation is given a unified treatment; the expectation of a random variable X is defined to be

$$\int_0^\infty P[X > x]dx - \int_{-\infty}^0 P[X \leqq x]dx,$$

provided that both of these improper Riemann integrals are finite. Formulas and properties in the discrete and absolutely continuous cases are then derived from this definition.

The contents of this book were used in a one-year course which I taught four times during the last six years and, except for the last half of Section 11.4, constitute no more nor no less than the material I actually presented in class. My colleague, Professor Richard C. Gilbert, taught this same course twice and based his lectures on notes of mine which eventually became this book. I have always been able to cover the material in this book in two semesters, each of fifteen weeks, in three hours of lecture per week. The fall semester always ends somewhere in the middle of Chapter 8. On the last day of the fall semester I always give a brief introduction to hypothesis testing and present the notion of randomized tests as given in the example in Section 11.4. In the spring semester I begin wherever I left off at the end of the fall semester and proceed to the end of the book. I usually spend from four to six weeks on Chapter 9 (Matrix Theory). Even when every student in the class already knows some matrix theory, I assume the contrary, and we proceed at a uniform rate through this chapter. (It usually turns out that my assumption was correct.) During the time spent on this chapter the homework assignments consist of complete, detailed proofs of the theorems covered each hour.

I wish to express my appreciation to my colleague, Professor Richard C. Gilbert, for many helpful discussions which greatly improved this book. I am indebted to Professor Sir Ronald A. Fisher, F. R. S., Cambridge, and to Dr. Frank Yates, F. R. S., Rothamsted, also to Messrs. Oliver and Boyd, Ltd., Edinburgh for permission to include Table IV which is an abridgment of their Table III from their book *Statistical Tables for Biological, Agricultural and Medical Research*. Mrs. Julia Rubalcava typed the manuscript speedily and accurately, and I wish to acknowledge my gratitude to her.

Riverside, California
January, 1962

HOWARD G. TUCKER

Contents

CHAPTER 1

Events and Probabilities

1.1 Combinatorial Probability

The notion of the probability of an event is approached by three different methods. One method, perhaps the first historically, is to repeat an experiment or game many times under identical conditions and compute the relative frequency with which an event occurs. This means: divide the total number of times that the specific event occurs by the total number of times the experiment is performed or the game is played. This ratio is called the *relative frequency*. Although this method of arriving at the notion of probability is the most primitive and unsophisticated, it is the most meaningful to the practical individual and the working scientist or engineer who has to apply the results of probability theory to real-life situations. Accordingly, whatever results one obtains in the theory of probability and statistics, one should be able to interpret them in terms of relative frequency.

A second way of approaching the notion of probability is from an axiomatic point of view. That is, a minimal list of axioms is set down which assumes certain properties of probabilities. From this minimal set of assumptions the further properties of probability are deduced and applied. The axiomatic approach will be used in this book.

The third method of arriving at the notion of probability is limited in application but is extremely useful. It is the subject considered in this section. This method is briefly stated as follows in terms of certain undefined words, which we introduce in quotation marks. Let us suppose that an experiment or game has a certain number of mutually exclusive "equally likely" outcomes. Let us also suppose that a certain event can occur in any one of a specified number of these "equally likely" outcomes. Then the probability of the event is *defined* to be the number of "equally likely" ways in which the event can occur divided by the total number of possible "equally likely" outcomes. It must be emphasized here that the number of equally likely ways in which the event can occur must be from *among* the total number of equally likely outcomes. When we mentioned above that this method is limited, we meant that in some games or experiments not all the possible outcomes are "equally likely." Before we give applications of this method, it will be necessary to review some notions from high school algebra.

Let us suppose that we have n different objects, and we want to arrange k of these in a row (where, of course, $k \leqq n$). We want to know in how many ways we can accomplish this feat. As an example, suppose there are five members of a club, call them A, B, C, D, E, and we want to know in how many ways we can select a chairman and a secretary. When we select the arrangement (C, A), we mean that C is the chairman and A is the secretary. In this case $n = 5$ and $k = 2$. The different arrangements are listed as follows:

$$\begin{array}{cccc} (A, B) & (A, C) & (A, D) & (A, E) \\ (B, A) & (B, C) & (B, D) & (B, E) \\ (C, A) & (C, B) & (C, D) & (C, E) \\ (D, A) & (D, B) & (D, C) & (D, E) \\ (E, A) & (E, B) & (E, C) & (E, D). \end{array}$$

One easily sees that there are 20 such arrangements. This number 20 can also be obtained by the following reasoning: there are five ways in which the chairman can be selected (which accounts for the five horizontal rows of pairs), *for each* chairman selected there are four ways of selecting the secretary (which accounts for the four vertical columns), and consequently there are 20 such pairs. In general, if we want to arrange k out of n objects, we reason as follows. There are n ways of selecting the first object. For each way we select the first object there are $n - 1$ ways of selecting the second object. Hence the total number of ways in which the first two objects can be selected is $n(n - 1)$. For every way in which the first two objects are selected, there are $n - 2$ ways of selecting the third object. Thus the number of ways in which the first three objects can be selected is $n(n - 1)(n - 2)$. From this one can easily observe that the number of ways in which the first k objects can be selected is $n(n - 1)(n - 2)\cdots(n - (k - 1))$, which can also be written as the ratio of factorials: $n!/(n - k)!$. (Recall: $5! = 1 \times 2 \times 3 \times 4 \times 5$.) This is also referred to as the number of permutations of n things taken k at a time.

In the above arrangements (or permutations), due regard must be given to the order in which the k items were selected. Suppose, however, that one is interested only in the number of ways k things can be selected but is not interested in the order or arrangement. For example, in the case of the club discussed above, the ways in which two members can be selected out of the five to form a committee are as follows:

$$\begin{array}{llll} (A, B) & (A, C) & (A, D) & (A, E) \\ (B, C) & (B, D) & (B, E) & \\ (C, D) & (C, E) & & \\ (D, E). & & & \end{array}$$

We do not list (D, B) as before because the committee denoted by (D, B) and the committee denoted by (B, D) are the same. Thus, now we have only half the number of selections. In general, if we want to find the number of ways in which we can select k things out of n things, we reason it out as follows: there are $n!/(n-k)!$ ways of arranging (or permuting) n things taken k at a time. However, we have too large a selection, since each time we obtain k particular things there are $k!$ ways of arranging them. Hence we want to divide the number of ways of permuting n things taken k at a time by $k!$ to obtain the desired answer. The number of ways in which we can select k objects out of n objects is usually referred to as the number of combinations of n things taken k at a time and is denoted by the binomial coefficient:

$$\binom{n}{k} = \frac{n!}{k!(n-k)!}.$$

We shall also need the binomial theorem which states that

$$(a+b)^n = \sum_{k=0}^{n} \binom{n}{k} a^k b^{n-k}$$

for every positive integer n, or, what amounts to the same thing,

$$(a+b)^n = \binom{n}{0} a^0 b^n + \binom{n}{1} a^1 b^{n-1} + \binom{n}{2} a^2 b^{n-2} + \cdots + \binom{n}{n} a^n b^0.$$

Naturally, $0!$ is defined to be equal to one.

Now let us solve some problems. In each case we shall want to find the probability, P, of a certain event. Accordingly, we first determine the total number of all "equally likely" outcomes. Then we determine that number of "equally likely" ways among these in which this event can occur. Finally, we divide this last number by the preceding number to obtain P.

Example 1. The numbers $1, 2, \cdots, n$ are arranged in random order, i.e., the $n!$ ways in which these n numbers can be arranged are assumed to be equally likely. We are to find the probability that the numbers 1 and 2 appear as neighbors in the order named.

As we have just noted, there are $n!$ ways in which these integers can be arranged. In order to compute that number of these ways in which the indicated event can occur, we reason as follows: there are $n - 1$ positions permitted for 1, for each position available for 1 there is only one position available for 2, and for every selection of positions for 1 and 2 there are $(n - 2)!$ ways in which the rest of the integers can be placed. Consequently,

$$P = \frac{(n-1)\cdot 1\cdot (n-2)!}{n!} = \frac{(n-1)!}{n!} = \frac{1}{n}.$$

Before beginning example 2, we should explain what is meant by selecting a random digit (or random number). One takes 10 tags and marks 0 on the first tag, 1 on the second tag, 2 on the third tag, $\cdots$, and 9 on the tenth tag. Then one puts these tags in a hat (or in an urn). If we say "select n random digits" or "sample n times with replacement," we mean that one selects a tag "at random," notes the number on it and records it, *returns the tag to the container*, and repeats this action $n - 1$ times more.

Example 2. We are to find the probability P that among k random digits neither 0 nor 1 appears.

The total number of possible outcomes is obtained as follows. There are 10 possibilities for selecting the first digit. *For each way* in which the first digit is selected there are 10 ways of selecting the second digit. So there are 10^2 ways of selecting the first two digits. For each way in which the first two digits are selected there are 10 ways of selecting the third digit. Consequently there are 10^3 ways of selecting the first three digits. In general, then, the number of ways in which the first k digits can be selected is 10^k. Now we consider the event: neither 0 nor 1 appears. In how many "equally likely" ways out of the 10^k possible outcomes can this event occur? In selecting the k random digits, it is clear that with the first random digit there are eight ways in which it can occur. The same goes for the second, third, and on up to the kth random digit. Hence, out of the 10^k total possible "equally likely" outcomes there are 8^k outcomes in which this event can occur. Thus $P = 8^k/10^k$.

Example 3. Now let us determine the probability P that among k random digits the digit zero appears exactly 3 times (where $3 \leqq k$).

Again, the total number of equally likely outcomes is 10^k. Among the k trials (i.e., k different objects) there are $\binom{k}{3}$ ways of selecting the 3 trials in which the zero appears. For each way of selecting the 3 trials in which only zero occurs there are 9^{k-3} ways in which the outcomes of the remaining $k - 3$ trials can occur. Thus $P = \binom{k}{3} 9^{k-3}/10^k$.

Example 4. A box contains 90 white balls and 10 red balls. If 9 balls are selected at random without replacement, what is the probability that 6 of them are white?

In this problem we easily compute that there are $\binom{100}{9}$ ways of selecting the 9 balls. Since there are $\binom{90}{6}$ ways of selecting 6 white balls out of 90 white balls, and since for each way one selects 6 white balls there are $\binom{10}{3}$ ways of selecting 3 red balls out of 10 red balls, we see that there are $\binom{90}{6}\binom{10}{3}$ ways of getting 6 white balls when we select 9 without replacement. Consequently,

$$P = \frac{\binom{90}{6}\binom{10}{3}}{\binom{100}{9}}.$$

Example 5. There are n men standing in a row, among whom are two men named A and B. We would like to find the probability P that there are r men between A and B.

There are two ways of solving this problem. In the first place there are $\binom{n}{2}$ ways in which one can select two places for A and B to stand, and among these there are $n - r - 1$ ways in which one can pick two positions with r positions between them. So $P = (n - r - 1)/\binom{n}{2}$. Another way of solving this problem is to say that there are $n!$ ways of arranging the n men, and that among these $n!$ ways there are two ways of selecting one of the men A or B. For each way of selecting one of A or B there are $n - r - 1$ ways of placing him, and for each way of selecting one of A or B and for each way of placing him there is one way in which the other man can be placed in order that there be r men between them, and there are $(n - 2)!$ ways of arranging the remaining $n - 2$ men. So

$$P = \frac{2(n - r - 1)(n - 2)!}{n!} = \frac{n - r - 1}{\binom{n}{2}}.$$

EXERCISES

1. An urn contains 4 black balls and 6 white balls. Two balls are selected without replacement. What is the probability that

(a) one ball is black and one ball is white?
(b) both balls are black?
(c) both balls are white?
(d) both balls are the same color?

2. In tossing a pair of fair dice what is the probability of throwing a 7 or an 11?

3. Two fair coins are tossed simultaneously. What is the probability that
(a) they are both heads?
(b) they match?
(c) one is heads and one is tails?

4. The numbers $1, 2, \cdots, n$ are placed in random order in a straight line. Find the probability that
(a) the numbers 1, 2, 3 appear as neighbors in the order given,
(b) the numbers 1, 2, 3 appear as neighbors in any order.

5. Among k random digits find the probability that
(a) no even digit appears,
(b) no digit divisible by 3 appears.

6. Among k random digits ($k \geqq 5$) find the probability that
(a) the digit 1 appears exactly five times,
(b) the digit 0 appears exactly two times and the digit 1 appears exactly three times.

7. A box contains 10 white tags and 5 black tags. Three tags are selected at random without replacement. What is the probability that two are black and one is white?

8. There are n men standing in a circle, among whom are two men named A and B. What is the probability that there are r men between them?

1.2 The Fundamental Probability Set and the Algebra of Events

We now leave the case where all individual outcomes are equally likely and consider the general case. However, before we may adequately discuss probabilities of events we must discuss the events themselves. This study constitutes what is known as the algebra of events.

Connected with any experiment or game is a set or space which is a collection of all possible individual outcomes of the experiment or game. Such a collection of all possible individual outcomes is called a *fundamental probability set* or *sure event* and will be denoted by the Greek letter Ω. We shall also use the expression *fundamental probability set* for any representation we might construct of the collection of all possible individual outcomes. For example, in a game consisting of one toss of a coin, a fundamental probability set consists of two individual outcomes which can conveniently be referred to as H (heads) and T (tails). If the game consists in tossing a coin twice, then the fundamental probability set consists of four individual outcomes. One of these outcomes could be denoted by (T, H), which means that "tails" occurs in the first toss of the coin and "heads" occurs on the second toss. The remaining three individual outcomes may be denoted by (H, H), (H, T), and (T, T), and the reader can now easily describe what the outcomes signify. In general, an arbitrary individual outcome will be denoted by the lower case Greek letter ω and will be referred to as an "elementary event." Thus Ω denotes the totality of all elementary events.

An event is simply a collection of certain elementary events. Different events are different collections of elementary events. (*Note:* One elementary event is not necessarily an event.) An event will usually be denoted (with or without subscripts) by an upper case Roman letter near the beginning of the alphabet. Consider the game where a coin is tossed twice. Then Ω consists of the elementary events:

$$(H, H) \qquad (H, T) \qquad (T, H) \qquad (T, T).$$

If A denotes the event: heads occurs in the first toss, then A consists of elementary events (H, H) and (H, T). If B denotes the event: at least one head appears, then B consists of the elementary events (H, H), (H, T), and (T, H). If C denotes the event: no heads appear, then C consists of just one elementary event, namely, (T, T). If D denotes the event: at least three heads occur, this is clearly an impossible event and is an empty collection of elementary events.

In general, we shall denote the fact that an elementary event ω belongs to the collection of elementary events which determine an event A by $\omega \in A$. If an elementary event ω occurs, and if $\omega \in A$, then we shall say that the event A occurs. It must be noted at this point that just because an event A occurs, it does *not* mean that no other events occur. In the previous example, if (H, H) occurs, then A occurs and so does B. The fundamental probability set Ω is called the *sure event* because whatever elementary event ω does occur, always $\omega \in \Omega$.

We now introduce some algebraic operations over events. If A is an event, then A^c will denote the event that the event A does not occur. Thus A^c consists of all those elementary events in the fundamental probability set which are not in A. For every elementary event ω in the fundamental probability set and for every event A, one and only one of the following is true: $\omega \in A$ or $\omega \in A^c$. An equivalent way of writing $\omega \in A^c$ is: $\omega \notin A$, and we say that ω is not an elementary event in A. Also, A^c is called the negation of A ("not A") or the complement of A.

If A and B are two events, then $A \cup B$ will denote the event that *at least* one of the two events A, B occur. By this we mean that A can occur and B not occur, or B can occur and A not occur, or both A and B can occur.

In the previous example considered, if E denotes the event that heads occurs in the second trial, then $A \cup E$ consists of the elementary events (H, H), (H, T), and (T, H). In other words, $A \cup E$ is the event that heads occurs at least once, and we might write $A \cup E = B$.

More generally, if $A_1, A_2, \cdots, A_n$ are any n events, then

$$A_1 \cup A_2 \cup \cdots \cup A_n$$

denotes the event that *at least one* of these n events occur. We usually write this event in the following notation:

$$\bigcup_{i=1}^{n} A_i.$$

Also, if $A_1, A_2, \cdots, A_n, \cdots$ denotes an infinite sequence of events, then $A_1 \cup A_2 \cup \cdots \cup A_n \cup \cdots$ or $\bigcup_{i=1}^{\infty} A_i$ denotes the event that at least one event in this sequence occurs.

Suppose A and B are events which cannot both occur, i.e., if $\omega \in A$, then $\omega \notin B$, and if $\omega \in B$, then $\omega \notin A$. In this case, A and B are said to be *incompatible* or *disjoint* or *mutually exclusive,* and instead of writing $A \cup B$ when we consider the event that at least one of them occurs, we shall write $A + B$. As a matter of fact, whenever we write the event $A + B$ we shall automatically imply that A and B are incompatible or disjoint or mutually exclusive. Thus $A + B$ denotes the event that at least one of the events occur and that at most one can occur. The symbol $\sum_{i=1}^{n} A_i$ means that the events $A_1, \cdots, A_n$ are disjoint and denotes the event that one of these events occur. The symbol $\sum_{n=1}^{\infty} A_n$ has the obvious meaning.

The notation $A \subset B$ means: if event A occurs, then B occurs. Other ways of saying this are: A implies B, A entails B, B is implied by A, and B is entailed by A. If $A \subset B$ and if $\omega \in A$, then $\omega \in B$. Thus in any situation where it is desired to prove that the relation $A \subset B$ holds, one should select an arbitrary $\omega \in A$ and then prove that $\omega \in B$.

The event that both the events A and B occur is denoted by $A \cap B$ or AB. The symbol ϕ will denote the impossible event, i.e., the event that contains no elementary events. It is clear that if $AB = \phi$, then A and B are incompatible. Finally, we define the equality of two events A and B and write $A = B$ if every elementary event in A is an elementary event in B and if every elementary event in B is an elementary event in A. It is clear then that $A = B$ if and only if $A \subset B$ and $B \subset A$; one should remember this fact when trying to prove equalities of events.

The following properties of the algebra of events are easily proved, and the proofs are left to the reader. The only tool one must have at his disposal is the following technique (already mentioned above): in order to prove $A \subset B$, take an arbitrary elementary event $\omega \in A$ and prove that $\omega \in B$.

In order to prove an equality $A = B$ one must prove that $A \subset B$ and $B \subset A$. Thus, for every trio of events A, B, C, we have:

1. $A \subset A$.
2. If $A \subset B$ and if $B \subset C$, then $A \subset C$.
3. $A \cap A = A$ and $A \cup A = A$.
4. $A \cup B = B \cup A$ and $A \cap B = B \cap A$.
5. $A \cap (B \cap C) = (A \cap B) \cap C$ and $A \cup (B \cup C) = (A \cup B) \cup C$.
6. $\phi \subset A \subset \Omega$.
7. $A \cap B \subset A \subset A \cup B$.
8. $\phi \cap A = \phi$ and $\phi \cup A = A$.
9. $\Omega \cap A = A$ and $\Omega \cup A = \Omega$.
10. $(A^c)^c = A$.
11. $(A \cup B)^c = A^c \cap B^c$ and $(A \cap B)^c = A^c \cup B^c$. (These are known as the DeMorgan laws.)
12. $A \cup B = A + BA^c$.
13. $B = AB + A^cB$.
14. $A \cap (B \cup C) = AB \cup AC$ and $A \cup (B \cap C) = (A \cup B) \cap (A \cup C)$.

In addition, letting $\{A_n\}$ denote a sequence of events and N denote a finite integer or ∞, we have

15. $\bigcup_{n=1}^{N} A_n = A_1 + \sum_{n=2}^{N} A_1^c \cdots A_{n-1}^c A_n$.

16. $\left(\bigcup_{n=1}^{N} A_n\right)^c = \bigcap_{n=1}^{N} A_n^c$ and $\left(\bigcap_{n=1}^{N} A_n\right)^c = \bigcup_{n=1}^{N} A_n^c$ (DeMorgan's laws).

EXERCISES

1–16. Prove the 16 propositions which appeared in this section.

1.3 The Axioms of a Probability Space

Before we list the basic axioms the reader should recall what the word "denumerable" means. A set or collection of objects is said to be *denumerable* if it can be put into one-to-one correspondence with the set of all positive integers. A denumerable set is infinite. The student has learned in other mathematics courses that the set of all rational numbers is denumerable while the set of all real numbers is not denumerable.

Let us consider some fixed fundamental probability set Ω. The following assumptions are made concerning all those collections of elementary events which we shall call events. Let $\mathcal{A}$ denote the collection of all events that we shall consider. We assume that

(i) *for every event A in $\mathfrak{A}$, (or for every $A \in \mathfrak{A}$), then also A^c is in $\mathfrak{A}$, (or $A^c \in \mathfrak{A}$),*

(ii) *if $A_1, A_2, \cdots, A_n, \cdots$ is any denumerable sequence of events in $\mathfrak{A}$, then*

$$\bigcup_{n=1}^{\infty} A_n \in \mathfrak{A},$$

and

(iii) $\phi \in \mathfrak{A}$.

A collection of events with properties (i), (ii), and (iii) is called a *sigma-field* of events.

The student should in particular note here that although an event is defined as a collection or set of elementary events, we have never said, and it is not necessarily true, that every collection of elementary events is an event. It is true that every collection of elementary events in a finite or denumerable fundamental probability set is an event. However, in case the fundamental probability set is uncountable (e.g., the set of real numbers in some interval of positive length), then this is not necessarily true.

There are some important consequences of the above three axioms which we now state and prove.

1. Theorem. *If $A_1, A_2, \cdots, A_n$ is any finite sequence of events in $\mathfrak{A}$, then*

$$\bigcup_{k=1}^{n} A_k \in \mathfrak{A}.$$

Proof. Since $\phi \in \mathfrak{A}$, let us define $\phi = A_{n+1} = A_{n+2} = \cdots$. Then, by hypothesis, (ii) and (iii), $\bigcup_{k=1}^{\infty} A_k \in \mathfrak{A}$. But $\bigcup_{k=1}^{\infty} A_k = \bigcup_{k=1}^{n} A_k$, which proves the theorem.

2. Theorem. *The sure event Ω is always in $\mathfrak{A}$, i.e., $\Omega \in \mathfrak{A}$.*

Proof. By (iii) $\phi \in \mathfrak{A}$, and thus by (i), $\phi^c \in \mathfrak{A}$. But $\phi^c = \Omega$.

3. Theorem. *If $A_1, A_2, \cdots, A_n, \cdots$ is any denumerable sequence of events in $\mathfrak{A}$, then $\bigcap_{k=1}^{\infty} A_k \in \mathfrak{A}$.*

Proof. Since $A_n \in \mathfrak{A}$ for $n = 1, 2, \cdots$, then $A_n^c \in \mathfrak{A}$ for $n = 1, 2, \cdots$. Then by axiom (ii)

$$\bigcup_{n=1}^{\infty} A_n^c \in \mathfrak{A}.$$

Axiom (i) then implies that

$$\left(\bigcup_{n=1}^{\infty} A_n^c\right)^c \in \mathfrak{A}.$$

By one of the DeMorgan laws (Proposition 16 in Section 1.2),

$$\left(\bigcup_{n=1}^{\infty} A_n^c \right)^c = \bigcap_{n=1}^{\infty} (A_n^c)^c = \bigcap_{n=1}^{\infty} A_n,$$

which proves the theorem.

Corollary to Theorem 3. *If $A_1, A_2, \cdots, A_n$ is any finite sequence of events in $\mathfrak{A}$, then $\bigcap_{k=1}^{n} A_k \in \mathfrak{A}$.*

The proof of this is trivial if one lets $\Omega = A_{n+1} = A_{n+2} = \cdots$ and then applies Theorem 3.

We now introduce the definition of probability.

Definition. *A probability P is a function which assigns to every event A in $\mathfrak{A}$ a number $P(A)$, called the probability of the event A, for which the following axioms are assumed:*

(i) $P(A) \geqq 0$ *for every* $A \in \mathfrak{A}$,

(ii) $P(\Omega) = 1$, *and*

(iii) *for every denumerable sequence of disjoint events* $A_1, A_2, \cdots, A_n, \cdots,$

$$P\left(\sum_{n=1}^{\infty} A_n \right) = \sum_{n=1}^{\infty} P(A_n).$$

It should be stressed that the above system of axioms for a probability is assumed to hold for any game or experiment, whether the elementary events are equally likely or not. We are now able to deduce a number of results from these axioms.

4. Theorem. $P(\phi) = 0$.

Proof. Let $A_1 = \phi$, $A_2 = \phi$, $A_3 = \phi$, $\cdots$. Clearly the denumerable sequence $\{A_n\}$ of events are disjoint. Thus by (iii) in the definition above,

$$P(\phi) = P\left(\sum_{n=1}^{\infty} A_n \right) = \sum_{n=1}^{\infty} P(A_n) = \sum_{n=1}^{\infty} P(\phi).$$

In order that this equality hold, the only value $P(\phi)$ can have is zero.

5. Theorem. *If $A_1, \cdots, A_n$ are any n incompatible events, then*

$$P(A_1 + A_2 + \cdots + A_n) = P(A_1) + P(A_2) + \cdots + P(A_n).$$

Proof. Let $A_{n+1} = \phi$, $A_{n+2} = \phi$, $\cdots$. Then the denumerable sequence $A_1, A_2, \cdots, A_n, \cdots$ is a disjoint sequence of events, and

$$P\left(\sum_{k=1}^{n} A_k \right) = P\left(\sum_{k=1}^{\infty} A_k \right) = \sum_{k=1}^{\infty} P(A_k) = \sum_{k=1}^{n} P(A_k),$$

which proves the theorem.

6. Theorem. *For every two events A and B,*

$$P(A \cup B) = P(A) + P(B) - P(AB).$$

Proof. Since $A \cup B = A + A^cB$ (by Proposition 12 in Section 1.2), then by Theorem 5 we have $P(A \cup B) = P(A) + P(A^cB)$. But by Proposition 13 of Section 1.2, $B = AB + A^cB$, so $P(B) = P(AB) + P(A^cB)$, or $P(A^cB) = P(B) - P(AB)$. Thus $P(A \cup B) = P(A) + P(B) - P(AB)$, as was to be proved.

First corollary to Theorem 6. (*Known as Boole's inequality.*)

$$P(A \cup B) \leqq P(A) + P(B).$$

Proof. This easily follows from Theorem 6 and the fact that $P(AB) \geqq 0$.

Second corollary to Theorem 6. *If A, B, and C are any three events, then*

$$P(A \cup B \cup C) \leqq P(A) + P(B) + P(C).$$

Proof. We need only apply Theorem 6 twice to obtain

$$P(A \cup B \cup C) \leqq P(A) + P(B \cup C) \leqq P(A) + P(B) + P(C).$$

7. Theorem. *If $A \subset B$, then $P(A) \leqq P(B)$.*

Proof. Since $B = BA + BA^c$, and since $BA = A$, we have $B = A + BA^c$. Thus, $P(B) = P(A) + P(BA^c)$. The conclusion follows by noting that $P(BA^c) \geqq 0$.

Corollary to Theorem 7. *For every event A, $P(A) \leqq 1$.*

Proof. Since every event $A \subset \Omega$, the conclusion follows directly from Theorem 7.

8. Theorem. *For every event A, $P(A^c) = 1 - P(A)$ and $P(A) = 1 - P(A^c)$.*

Proof. Since $\Omega = A + A^c$, we have $1 = P(\Omega) = P(A) + P(A^c)$, from which the two conclusions follow.

All of these theorems are extremely important and shall be used in the subsequent development.

EXERCISES

1. Write out a complete proof of the first corollary to Theorem 6.

2. Use Proposition 15 of Section 1.2 to prove that $P(\bigcup_{n=1}^{N} A_n) \leqq \sum_{n=1}^{N} P(A_n)$, where N is a finite integer or ∞. (Boole's Inequality).

3. Prove: If A, B, and C are any three events, then

$$\begin{aligned} P(A \cup B \cup C) = {} & P(A) + P(B) + P(C) \\ & - P(AB) - P(AC) - P(BC) \\ & + P(ABC). \end{aligned}$$

4. Write out a proof of the corollary to Theorem 3 using Theorem 1.

CHAPTER 2

Dependent and Independent Events

2.1 Conditional Probability

The notion of conditional (or relative) probability arises in the following manner. One has at his disposal some information, and he wants to know, on the basis of this information, what the probability of a certain event is. To be specific, the information at one's disposal is some event, and one wants to know the probability of the latter event, given the occurrence of this specific event. What does such a probability mean to the practical man when he considers the probability of an event E given the occurrence of an event (or "hypothesis") H? He would repeat the game or experiment a large number of times, say, N times. Among these N repetitions of the experiment or game he would note the number N_H of times that the event H occurs. Then from among this number of times in which H occurs he would note the number N_{EH} of times in which E occurs. Then he would observe the ratio N_{EH}/N_H. This ratio is called the relative frequency that E occurs among those times that H occurs. In a practical sense this ratio approximates what we would like to call the conditional probability that E occurs, given the information that H occurs. At this point one should notice that N_{EH} denotes the number of times among the N trials that both E and H occur. But

$$N_{EH}/N_H = \frac{N_{EH}/N}{N_H/N}.$$

One should recall from the very first section that N_{EH}/N approximates the probability of the event EH (in a relative frequency sense) and N_H/N approximates the probability of the event H. This consideration leads us to the following definition.

Definition. *If $P(B) > 0$, then we define the conditional probability of the event A given the event B, $P(A|B)$, by*

$$P(A|B) = \frac{P(AB)}{P(B)}.$$

With the formal definition above we can derive many useful properties of conditional probabilities.

1. Theorem. *If $P(B) > 0$, then $P(\cdot|B)$ is a probability, i.e.,*
(i) $P(A|B) \geqq 0$ *for every* $A \in \mathfrak{A}$,
(ii) $P(\Omega|B) = 1$, *and*
(iii) $P(\sum_{k=1}^{\infty} A_k|B) = \sum_{k=1}^{\infty} P(A_k|B)$ *for every denumerable sequence of disjoint events.*

Proof. (i) Since $AB \in \mathfrak{A}$, we have that $P(AB) \geqq 0$. If one divides through by $P(B)$ and uses the above definition, the conclusion is obtained.

(ii) $P(\Omega|B) = \dfrac{P(\Omega B)}{P(B)} = \dfrac{P(B)}{P(B)} = 1.$

(iii) One easily obtains

$$P\left(\sum_{n=1}^{\infty} A_n|B\right) = P\left(\sum_{n=1}^{\infty} A_nB\right)/P(B)$$
$$= \left\{\sum_{n=1}^{\infty} P(A_nB)\right\}/P(B) = \sum_{n=1}^{\infty} P(A_n|B),$$

and thus all three assertions of the theorem are proved.

The above theorem states that every conditional probability is a probability. Thus every theorem which was proved for an ordinary probability will also be true for any conditional probability. In addition, there are three important results for conditional probabilities which we shall now prove; they are the *multiplication rule*, the *theorem of total probabilities*, and *Bayes' rule*.

2. Theorem. (Multiplication Rule.) *For every $n + 1$ events $A_0, A_1, \cdots, A_n$ for which $P(A_0A_1 \cdots A_{n-1}) > 0$, then*

$$P(A_0A_1 \cdots A_n) = P(A_0)P(A_1|A_0)P(A_2|A_0A_1) \cdots P(A_n|A_0A_1 \cdots A_{n-1}).$$

Proof. Since $A_0A_1 \cdots A_{n-1} \subset A_0A_1 \cdots A_{n-2} \subset \cdots \subset A_0A_1 \subset A_0$, then $0 < P(A_0A_1 \cdots A_{n-1}) \leqq \cdots \leqq P(A_0A_1) \leqq P(A_0)$, and consequently all the conditional probabilities involved in the statement of the theorem are well defined. The proof of this theorem will be accomplished by use of the axiom of induction (i.e., by so-called "mathematical induction"). The axiom of induction states that if S is a set of integers, if $1 \in S$, and if

$n \in S$ implies that $n + 1 \in S$, then S contains all positive integers. In order to prove the theorem let S denote those values of n for which the theorem is true. Clearly $1 \in S$, since $P(A_0A_1) = P(A_0)P(A_1|A_0)$ by the very definition of conditional probability. Let n be any integer in S. Then by the definition of conditional probability,

$$P(A_0A_1 \cdots A_nA_{n+1}) = P(A_0A_1 \cdots A_n)P(A_{n+1}|A_0A_1 \cdots A_n).$$

Since $n \in S$, then $P(A_0A_1 \cdots A_n)$ on the right-hand side of this equation is equal to

$$P(A_0)P(A_1|A_0) \cdots P(A_n|A_0A_1 \cdots A_{n-1}).$$

Consequently $n + 1 \in S$, and, by the axiom of induction, S contains all positive integers. This proves the theorem.

Example. In Polya's urn scheme, an urn initially contains r red balls and b black balls. At each trial a ball is selected at random, its color is noted, and it is *replaced along with* c additional balls of the same color. Let us find the probability that one obtains a red ball in each of the first three trials. Let R_i denote the event that a red ball is selected in the ith trial. Then we want to find the probability $P(R_1R_2R_3)$. By the multiplication rule,

$$\begin{aligned} P(R_1R_2R_3) &= P(R_1)P(R_2|R_1)P(R_3|R_1R_2) \\ &= \frac{r}{r+b}\,\frac{r+c}{r+b+c}\,\frac{r+2c}{r+b+2c}. \end{aligned}$$

3. Theorem. (Theorem of Total Probabilities.) *If $P(\sum_{n=1}^{N} H_n) = 1$, where N is a positive integer or ∞, and if $P(H_n) > 0$ for every n, then for every event A,*

$$P(A) = \sum_{n=1}^{N} P(A|H_n)P(H_n).$$

Proof. Since $P((\sum_{n=1}^{N} H_n)^c) = 0$, then

$$\begin{aligned} P(A) &= P\left(A \sum_{n=1}^{N} H_n\right) + P\left(A \left(\sum_{n=1}^{N} H_n\right)^c\right) \\ &= P\left(\sum_{n=1}^{N} AH_n\right) = \sum_{n=1}^{N} P(AH_n) \\ &= \sum_{n=1}^{N} P(A|H_n)P(H_n), \end{aligned}$$

which completes the proof.

Example. A box contains n_1 tags numbered 1 and n_2 tags numbered 2. A tag is selected at random. If it is a number 1 tag, one goes to urn number 1 which contains r_1 red balls and b_1 black balls and selects a ball at random; if it is a number 2 tag, one goes to urn number 2 which contains r_2 red balls and b_2 black balls and selects a ball at random. The problem is to find the probability that one obtains a red ball. Accordingly, let R denote the event that a red ball is selected, let H_1 denote the event that a number 1 tag is selected, and let H_2 denote the event that a number 2 tag is selected. By the theorem of total probabilities,

$$\begin{aligned} P(R) &= P(R|H_1)P(H_1) + P(R|H_2)P(H_2) \\ &= \frac{r_1}{r_1 + b_1}\frac{n_1}{n_1 + n_2} + \frac{r_2}{r_2 + b_2}\frac{n_2}{n_1 + n_2}. \end{aligned}$$

It should be pointed out that this problem would be more difficult to solve if one used the "equally likely outcomes" method on it.

4. Theorem. (Bayes' Rule.) *If* $P(\sum_{n=1}^{N} H_n) = 1$, *where* N *is a positive integer or* ∞, *if* $P(A) > 0$, *and if* $P(H_n) > 0$ *for every* n, *then*

$$P(H_j|A) = \frac{P(A|H_j)P(H_j)}{\sum_{n=1}^{N} P(A|H_n)P(H_n)}$$

for every integer j.

Proof. Using the definition of conditional probability and the theorem of total probabilities, we obtain

$$\begin{aligned} P(H_j|A) &= \frac{P(AH_j)}{P(A)} \\ &= \frac{P(A|H_j)P(H_j)}{\sum_{n=1}^{N} P(A|H_n)P(H_n)} \end{aligned}$$

which proves the theorem.

Example. A box contains $N = n_1 + n_2 + n_3$ tags, where n_1 tags are numbered 1, n_2 tags are numbered 2, and n_3 tags are numbered 3. There are three urns, and they are numbered 1, 2, and 3. Urn number i contains r_i red balls and b_i black balls. A tag is selected at random from the box, and then a ball is selected at random from the urn of the same number as the tag selected. The problem is: if the ball selected is red, what is the probability that it came from urn number 2? Let R denote the event that the ball selected is red, and let H_1, H_2, H_3 denote events that a number 1, a number 2, a number 3 tag is selected, respectively. In this problem we are interested in computing $P(H_2|R)$. Using Bayes' rule we obtain

$$\begin{aligned} P(H_2|R) &= \frac{P(R|H_2)P(H_2)}{P(R|H_1)P(H_1) + P(R|H_2)P(H_2) + P(R|H_3)P(H_3)} \\ &= \frac{\dfrac{r_2}{r_2 + b_2} \cdot \dfrac{n_2}{n_1 + n_2 + n_3}}{\sum_{m=1}^{3} \dfrac{r_m}{r_m + b_m} \cdot \dfrac{n_m}{n_1 + n_2 + n_3}}. \end{aligned}$$

EXERCISES

1. In Polya's urn scheme, used in an example in this section, find the probability that

(a) a red ball is selected in the second trial,
(b) a red ball is selected in the Nth trial,
(c) a red ball is selected in the second trial and a black ball is selected in the third trial.

2. In Polya's urn scheme find the conditional probability that

(a) a red ball is selected in the first trial, given that a red ball is selected in the second trial,
(b) a red ball is selected in the first trial, given that a red ball is selected in the Nth trial ($N \geqq 2$).

3. In tossing a penny, what is the conditional probability that the first head occurs on the Nth trial given that at least one head occurs during the first $M + N$ trials?

4. In Polya's urn scheme, find the conditional probability that

(a) at least one red ball is selected during the first two trials, given that *one and only one* is selected during the first three trials,
(b) the first red ball is selected at the second trial, given that *at least one red ball* is selected during the first three trials.

5. A tennis tournament is held with 2^n players of equal ability. In the first play, the opposing pairs of players are randomly selected, and in each succeeding play the opposing pairs are randomly selected from among the winners of the previous games. If A and B are two of the 2^n players, what is the probability that they will play against each other?

6. Prove the following simple form of Bayes' rule: if $P(A) > 0$ and $P(B) > 0$, then $P(B|A) = P(B)P(A|B)/P(A)$.

2.2 Stochastic Independence

The notion of independence arose from those cases where the outcomes are equally likely. Accordingly, before giving the definition of independence and deriving certain of its properties we consider just such a case.

Let g_1 denote some game in which there are N_1 equally likely outcomes. If A is an event which may or may not occur when the game g_1 is played, and if A can occur in N_A equally likely outcomes, then the probability of A occurring is N_A/N_1. Now let g_2 and g_3 denote two additional games in which there are N_2 and N_3 equally likely outcomes, respectively. Suppose that each game can be played in a manner which does not depend on the outcomes of the other games. In such a situation the occurrence or nonoccurrence of an event A in game g_1 does not depend on and does not influence the occurrence or nonoccurrence of an event B in game g_2, and the occurrence or nonoccurrence of either or both of events A and B does not influence and is not influenced by the occurrence of some event C in game g_3. In other words, we might say that the events A, B, and C are *independent* of each other. Let us compute the probabilities of A, B, and C when the three games are played in succession. If N_B and N_C denote the number of equally likely ways in which event B and event C can occur in game g_2 and game g_3, respectively, then easily

$$P(A) = \frac{N_A N_2 N_3}{N_1 N_2 N_3} = \frac{N_A}{N_1},$$

$$P(B) = \frac{N_1 N_B N_3}{N_1 N_2 N_3} = \frac{N_B}{N_2},$$

and

$$P(C) = \frac{N_1 N_2 N_C}{N_1 N_2 N_3} = \frac{N_C}{N_3}.$$

However, since

$$P(ABC) = \frac{N_A N_B N_C}{N_1 N_2 N_3},$$

we discover that

$$P(ABC) = P(A)P(B)P(C).$$

In other words, if three events occur independently of each other in this "equally likely" situation, we shall want to write that the probability of the joint occurrence of all three of them is equal to the product of their individual probabilities. One can easily see that such a multiplication rule would be true for four or five such games or, in short, for any finite number of games.

Now we may begin a formal treatment.

Definition. *Let $\mathcal{C}$ denote a collection of events. The events in $\mathcal{C}$ are said to be independent if the probability of the joint occurrence of any finite number of them equals the product of their probabilities.*

As an example, if $\mathcal{C}$ consists of only two events A and B, then these events are defined to be independent if $P(AB) = P(A)P(B)$. If $\mathcal{C}$ consists of three events A, B, and C, then these events are said to be independent if $P(AB) = P(A)P(B)$, $P(AC) = P(A)P(C)$, $P(BC) = P(B)P(C)$, and $P(ABC) = P(A)P(B)P(C)$. The reader can easily write out for himself the defining equations when a class of four events are independent. The class $\mathcal{C}$ of events quite frequently possesses infinitely many events, and the only way to state that these events are independent is to state that

$$P(A_1 A_2 \cdots A_n) = P(A_1)P(A_2) \cdots P(A_n)$$

for every finite collection $A_1, A_2, \cdots, A_n$ in $\mathcal{C}$.

We now obtain some consequences of the definition of independence.

1. Theorem. *If A and B are independent events, then so are events A and B^c.*

Proof. First let us write $A = AB + AB^c$, which we may do by Proposition 13 in Section 1.2. Then we take the probability of both sides,

$$P(A) = P(AB) + P(AB^c),$$

and since A and B are independent by hypothesis, we may write

$$P(AB^c) = P(A) - P(A)P(B) = P(A)P(B^c).$$

This completes the proof.

The proof of the above theorem is essentially the proof of the following theorem, whose proof we omit. (See problem 4 in the exercises.)

2. Theorem. *Assume that the events of some class $\mathcal{C}$ of events are independent. If any or all of the events in $\mathcal{C}$ are replaced by their negations, the events in the resulting class are still independent.*

A most convincing theorem on independence and conditional probability is the next one.

3. Theorem. *Assume $P(B) > 0$. A necessary and sufficient condition that events A and B be independent is that $P(A|B) = P(A)$.*

Proof. We first show that the condition is necessary. Assuming that A and B are independent, we obtain

$$P(A|B) = \frac{P(AB)}{P(B)} = \frac{P(A)P(B)}{P(B)} = P(A).$$

We now show that the condition is sufficient. Assuming that $P(A|B) = P(A)$, we obtain

$$P(AB) = P(A|B)P(B) = P(A)P(B),$$

which proves the theorem.

At this point one might inquire whether we have required too much in our definition of independence. In other words, perhaps all we needed was to stipulate that $P(AB) = P(A)P(B)$ for every pair of events in $\mathcal{C}$, from which we could possibly deduce the much stronger definition given. One person who raised this question and answered it in the negative was the eminent Soviet mathematician, S. N. Bernstein, who constructed the following example. Suppose Ω consists of four equally likely elementary events denoted by $\omega_1, \omega_2, \omega_3, \omega_4$. Let $A = \{\omega_1, \omega_2\}$, $B = \{\omega_1, \omega_3\}$ and $C = \{\omega_1, \omega_4\}$. Clearly $P(A) = P(B) = P(C) = \frac{1}{2}$. Since $AB = AC = BC = \{\omega_1\}$, then

$$\begin{aligned} P(AB) &= P(AC) = P(BC) = \tfrac{1}{4} \\ &= P(A)P(B) = P(A)P(C) = P(B)P(C). \end{aligned}$$

However,

$$P(ABC) = P(\{\omega_1\}) = \tfrac{1}{4} \neq P(A)P(B)P(C) = \tfrac{1}{8}.$$

Thus in our definition of an independent collection of events we have to state that the probability of the joint occurrence of *every finite collection of events* in $\mathcal{C}$ equals the product of their individual probabilities.

EXERCISES

1. If $\mathcal{C}$ consists of events A, B, C, D, *what equations* must be satisfied in order that these events be independent?

2. If $\mathcal{C}$ consists of $n \geqq 2$ events $A_1, \cdots, A_n$, *how many* equations must be satisfied in order that these events be independent?

3. Prove the *lemma:* If $A_1, A_2, \cdots, A_n, B_1, \cdots, B_m$ are $m + n$ independent events, then $A_1^c, \cdots, A_n^c, B_1, \cdots, B_m$ are independent also. (*Hint of proof:* Do this by induction on n, but be careful.)

4. Prove Theorem 2 using the lemma of problem 3.

5. Prove: If $P(B) = 0$ (*note:* B is not necessarily the same as ϕ here), then, for any event A, A and B are independent.

2.3 An Application in Physics of the Notion of Independence

In any physical application of probability theory, if one can make the assumption of independence of events, the resulting mathematics is usually easier. However, one must test the mathematical model afterwards by experimentation in order to justify the assumptions made. In this section we construct a mathematical model for a physical phenomenon, assuming independence of certain events, and then show by experimental data that the assumption, and consequently the model, is a good one.

Consider an amount of radium which at some initial time, say $t = 0$, has a mass denoted by M. At any time t let the mass of whatever remains after radioactive disintegration be denoted by $M(t)$. The problem is to be able to predict the value of $M(t)$ for any value of t, i.e., to find, if possible, a "formula" for $M(t)$. We shall consider this problem from two points of view: the long-range view where time is measured in terms of years, and the short-range view where time t is measured in terms of seconds.

The problem from the long-range point of view is not a probability problem but is what is called a *deterministic* problem. In this case it seems reasonable to assume that the rate of disintegration at any time t is proportional to the mass $M(t)$ at that time. Accordingly, we may write

$$\frac{dM(t)}{dt} = -KM(t),$$

where $K > 0$ and $-K$ is the (unknown) constant of proportionality. Thus we write

$$\frac{1}{M(t)}\frac{dM(t)}{dt} = -K$$

and integrate both sides by writing

$$\int_0^t \frac{1}{M(\tau)}\frac{dM(\tau)}{d\tau}\,d\tau = \int_0^t (-K)\,d\tau.$$

We obtain

$$\log M(t) - \log M(0) = -Kt,$$

or

$$\log \frac{M(t)}{M(0)} = -Kt.$$

Since $M = M(0)$, we finally obtain

$$M(t) = Me^{-Kt}.$$

In order to evaluate K we must take a mass M of radium, and after t_1 years we measure its mass $M(t_1)$. Then we solve the equation

$$M(t_1) = Me^{-Kt_1}$$

to obtain

$$K = \frac{1}{t_1}\log\frac{M(0)}{M(t_1)},$$

and thus we have evaluated K. A graph of $M(t) = Me^{-Kt}$ is shown in Fig. 1.

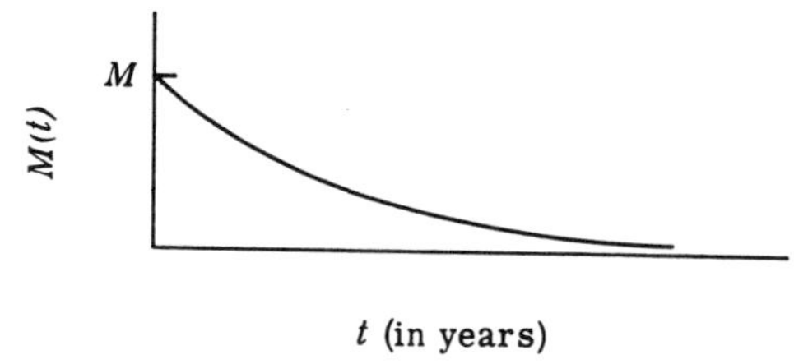

Fig. 1

The formula derived for $M(t)$ has been demonstrated by physical experimentation to give an adequate picture of the phenomenon.

Now suppose that we are interested in the decrease of mass during a very short period of time, say, when time is most conveniently measured in seconds. An experimental observation on an original mass of magnitude M might appear as in Fig. 2. Each instantaneous decrease in mass is due to emission of an alpha particle. The amount of each instantaneous decrease is the same, namely, the mass decrease due to loss of an alpha particle. The times (i.e., values of t) at which these instantaneous decreases of mass occur are not deterministic, i.e., if one made another observation on a mass of magnitude M, the graph in Fig. 2 would be entirely different.

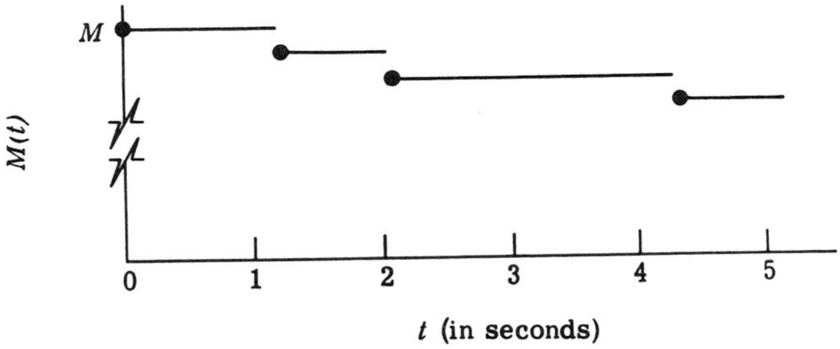

Fig. 2

However, if one duplicates this experiment many times, one would find that the relative frequency with which 0, 1, 2, etc., alpha particles are emitted during a specified time interval remain "relatively constant." So the problem changes. We cannot hope to find the exact number of particles which are emitted after t seconds, but we might be interested in the next best thing, the probability $P_n(t)$ that n particles are emitted after a time interval of length t.

We now construct a mathematical model for the phenomenon. This consists in stating certain mathematical assumptions concerning the physical phenomenon and then deriving the required results. The following assumptions seem reasonable:

(i) If $0 < t_1 < t_2$, the number of alpha particles emitted during the time interval $[t_1, t_2]$ does not depend on the number of particles emitted during the time interval $[0, t_1]$.

(ii) The probability that exactly one alpha particle is emitted during the time interval $[t, t + h]$, for $h > 0$, is $\lambda h + o(h)$, where λ is an unknown positive constant, and $o(h)$ possesses the property that

$$\lim_{h \to 0} \frac{o(h)}{h} = 0.$$

(iii) The probability that more than one particle is emitted during the time interval $[t, t + h]$, with $h > 0$, is $o(h)$.

(iv) For every n, $P_n(t)$ is differentiable in t, where $P_n(t)$ is the probability that exactly n particles are emitted during the time interval $[0, t]$.

For $0 \leqq t_1 < t_2$, let $A_k(t_1, t_2)$ denote the event that exactly k alpha particles are emitted during the time interval $[t_1, t_2]$. We may write

(1) $$A_0(0, t + h) = A_0(0, t)A_0(t, t + h),$$

and in case $n \geqq 1$ we may write

$$(2) \qquad \begin{aligned} A_n(0, t+h) &= A_n(0, t)A_0(t, t+h) \\ &\quad + A_{n-1}(0, t)A_1(t, t+h) \\ &\quad + \sum_{k=2}^{n} A_{n-k}(0, t)A_k(t, t+h). \end{aligned}$$

For $n = 0, 1, 2, \cdots$, let $P_n(t) = P(A_n(0, t))$. Then using the first three assumptions we may take probabilities of both sides of (1) and obtain

$$\begin{aligned} P_0(t+h) &= P(A_0(0, t))P(A_0(t, t+h)) \\ &= P_0(t)(1 - \lambda h - o(h)) \end{aligned}$$

which, rearranged, yields

$$(3) \qquad \frac{P_0(t+h) - P_0(t)}{h} = -\lambda P_0(t) - \frac{o(h)}{h} P_0(t).$$

We next obtain a similar equation for $P_n(t)$, $n \geqq 1$. We first show that

$$P\left(\sum_{k=2}^{n} A_{n-k}(0, t)A_k(t, t+h) \right) = o(h).$$

This easily follows from the fact that

$$\sum_{k=2}^{n} A_{n-k}(0, t)A_k(t, t+h) \subset \sum_{k=2}^{n} A_k(t, t+h) \subset \sum_{k=2}^{\infty} A_k(t, t+h),$$

and by assumption (iii). We now take probabilities of both sides of (2). In the same manner in which we derived (3) we obtain, for $n = 1, 2, \cdots$,

$$\begin{aligned} P_n(t+h) &= P_n(t)(1 - \lambda h - o(h)) \\ &\quad + P_{n-1}(t)(\lambda h + o(h)) + o(h). \end{aligned}$$

Subtracting $P_n(t)$ from both sides and dividing both sides by h we obtain

$$(4) \qquad \frac{P_n(t+h) - P_n(t)}{h} = -\lambda P_n(t) + \lambda P_{n-1}(t) + \frac{o(h)}{h}.$$

Assumption (iv) allows us to take the limit of both sides of (3) and (4) as $h \to 0$ to obtain

$$(5) \qquad \begin{cases} P_0'(t) = -\lambda P_0(t), \\ P_n'(t) = -\lambda P_n(t) + \lambda P_{n-1}(t), \qquad n = 1, 2, \cdots. \end{cases}$$

In (5) we have an infinite system of differential equations. We now propose to solve these to obtain the probabilities we seek, namely, $\{P_n(t), n = 0, 1, 2, \cdots\}$.

We first impose two initial conditions. It seems only reasonable to require that $P_0(0) = 1$ and $P_n(0) = 0$ if $n \geqq 1$. The differential equation $P_0'(t) = -\lambda P_0(t)$ is easy to solve. We first rewrite it as $P_0'(t) + \lambda P_0(t) = 0$, then multiply both sides by $e^{\lambda t}$, and finally notice that what we have may be written as

$$\frac{d}{dt}(P_0(t)e^{\lambda t}) = 0.$$

If we integrate both sides from 0 to t, we obtain $P_0(t)e^{\lambda t} - P_0(0) = 0$, or

$$P_0(t) = e^{-\lambda t}.$$

We can now solve the differential equation

$$P_n'(t) = -\lambda P_n(t) + \lambda P_{n-1}(t)$$

for $n = 1$, i.e., we solve

$$P_1'(t) = -\lambda P_1(t) + \lambda P_0(t).$$

Since we now know that $P_0(t) = e^{-\lambda t}$, we may write

$$P_1'(t) + \lambda P_1(t) = \lambda e^{-\lambda t}.$$

Again, multiply both sides by $e^{\lambda t}$ to obtain

$$\frac{d}{dt}(P_1(t)e^{\lambda t}) = \lambda.$$

Upon integrating both sides between 0 and t, one obtains $P_1(t)e^{\lambda t} - P_1(0) = \lambda t$. Since $P_1(0) = 0$ we finally obtain

$$P_1(t) = e^{-\lambda t}\lambda t.$$

By this time the student should be able to solve the differential equation

$$P_2'(t) = -\lambda P_2(t) + \lambda P_1(t)$$

and obtain the solution

$$P_2(t) = \frac{e^{-\lambda t}(\lambda t)^2}{2!}.$$

By mathematical induction the student should be able to prove that

$$P_n(t) = \frac{e^{-\lambda t}(\lambda t)^n}{n!}, \qquad n = 0, 1, 2, \cdots. \tag{6}$$

Thus we have found our answer in (6). In other words, starting from assumptions (i), (ii), (iii), and (iv), (6) is a good mathematical answer. But is it a good physical answer? Yes, it is, in a practical sense. Table 1 should convince the student of this. The explanation of the table is easy. This is data collected by Rutherford and Geiger. They observed the number of alpha particles emitted during time intervals which were 7.5 seconds of duration. They made 2608 (independent) observations on such intervals, i.e., they observed the number of alpha particles emitted during 2608 disjoint intervals. The first column, n, of Table 1 lists the number of par-

TABLE 1

RUTHERFORD AND GEIGER EXPERIMENTAL DATA

n	Number of periods	Experimental relative frequency	$P_n(7.5)$ with $\lambda = .516$
0	57	.0219	.0209
1	203	.0778	.0807
2	383	.1469	.1562
3	525	.2013	.2015
4	532	.2040	.1949
5	408	.1564	.1509
6	273	.1047	.0973
7	139	.0533	.0538
8	45	.0173	.0260
9	27	.0104	.0112
10	10	.0038	.0065
11	4	.0015	.
12	2	.0008	.
.			.
.			.
.			.
Total	2608		

ticles which *could* be emitted during a 7.5-second time interval, namely, $n = 0, 1, 2, \cdots$. The second column denotes the number of 7.5-second periods during which n particles were emitted, i.e., during 57 out of the total 2608 periods no alpha particles were emitted, in 203 out of the 2608 7.5-second intervals exactly one alpha particle was emitted, in 383 intervals two particles were emitted, etc. In the third column, the experimental relative frequency is tabulated, i.e., $.0219 = 57/2608$, $.0778 = 203/2608$, etc. In other words, the figures given in the third column are crude estimates of the probability that n particles are emitted during a 7.5-second interval for $n = 0, 1, 2, \cdots$. In the fourth column we list the theoretical probabilities for n particles to be emitted during a 7.5-second interval, making use of formula (6). In this formula we use, as a value for λ, $\lambda = .516$. Although the last two columns are not identical, the student should be impressed by the fact that they are quite close to each other, thus in a sense confirming the assumptions made.

We cannot close this section without pointing out a moral which seems to be best expressed by R. P. Agnew in his book "*Differential Equations*" (McGraw-Hill, New York, 1942, p. 30). Professor Agnew wrote, ". . . much of the progress in science is due to men who have the courage to make assumptions, the good sense to make reasonable assumptions, and the ability to draw correct conclusions from the assumptions."

EXERCISES

1. Write a formal proof, using mathematical induction, that $P_n(t) = e^{-\lambda t}(\lambda t)^n/n!$, $n = 0, 1, \cdots$.

2. Prove: $\sum_{n=0}^{\infty} P_n(t) = 1$.

3. Prove:

(a) $\sum_{n=0}^{\infty} nP_n(t) = \lambda t$,

(b) $\sum_{n=0}^{\infty} n^2P_n(t) = \lambda t + \lambda^2 t^2$.

CHAPTER 3

Random Variables and Probability Distributions

3.1 The Definition of a Function

The treatment of the notion of random variable varies from book to book on probability and statistics at the undergraduate level. In this book the notion of random variable will be treated as a function. In addition, the notion of function will be developed in terms of the theory of sets. This chapter is primarily concerned with random variables, and this initial section must necessarily deal with the definition of function.

The basic objects out of which all mathematical notions are developed are sets. For our purposes a set will remain an undefined entity. Loosely speaking, a set may be considered as a collection of objects. One example of a set has already been encountered by the student, namely, an event, which is a set of elementary events. Other examples of sets are a set of numbers, a set of events, and a set of students. An arbitrary set will be denoted by a capital italic letter, e.g., A, B, and if the set is denoted by the objects it contains, then these objects are enclosed by braces, $\{\ \}$. For example, $\{1, 2, 3\}$ is a set of three objects, these objects being the symbols 1, 2, 3. Associated with the undefined notion of set is the undefined relation "belongs to." For any object and any set, one and only one of the following is true: (i) the object "belongs to" the set, or (ii) the object does not belong to the set. The objects which belong to a set (or out of which the set is formed) are called the elements (or members) of the set. If the object or element denoted by a belongs to a set denoted by A, we shall record this fact by writing $a \in A$. Any collection of elements of a set will be called a subset of the set.

Let us consider the set $\{a, b\}$ consisting of the elements a and b. The set of all subsets $\mathcal{S}\{a, b\}$ of the set $\{a, b\}$ consists of elements ϕ (the empty set), $\{a\}$, $\{b\}$, and $\{a, b\}$, i.e.,

$$\mathcal{S}\{a, b\} = \{\phi, \{a\}, \{b\}, \{a, b\}\}.$$

A certain *subset* of $\mathcal{S}\{a, b\}$ will occupy our interest for the remainder of this section.

Definition. *The ordered pair* $\langle a, b\rangle$ *is defined to be the subset* $\{\{a\}, \{a, b\}\}$ *of* $\mathcal{S}\{a, b\}$.

One usually refers to a as the first element or first coordinate of $\langle a, b\rangle$ and to b as the second element or second coordinate of $\langle a, b\rangle$.

Definition. *Let A and B be sets. The Cartesian product* $A \times B$ *of A and B is defined to be the set of all possible ordered pairs* $\langle a, b\rangle$ *formed from elements a which belong to the set A and elements b which belong to the set B.*

Symbolically, this definition may be written

$$A \times B = \{\langle a, b\rangle | a \in A, b \in B\}.$$

For example, if A is a finite set consisting of m elements $a_1, a_2, \cdots, a_m$, and if B is a finite set containing n elements $b_1, b_2, \cdots, b_n$, then $A \times B$ is a *set* consisting of the following mn elements:

$$\begin{array}{cccc} \langle a_1, b_1\rangle & \langle a_1, b_2\rangle & \cdots & \langle a_1, b_n\rangle \\ \langle a_2, b_1\rangle & \langle a_2, b_2\rangle & \cdots & \langle a_2, b_n\rangle \\ \cdot & \cdot & & \cdot \\ \cdot & \cdot & & \cdot \\ \cdot & \cdot & & \cdot \\ \langle a_m, b_1\rangle & \langle a_m, b_2\rangle & \cdots & \langle a_m, b_n\rangle. \end{array}$$

Definition. *A relation R between the set A and the set B is a subset of* $A \times B$.

Definition. *The domain* dom R *of a relation R between sets A and B is defined as the set of those elements* $a \in A$ *such that for some* $b \in B$, $\langle a, b\rangle \in R$, *or, in symbols,*

$$\text{dom } R = \{a \in A | \textit{for some } b \in B, \langle a, b\rangle \in R\}.$$

In other words, the domain of relation R, dom R, is the set of all first coordinates of the ordered pairs in R.

Definition. *The range of a relation R, denoted by* range R, *is defined as the set of those elements* $b \in B$ *such that for some* $a \in A$, $\langle a, b\rangle \in R$, *or in symbols,*

$$\text{range } R = \{b \in B | \textit{for some } a \in A, \langle a, b\rangle \in R\}.$$

In other words, the range of a relation R is the set of all second coordinates found in the ordered pairs in R.

Definition. *A function f from A to B (or a function f whose domain is A and whose range is in B) is defined as a relation between A and B for which* dom $f = A$ *and such that if* $\langle a, b_1 \rangle \in f$ *and if* $\langle a, b_2 \rangle \in f$, *then* $b_1 = b_2$.

Another way of saying this is to say that a function f is a relation in which no two distinct ordered pairs have the same first coordinate. Thus, if $a \in \text{dom} f$, there is one and only one element $b \in B$ such that $\langle a, b \rangle \in f$. This element b is usually denoted by $f(a)$; i.e., if $a \in \text{dom} f$, then $f(a)$ is the one and only element in B such that $\langle a, f(a) \rangle \in f$.

EXERCISES

1. Is a Cartesian product associative, i.e., if A, B, and C are sets, does $(A \times B) \times C = A \times (B \times C)$?

2. Let $A = \{\alpha, \beta, \gamma\}$ and $B = \{x, y, z, w\}$. How many elements are in $A \times B$? List them.

3. By $[a, b]$ we mean the set of all real numbers not less than a nor greater than b. Let $A = [-.5, 1.5]$ and $B = [2, 4]$. Draw a picture of $A \times B$.

4. Let $A = [-1, 1]$ and $B = [-1, 1]$. Let relation R between A and B be defined by $R = \{\langle x, y \rangle | x^2 + y^2 \leqq \frac{1}{4}\}$. Shade in $A \times B$ with horizontal lines, and shade in R with vertical lines.

5. Check whether the relation R in problem 4 is a function or not.

6. Let $A = B =$ the set of all real numbers. Let $\mathbf{I}$ denote the relation

$$\mathbf{I} = \{\langle x, x \rangle | x \in A\}$$

between A and B. Also, for every real number t, let $\mathbf{t}$ denote the relation

$$\mathbf{t} = \{\langle \theta, t \rangle | \theta \in A\}.$$

Are $\mathbf{I}$ and $\mathbf{t}$ functions? If so, prove it. Draw pictures of $\mathbf{I}$, $\mathbf{2}$, $\mathbf{-7.9}$.

7. Prove the fundamental property of ordered pairs: $\langle a, b \rangle = \langle c, d \rangle$ if and only if $a = c$ and $b = d$.

3.2 The Definition of a Random Variable

Now we return to probability theory. The purpose of this section is to define random variable and to prove some theorems which present equivalent definitions to the one which will be given. First, a general warning should be sounded that the expression "random variable" is a misnomer. A random variable is not "random," nor is it a "variable," whatever the last quoted word might mean. A random variable is simply a function with a certain restrictive property. The formal definition is now presented.

Let Ω be an arbitrary fundamental probability set, and let $\mathcal{A}$ be a sigma-field of events over Ω.

Definition. *A random variable X is a function whose domain is Ω and whose range is a nonempty set of real numbers such that for every real number x the set of elementary events ω for which $X(\omega) \leqq x$ is an event, i.e., an element of $\mathcal{A}$. This last requirement may be written: $\{\omega \in \Omega | X(\omega) \leqq x\} \in \mathcal{A}$.*

Let us consider an example. The simplest game is that of tossing a coin once. In this case, $\Omega = \{H, T\}$, and $\mathcal{A}$ is the set of all subsets. Let the random variable X in this case denote "the number of heads in $\cdots$." Then X is a function over Ω defined by: $X(H) = 1$ and $X(T) = 0$. Thus

$$\{\omega \in \Omega | X(\omega) \leqq x\} = \begin{cases} \phi & \text{if } x < 0 \\ \{T\} & \text{if } 0 \leqq x < 1 \\ \{H, T\} & \text{if } x > 1. \end{cases}$$

Let us consider yet another example. We consider the game of tossing a pair of dice. A fundamental probability space Ω for this game is listed below:

(1, 1)	(1, 2)	(1, 3)	(1, 4)	(1, 5)	(1, 6)
	(2, 2)	(2, 3)	(2, 4)	(2, 5)	(2, 6)
		(3, 3)	(3, 4)	(3, 5)	(3, 6)
			(4, 4)	(4, 5)	(4, 6)
				(5, 5)	(5, 6)
					(6, 6).

In this game, $\mathcal{A}$ is the set of all subsets of Ω, i.e., every collection of elementary events is an event. Let us consider the random variable X as the sum of the upturned faces. Thus, for each elementary event (i, j) we have $X(i, j) = i + j$. Now let us take some special values of x to obtain

$$\{\omega \in \Omega | X(\omega) \leqq 1.2\} = \phi,$$
$$\{\omega \in \Omega | X(\omega) \leqq 3.1\} = \{(1, 1), (1, 2)\}$$

since $X(1, 1) = 2$ and $X(1, 2) = 3$, and

$$\{\omega \in \Omega | X(\omega) \leqq 4\} = \{(1, 1), (1, 2), (1, 3), (2, 2)\}.$$

Notation. From now on we shall use the notation $[X \leqq x]$ in place of the expression $\{\omega \in \Omega | X(\omega) \leqq x\}$. Also, we shall denote $\{\omega \in \Omega | X(\omega) < x\}$ by $[X < x]$, $\{\omega \in \Omega | X(\omega) \geqq x\}$ by $[X \geqq x]$, and $\{\omega \in \Omega | X(\omega) > x\}$ by $[X > x]$. In general, if S is any set of real numbers, then we shall denote $\{\omega \in \Omega | X(\omega) \in S\}$ by $[X \in S]$.

We now derive conditions equivalent to that given in the definition of random variable. First we need two lemmas.

1. Lemma. *If X is any function whose domain is Ω and whose range is a nonempty set of real numbers, then*

$$\bigcup_{n=1}^{\infty} [X \leqq x - 2^{-n}] = [X < x]$$

for every real number x.

Proof. Let $\omega \in \bigcup_{n=1}^{\infty} [X \leqq x - 2^{-n}]$. Then there is at least one integer n such that $\omega \in [X \leqq x - 2^{-n}]$. This means that $X(\omega) \leqq x - 2^{-n}$, which implies that $X(\omega) < x$, or $\omega \in [X < x]$. On the other hand, if $\omega \in [X < x]$, then $X(\omega) < x$. Select m large enough so that $2^{-m} \leqq x - X(\omega)$. Then $a \in [X \leqq x - 2^{-m}] \subset \bigcup_{n=1}^{\infty} [X \leqq x - 2^{-n}]$, which completes the proof.

2. Lemma. *If X is any function whose domain is Ω and whose range is a nonempty set of real numbers, then*

$$\bigcap_{n=1}^{\infty} [X < x + 2^{-n}] = [X \leqq x]$$

for every real number x.

Proof. Let $\omega \in [X \leqq x]$. Then $X(\omega) \leqq x < x + 2^{-n}$ for every positive integer n. Thus $\omega \in \bigcap_{n=1}^{\infty} [X < x + 2^{-n}]$. On the other hand, if $\omega \in \bigcap_{n=1}^{\infty} [X < x + 2^{-n}]$, then $X(\omega) < x + 2^{-n}$ for $n = 1, 2, \cdots$. This makes it impossible for the inequality $X(\omega) > x$ to be true, for if it *were*, we could find an n such that $2^{-n} < X(\omega) - x$, thus violating the inequality in the preceding sentence. Hence $X(\omega) \leqq x$, which implies that $\omega \in [X \leqq x]$. This completes the proof.

3. Theorem. *Let X be a function whose domain is Ω and whose range is a nonempty set of real numbers. Then X is a random variable if and only if, for every real number x, $[X < x] \in \mathcal{A}$.*

Proof. We first prove the "only if" part. If X is a random variable, then $[X \leqq x - 2^{-n}] \in \mathcal{A}$ for $n = 1, 2, \cdots$. Since a denumerable union of events is an event, we have

$$\bigcup_{n=1}^{\infty} [X \leqq x - 2^{-n}] \in \mathcal{A}.$$

Lemma 1 allows us to conclude that $[X < x] \in \mathcal{A}$. Conversely, if $[X < t] \in \mathcal{A}$ for every real number t, then $[X < x + 2^{-n}] \in \mathcal{A}$ for $n = 1, 2, \cdots$. This implies that

$$\bigcap_{n=1}^{\infty} [X < x + 2^{-n}] \in \mathcal{A},$$

which, with Lemma 2, implies that $[X \leqq x] \in \mathcal{A}$. This proves the theorem.

The proofs of the next two theorems are based directly on the definition of random variable, Theorem 3, and the fact that $A \in \mathcal{A}$ implies that $A^c \in \mathcal{A}$. These proofs are left to the student.

4. Theorem. *Let X be a function whose domain is Ω and whose range is a nonempty set of real numbers. Then X is a random variable if and only if $[X \geqq x] \in \mathcal{A}$ for every real number x.*

5. Theorem. *Let X be a function whose domain is Ω and whose range is a nonempty set of real numbers. Then X is a random variable if and only if $[X > x] \in \mathcal{A}$ for every real number x.*

EXERCISES

1. Prove Theorem 4.

2. Prove Theorem 5.

3. Let X denote the number of heads in three tosses of a coin.
(a) List the elementary events in Ω.
(b) What values does X assign to the elementary events in Ω?
(c) What elementary events are in the event $[X \leqq 1.78]$?
(d) What elementary events are in $[X \leqq 2.65]$?

4. Prove the Theorem: *Let X be a function whose domain is Ω and whose range is a nonempty set of real numbers. Then X is a random variable if and only if $[a < X \leqq b] \in \mathcal{A}$ for every pair of real numbers a, b where $a < b$.*

3.3 Combinations of Random Variables

The purpose of this section is to define algebraic operations on random variables and to prove that the new functions formed are also random variables. We shall conclude this section by introducing the simplest kind of random variables, the indicators, with a brief outline of their properties.

By the sum of two random variables X and Y we mean the function which assigns to every elementary event $\omega \in \Omega$ the number $X(\omega) + Y(\omega)$. Formally, we define the sum of X and Y, $X + Y$, by

$$X + Y = \{\langle \omega, X(\omega) + Y(\omega)\rangle | \omega \in \Omega\}.$$

1. Theorem. *If X and Y are random variables, then $X + Y$ is a random variable.*

Proof. Let us consider the set

$$A = \bigcup_r [X < r][Y < z - r]$$

where r runs through the set of all rational numbers. Since the set of all rational numbers is denumerable, $A \in \mathcal{A}$. Because of this and Theorem 3 in Section 3.2 we need only prove that

$$A = [X + Y < z].$$

First, it is clear that $A \subset [X + Y < z]$, so we need only prove inclusion in the reverse direction. Let $\omega \in [X + Y < z]$. Then $X(\omega) + Y(\omega) < z$. Let r_0 be any rational number satisfying the inequality $X(\omega) < r_0 < z - Y(\omega)$. Then $X(\omega) < r_0$ and $Y(\omega) < z - r_0$, so $\omega \in [X < r_0][Y < z - r_0] \subset A$. This proves the theorem.

If X is a random variable and K is any real number, then by KX we mean the function which assigns to every $\omega \in \Omega$ the number $KX(\omega)$. Formally,

$$KX = \{\langle\omega, KX(\omega)\rangle | \omega \in \Omega\}.$$

2. Theorem. *If X is a random variable, and if K is any real number. then KX is a random variable.*

Proof. We consider three cases.

(i) $K = 0$. In this case

$$[KX \leqq x] = \begin{cases} \phi \in \mathcal{A} & \text{if } x < 0 \\ \Omega \in \mathcal{A} & \text{if } x \geqq 0. \end{cases}$$

(ii) $K > 0$. In this case, for every real x,

$$[KX \leqq x] = [X \leqq x/K] \in \mathcal{A}.$$

(iii) $K < 0$. In this case, for every real x,

$$[KX \leqq x] = [X \geqq x/K] \in \mathcal{A}.$$

The proofs in these three cases prove the theorem.

If X and Y are random variables, then the function XY is a function which assigns to every $\omega \in \Omega$ the number $X(\omega)Y(\omega)$. This may be written as

$$XY = \{\langle\omega, X(\omega)Y(\omega)\rangle | \omega \in \Omega\}.$$

3. Theorem. *If X is a random variable, then X^2 is a random variable.*

Proof. This easily follows from the fact that for every $x < 0$, $[X^2 \leqq x] = \phi \in \mathcal{A}$, and for every $x \geqq 0$,

$$[X^2 \leqq x] = [-\sqrt{x} \leqq X \leqq \sqrt{x}] = [X \leqq \sqrt{x}][X \geqq -\sqrt{x}] \in \mathcal{A}.$$

4. Theorem. *If X and Y are random variables, then XY is a random variable.*

Proof. Repeated use of Theorems 1, 2, and 3 allows us to make the following sequence of statements:

(i) $X + Y$ and $X - Y$ are random variables,
(ii) $(X + Y)^2$ and $(X - Y)^2$ are random variables, and
(iii) $\{(X + Y)^2 - (X - Y)^2\}/4$ is a random variable.

But this last random variable obviously equals XY, and thus XY is a random variable.

If X and Y are random variables, then X/Y is a function which assigns to every $\omega \in \Omega$ the number $X(\omega)/Y(\omega)$, provided $Y(\omega) \neq 0$. We may also write

$$X/Y = \{\langle \omega, X(\omega)/Y(\omega)\rangle | \omega \in \Omega \quad \text{and} \quad Y(\omega) \neq 0\}.$$

The reader should note that dom $X/Y = [Y \neq 0]$.

5. Theorem. *If X and Y are random variables and $[Y = 0] = \phi$, then X/Y is a random variable.*

Proof. One may write

$$\begin{aligned}[X/Y \leqq x] &= [X/Y \leqq x][Y < 0] + [X/Y \leqq x][Y > 0] \\ &= [X \geqq xY][Y < 0] + [X \leqq xY][Y > 0] \\ &= [X - xY \geqq 0][Y < 0] + [X - xY \leqq 0][Y > 0].\end{aligned}$$

Each of these last four collections of elementary events are events because of theorems of Sections 3.2 and 3.3, which in turn implies that $[X/Y \leqq x] \in \mathcal{A}$.

For two random variables X and Y we define the function max $\{X, Y\}$ to be the function which assigns to every $\omega \in \Omega$ the larger of the two numbers $X(\omega)$, $Y(\omega)$.

6. Theorem. *If X and Y are random variables, then* max $\{X, Y\}$ *is a random variable.*

Proof. This theorem follows from the fact that

$$[\max \{X, Y\} \leqq z] = [X \leqq z][Y \leqq z] \in \mathcal{A}.$$

The simplest type of random variable is that which indicates an event. Suppose A is a set of elementary events in Ω (and not necessarily an event). Then the indicator of A, I_A, is a function defined as:

$$I_A(\omega) = \begin{cases} 1 & \text{if} \quad \omega \in A \\ 0 & \text{if} \quad \omega \in A^c. \end{cases}$$

Truly, I_A "indicates" A. If A occurs, then an elementary event ω in A occurs and $I_A(\omega) = 1$; if A does not occur, then an elementary event ω in A^c occurs and $I_A(\omega) = 0$.

The following theorems are so obvious and easy to prove that their proofs are left to the student.

7. Theorem. *Let A be a set of elementary events in Ω. Then I_A is a random variable if and only if $A \in \mathcal{A}$.*

Hint of proof: Use the relation

$$[I_A \leqq x] = \begin{cases} \phi & \text{if } x < 0 \\ A^c & \text{if } 0 \leqq x < 1 \\ \Omega & \text{if } 1 \leqq x. \end{cases}$$

8. Theorem. $I_\Omega = 1$, *i.e.*, $I_\Omega(\omega) = 1$ *for every* $\omega \in \Omega$.

9. Theorem. $(I_A)^2 = I_A$ *for every* $A \in \mathcal{A}$.

10. Theorem. $1 - I_A = I_{A^c}$ *for every* $A \in \mathcal{A}$.

11. Theorem. $I_A I_B = I_{AB}$ *for every* $A \in \mathcal{A}$ *and every* $B \in \mathcal{A}$.

12. Theorem. $I_{A \cup B} = \max \{I_A, I_B\}$ *for every* $A \in \mathcal{A}$ *and every* $B \in \mathcal{A}$.

13. Theorem. $I_A + I_B = I_{A+B}$ *for every disjoint pair of events* A, B.

EXERCISES

1. Prove: If X and Y are random variables, then $[\min (X, Y) \leqq z] = [X \leqq z] \cup [Y \leqq z]$.

2. Using problem 1, prove that if X and Y are random variables, then $\min (X, Y)$ is a random variable.

3. Prove: If X and Y are random variables, then

$$-\max(-X, -Y) = \min(X, Y).$$

Then use this fact to deduce problem 2 as a corollary to Theorem 6.

4–10. Prove Theorems 7–13.

3.4 Distribution Functions

Although the notion of random variable is the central notion of probability and statistics, it is not considered of interest by itself. With every random variable is associated another function known as its distribution function. The study of probability (and statistics) thus becomes distinct from a usual course in analysis in that properties of functions (random variables) are considered in terms of corresponding distribution functions.

Definition. *If X is a random variable, then the distribution function of X, F_X is a function defined by*

$$F_X(x) = P[X \leqq x]$$

for every real number x. (The reader should note that it is at this point that we need the requirement $[X \leqq x] \in \mathcal{A}$ for every real x in our definition of random variable.)

Let us consider an example of the game where a fair (or unbiased) coin is tossed three times. In this case Ω consists of the following eight elementary events:

$$\begin{array}{cccc} (HHH) & (HHT) & (HTH) & (HTT) \\ (THH) & (THT) & (TTH) & (TTT). \end{array}$$

Let X denote the number of heads which appear in the three tosses of the coin. Thus $X(HHH) = 3$, $X(HHT) = 2$, $X(HTH) = 2$, $X(HTT) = 1, \cdots, X(TTT) = 0$. Suppose $x < 0$, say $x = -2.718$. Then $[X \leqq x] = \phi$ and $P[X \leqq x] = 0$. If $0 \leqq x < 1$, say $x = .518$, then $[X \leqq x] = \{(TTT)\}$ and $P[X \leqq x] = \frac{1}{8}$. If $1 \leqq x < 2$, then $[X \leqq x] = \{(TTT), (HTT), (THT), (TTH)\}$, and $P[X \leqq x] = \frac{1}{2}$. If $2 \leqq x < 3$, then $[X \leqq x] = \{(HHT), (HTH), (HTT), (THH), (THT), (TTH), (TTT)\}$, and $P[X \leqq x] = \frac{7}{8}$. Finally if $x \geqq 3$, then $[X \leqq x] = \Omega$ and $P[X \leqq x] = 1$. Thus the distribution function is:

$$F_X(x) = \begin{cases} 0 & \text{if} \quad -\infty < x < 0 \\ \frac{1}{8} & \text{if} \quad 0 \leqq x < 1 \\ \frac{1}{2} & \text{if} \quad 1 \leqq x < 2 \\ \frac{7}{8} & \text{if} \quad 2 \leqq x < 3 \\ 1 & \text{if} \quad 3 \leqq x. \end{cases}$$

The graph of $F_X(x)$ is shown in Fig. 3. This is but just one particular case of a distribution function. We now prove some properties of distribution functions.

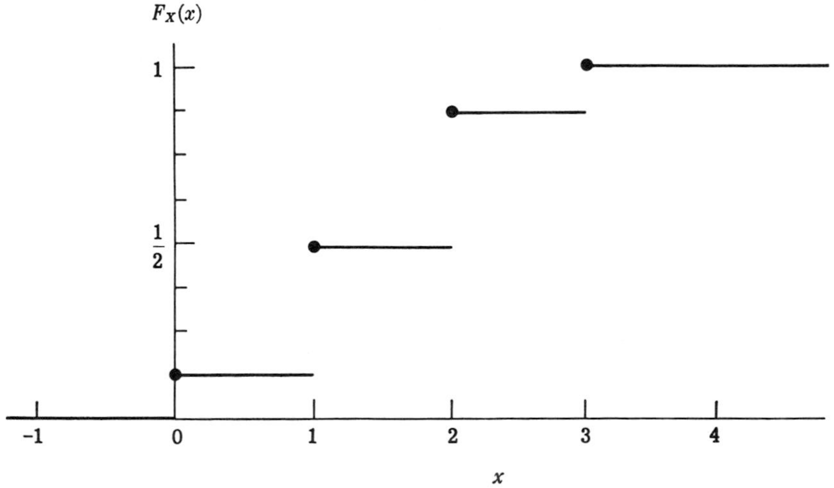

Fig. 3

1. Theorem. *Let X be a random variable and F_X its distribution function. If $x_1 < x_2$, then $F_X(x_1) \leqq F_X(x_2)$.*

Proof. Since one can write

$$[X \leqq x_2] = [X \leqq x_1] + [x_1 < X \leqq x_2],$$

then, upon taking probabilities of both sides, we obtain

$$P[X \leqq x_2] = P[X \leqq x_1] + P[x_1 < X \leqq x_2] \geqq P[X \leqq x_1],$$

which proves the theorem.

2. Theorem. *If F_X is the distribution function of a random variable X, then $\lim_{x \to \infty} F_X(x) = 1$.*

Proof. First let us recall the definition of $\lim_{x \to \infty} g(x) = L$. By this we mean that for every $\epsilon > 0$ there exists a value of x, say x_ϵ, such that $L - \epsilon < g(x) < L + \epsilon$ for every $x > x_\epsilon$. Since $F_X(x)$ is a probability we need only show that for arbitrary $\epsilon > 0$, there exists a real number x_ϵ such that $1 - \epsilon < F_X(x)$ for all $x > x_\epsilon$. Since X is a random variable, and since $X(\omega)$ is finite for every $\omega \in \Omega$, we see that it is possible to write

$$\Omega = [X \leqq 0] + \sum_{n=1}^{\infty} [n - 1 < X \leqq n].$$

Taking the probabilities of both sides we obtain

$$1 = P[X \leqq 0] + \sum_{n=1}^{\infty} P[n - 1 < X \leqq n].$$

Thus the infinite series is convergent, and we see that there exists an integer N_ϵ such that for all $n > N_\epsilon$,

$$P[X \leqq 0] + \sum_{k=1}^{n} P[k - 1 < X \leqq k] > 1 - \epsilon,$$

or

$$P[X \leqq n] > 1 - \epsilon.$$

Select $x_\epsilon = N_\epsilon + 1$. Applying Theorem 1 we obtain $F_X(x) > 1 - \epsilon$ for all $x > x_\epsilon$, which concludes the proof of the theorem.

3. Theorem. *If F_X is the distribution function of a random variable X, then*

$$\lim_{x \to -\infty} F_X(x) = 0.$$

Proof. Let $\epsilon > 0$ be arbitrary. We must show that there exists a real number x_ϵ such that $F_X(x) < \epsilon$ for all $x < x_\epsilon$. By the same reasoning as above, we note that

$$\Omega = [X > 0] + \sum_{k=0}^{\infty} [-(k+1) < X \leqq -k].$$

If we take the probability of both sides we obtain

$$1 = P[X > 0] + \sum_{k=0}^{\infty} P[-(k+1) < X \leqq -k].$$

Since this is a convergent series, there is an integer N_ϵ such that

$$P[X > 0] + \sum_{k=0}^{n} P[-(k+1) < X \leqq -k] > 1 - \epsilon$$

for all $n > N_\epsilon$. This is the same as writing

$$P[X \leqq -(n+1)] < \epsilon$$

for all $n > N_\epsilon$. Let $x_\epsilon = -(N_\epsilon + 1)$. Then, by Theorem 1, $F_X(x) < \epsilon$ for all $x < x_\epsilon$.

EXERCISES

1. Let X denote the number of heads which appear during two tosses of an unbiased coin.

(a) List the elementary events in Ω.
(b) Evaluate $X(\omega)$ for every $\omega \in \Omega$.
(c) Evaluate $F_X(x)$ and graph it.

2. Let Y denote the sum of the faces when two fair dice are tossed. Answer questions 1(a), 1(b), and 1(c) for Y.

3. Prove: If X is a random variable, then $F_X(x)$ is continuous from the right, i.e., at each x and for every $\epsilon > 0$ there is a $\delta > 0$ (which depends on x and ϵ) such that $F(x + h) - F(x) < \epsilon$ for all h for which $0 < h < \delta$. (*Hint:* use the relation

$$[x < X \leqq x + 1] = \sum_{n=1}^{\infty} \left[x + \frac{1}{n+1} < X \leqq x + \frac{1}{n}\right]$$

and the fact that the "tail" of a convergent series converges to zero.)

4. In Polya's urn scheme (see Section 2.1), let $r = 3$, $b = 2$, $c = 1$. Let Z denote the number of red balls selected in the first three trials. Answer questions 1(a), 1(b), and 1(c) for Z.

3.5 Multivariate Distribution Functions

Random variables not only possess individual distribution functions but also joint distribution functions. We first consider the so-called bivariate distributions, namely, the joint distribution functions of two random variables.

Definition. *If X and Y are two random variables, then their joint (or bivariate) distribution function $F_{X,Y}(x, y)$ is defined by*

$$F_{X,Y}(x, y) = P([X \leqq x][Y \leqq y]).$$

Joint distribution functions have much the same properties as distribution functions of one random variable (or, the so-called univariate distribution function). The proofs of the following three theorems are so much like the proofs of the three theorems in Section 3.4 that only hints of the proofs will be supplied. Formal proofs of these theorems are left to the student.

1. Theorem. *If X and Y are random variables, if $x_1 \leqq x_2$ and if $y_1 \leqq y_2$, then*

$$F_{X,Y}(x_1, y_1) \leqq F_{X,Y}(x_2, y_2).$$

Hint of proof: Use the fact that

$$[X \leqq x_1][Y \leqq y_1] \subset [X \leqq x_2][Y \leqq y_2].$$

2. Theorem. *If X and Y are random variables, then*

(a) $\lim_{x \to \infty} F_{X,Y}(x, y) = F_Y(y)$ *for every y,*

and

(b) $\lim_{y \to \infty} F_{X,Y}(x, y) = F_X(x)$ *for every x.*

Hint of proof: In order to prove part (a), one should use the fact that

$$[Y \leqq y] = [X \leqq 0][Y \leqq y] + \sum_{k=1}^{\infty} [k - 1 < X \leqq k][Y \leqq y]$$

and then follow closely the steps in the proof of Theorem 2 in Section 3.4. In order to prove part (b), one should use the result in part (a) and the fact that $F_{X,Y}(x, y) = F_{Y,X}(y, x)$.

3. Theorem. *If X and Y are random variables, then*

(a) $\lim_{x \to -\infty} F_{X,Y}(x, y) = 0,$

and

(b) $\lim_{y \to -\infty} F_{X,Y}(x, y) = 0.$

The proof of this theorem is very much like the proof of Theorem 3 in Section 3.4.

We need not present a formal development at this time of the general notion of multivariate distributions. After carefully going through the development presented this far, the reader should be able to supply a definition of the joint distribution function of three random variables X_1, X_2, X_3 and should be able to prove theorems analogous to Theorems 1, 2, and 3. In fact, the student is urged to carry through this development for three random variables. Then the general picture for four or more random variables will appear clearly to him.

We conclude this section on multivariate distributions by introducing the notion of independent random variables.

Definition. *Let $X_1, X_2, \cdots, X_n, \cdots$ denote a (finite or infinite) set of random variables. These random variables are said to be* **independent** *(or* **stochastically independent***) if for all possible selections of corresponding pairs of real numbers*

$$(a_1, b_1), (a_2, b_2), \cdots, (a_n, b_n), \cdots,$$

where $a_i \leqq b_i$ for all i, and where the values $\pm\infty$ are allowed, the events $[a_1 < X_1 \leqq b_1], [a_2 < X_2 \leqq b_2], \cdots, [a_n < X_n \leqq b_n], \cdots$ are independent. We insert in this definition an equivalent statement whose proof is too complicated to be included: these random variables are said to be independent if for every sequence of intervals $I_1, I_2, \cdots, I_n, \cdots,$ where each I_n can be of the form (a, b), $[a, b]$, $(a, b]$ or $[a, b)$, the events

$$[X_1 \in I_1], [X_2 \in I_2], \cdots, [X_n \in I_n], \cdots$$

are independent.

4. Theorem. *Let $X_1, X_2, \cdots, X_m$ denote any m random variables. A necessary and sufficient condition that these random variables be independent is that for every m-tuple $(x_1, x_2, \cdots, x_m)$ of real numbers the equality*

$$F_{X_1,X_2,\ldots,X_m}(x_1, x_2, \cdots, x_m) = \prod_{j=1}^{m} F_{X_j}(x_j)$$

holds.

Proof. We first prove that the condition is necessary. Accordingly, we assume the random variables are independent and prove that the above equality holds. In this case, let $-\infty = a_1 = a_2 = \cdots = a_m$ and $x_i = b_i$ for $1 \leqq i \leqq m$. Then by the definition of independence and joint distribution we have

$$\begin{aligned} &F_{X_1,X_2,\ldots,X_m}(x_1, x_2, \cdots, x_m) \\ &= P\left(\bigcap_{k=1}^{m} [-\infty < X_k \leqq x_k]\right) \\ &= \prod_{k=1}^{m} P[X_k \leqq x_k] = \prod_{k=1}^{m} F_{X_k}(x_k), \end{aligned}$$

which establishes the condition. We now prove that the equation in the theorem implies independence of the random variables. We first remark that if $(i_1, i_2, \cdots, i_k)$ is a subset of the integers $(1, 2, \cdots, m)$, then

$$F_{X_{i_1}, X_{i_2}, \ldots, X_{i_k}}(x_{i_1}, x_{i_2}, \cdots, x_{i_k}) = \prod_{j=1}^{k} F_{X_{i_j}}(x_{i_j}).$$

This easily follows from the condition given in the theorem by taking the limit of both sides as $x_\alpha \to \infty$ where $\alpha \notin \{i_1, i_2, \cdots, i_k\}$ and by using Theorem 2 and Theorem 1 of this section. We next prove that

$$P([a_1 < X_1 \leqq b_1][a_2 < X_2 \leqq b_2]) = \prod_{j=1}^{2} P[a_j < X_j \leqq b_j].$$

Accordingly, we obtain from the above remark that $F_{X_1,X_2}(x_1, x_2) = F_{X_1}(x_1)F_{X_2}(x_2)$ for every x_1 and x_2. We first note that the following equalities hold:

$$\text{(a)} \qquad \begin{cases} F_{X_1,X_2}(b_1, b_2) = F_{X_1}(b_1)F_{X_2}(b_2) \\ F_{X_1,X_2}(a_1, b_2) = F_{X_1}(a_1)F_{X_2}(b_2) \\ F_{X_1,X_2}(b_1, a_2) = F_{X_1}(b_1)F_{X_2}(a_2) \\ F_{X_1,X_2}(a_1, a_2) = F_{X_1}(a_1)F_{X_2}(a_2). \end{cases}$$

Also, it is easy to verify that

$$\text{(b)} \qquad \begin{aligned} [X_1 \leqq b_1][X_2 \leqq b_2] = {} & [a_1 < X_1 \leqq b_1][a_2 < X_2 \leqq b_2] \\ & + [a_1 < X_1 \leqq b_1][X_2 \leqq a_2] \\ & + [X_1 \leqq a_1][a_2 < X_2 \leqq b_2] \\ & + [X_1 \leqq a_1][X_2 \leqq a_2]. \end{aligned}$$

Since

$$\begin{aligned} [X_1 \leqq b_1][X_2 \leqq a_2] = {} & [X_1 \leqq a_1][X_2 \leqq a_2] \\ & + [a_1 < X_1 \leqq b_1][X_2 \leqq a_2], \end{aligned}$$

we obtain, after taking probabilities of both sides, that

$$\text{(c)} \qquad P([a_1 < X_1 \leqq b_1][X_2 \leqq a_2]) = F_{X_1,X_2}(b_1, a_2) - F_{X_1,X_2}(a_1, a_2).$$

In a similar manner we obtain

$$\text{(d)} \qquad P([X_1 \leqq a_1][a_2 < X_2 \leqq b_2]) = F_{X_1,X_2}(a_1, b_2) - F_{X_1,X_2}(a_1, a_2).$$

Now if we take probabilities of both sides of Eq. (b) and make use of (c), (d), and (a), we finally obtain

$$\begin{aligned} P([a_1 < X_1 \leqq b_1][a_2 < X_2 \leqq b_2]) & \\ = {} & F_{X_1}(b_1)F_{X_2}(b_2) - F_{X_1}(a_1)F_{X_2}(b_2) \\ & - F_{X_1}(b_1)F_{X_2}(a_2) + F_{X_1}(a_1)F_{X_2}(a_2) \\ = {} & (F_{X_1}(b_1) - F_{X_1}(a_1))(F_{X_2}(b_2) - F_{X_2}(a_2)) \\ = {} & P[a_1 < X_1 \leqq b_1]P[a_2 < X_2 \leqq b_2]. \end{aligned}$$

If, in the above proof, one replaces X_1 by X_{i_1} and X_2 by X_{i_2}, then one proves that

$$P\left(\bigcap_{j=1}^{2} [a_{i_j} < X_{i_j} \leqq b_{i_j}]\right) = \prod_{j=1}^{2} P[a_{i_j} < X_{i_j} \leqq b_{i_j}].$$

The proof that

$$P\left(\bigcap_{j=1}^{k} [a_{i_j} < X_{i_j} \leqq b_{i_j}]\right) = \prod_{j=1}^{k} P[a_{i_j} < X_{i_j} \leqq b_{i_j}]$$

for $3 \leqq k \leqq m$ is the same but more complicated and is more a problem of complicated notation than one of mathematics. Consequently the proof of the above equation for $k \geqq 3$ will not be given here. However, the student is urged to try his hand at proving this in the case $k = 3$.

EXERCISES

1–3. Write out formal proofs of Theorems 1, 2, and 3, respectively.

4. State the definition of the joint distribution function for the random variables X, Y, Z.

5–7. State and prove theorems analogous to Theorems 1, 2, and 3 in the case of three random variables X, Y, Z.

8. Prove: If X, Y, Z are three random variables such that

$$F_{X,Y,Z}(x, y, z) = F_X(x)F_Y(y)F_Z(z)$$

for all real x, y, z, then X, Y, Z are independent.

CHAPTER 4

Discrete Distributions

4.1 Univariate Discrete Distributions

A random variable X will be called *discrete*, and its distribution function $F_X(x)$ will be called *discrete*, if the range of X is finite or denumerable. This means that there is a finite or denumerable set of real numbers $x_1, x_2, \cdots, x_n, \cdots$ such that $\sum_n [X = x_n] = \Omega$, where the union is taken over a finite set of integers in case the range of X is finite and over all positive integers in case the range of X is denumerable. For such a random variable the distribution function can be represented by

$$F_X(x) = \sum P[X = x_n]$$

where the sum is taken over those values of n for which $x_n \leqq x$. One way of writing this is

$$F_X(x) = \sum_{\{n|x_n \leqq x\}} P[X = x_n].$$

Associated with a discrete random variable or a discrete distribution is a function called the *discrete density function* or *discrete frequency function*, $f_X(x)$, which is defined by

$$f_X(x) = \begin{cases} P[X = x_n] & \text{if} \quad x = x_n, \\ 0 & \text{if} \quad x \neq x_n \text{ for all } n. \end{cases}$$

Then $\sum_n f_X(x_n) = 1$, and

$$\sum_{\{n|x_n \leqq x\}} f_X(x_n) = F_X(x).$$

Before we give the important discrete distributions of this chapter, let us consider the following useful notation. If x is a real number, then $[x]$ will denote the largest integer equal to or less than x. For example, $[3.17] = 3$, $[-2.718] = -3$, and $[100] = 100$. This notation will be used in cases where the range of a random variable X is the set of nonnegative integers, i.e., $x_0 = 0$, $x_1 = 1$, $x_2 = 2, \cdots, x_n = n, \cdots$. In such a case the distribution function of a discrete random variable is written

$$F_X(x) = \sum_{k=0}^{[x]} P[X = k] = \sum_{k=0}^{[x]} f_X(k).$$

It should also be noted that any discrete random variable can be represented in terms of indicators. For example, if $\{x_n\}$ is a sequence (finite or denumerable) of real numbers for which

$$\sum_n [X = x_n] = \Omega,$$

then X can be written as

$$X = \sum_n x_n I_{[X=x_n]}.$$

In order to see this, suppose that $\omega \in [X = x_1]$, i.e., suppose $X(\omega) = x_1$. Then

$$I_{[X=x_1]}(\omega) = 1 \quad \text{and} \quad I_{[X=x_n]}(\omega) = 0 \quad \text{for} \quad n \neq 1.$$

Thus, by the above representation,

$$\sum_n x_n I_{[X=x_n]}(\omega) = x_1 I_{[X=x_1]}(\omega) = x_1.$$

In general, if ω is such that $X(\omega) = x_k$, then

$$\sum_n x_n I_{[X=x_n]}(\omega) = x_k I_{[X=x_k]}(\omega) = x_k.$$

Representations such as these will be seen to be useful.

EXERCISES

1. Let X denote the number of heads minus the number of tails obtained in a game where a fair coin is tossed three times.

(a) Write X as a sum of products of constants and indicators.
(b) Find the discrete density function of X.
(c) Find the distribution function of X.

2. In a game where a pair of fair dice is tossed, let Y denote the smallest even number equal to or greater than the sum of the upturned faces of the dice. Answer questions 1(a), 1(b), and 1(c) for Y.

3. Evaluate the following: [3.67], [100], [9.99], [−2], and [−7.21].

4.2 The Binomial and Pascal Distributions

By a univariate distribution function we mean the distribution function of a single random variable. When we write "distribution" of a random variable we refer either to its distribution function or its discrete density function.

Definition. *By a sequence of n Bernoulli trials we mean a game (or experiment) consisting of n trials which satisfy the following three requirements:*

(i) one of two possible incompatible events, denoted by S and F, occurs as the outcome of each trial,

(ii) the outcome of each trial is independent of the outcomes of the other trials, and

(iii) the probability of S occurring at a trial does not change from trial to trial.

As an example of a sequence of n Bernoulli trials, the simplest is that of tossing a coin n times. Each toss of the coin is a trial. If heads occurs at a trial (i.e., a toss of the coin) we might call this outcome S; if tails occurs, we would then call this outcome F. It is easy to see that requirements (i), (ii), and (iii) of the above definition are satisfied in this case. Another example of a sequence of n Bernoulli trials is when one samples n times *with replacement* from a lot which contains both defective and nondefective items. If a defective item is obtained at a trial (selection), this outcome might be called S, while the outcome of obtaining a nondefective item would be called F.

In this definition the event S is usually referred to as "success" and F is usually referred to as "failure." The probability of S occurring in a trial is usually denoted by p, and the probability of F is usually denoted by q, where $q = 1 - p$. In a game or experiment consisting of n Bernoulli trials, the fundamental probability set Ω can be represented as the set of all possible n-tuples of letters involving S and F only. By the same reasoning as that used in Section 1.1 the reader should be able to see that there are 2^n elementary events in Ω. The event "success occurs in the kth trial," S_k, consists of all those elementary events or n-tuples in which S occurs in the kth place. If an elementary event has k S's and $n - k$ F's (where $0 \leqq k \leqq n$), then the probability of this elementary event is $p^k(1 - p)^{n-k}$ or $p^k q^{n-k}$.

Let us consider a sequence of n Bernoulli trials, where the probability of S (success) in each trial is p, $0 < p < 1$. Over the fundamental probability set Ω for this game or experiment let us define a random variable X, known as the number of S's (or number of successes) in the game. To every elementary event, X assigns an integer equal to the number of S's in the n-tuple involving S's and F's only. The event $[X = k]$ denotes that collection of n-tuples in each of which there are exactly k S's. It is easily seen that

$$\sum_{k=0}^{n} [X = k] = \Omega.$$

The number of elementary events in $[X = k]$ is easy to compute. In n trials there are $\binom{n}{k}$ ways of selecting k trials at which S occurs. Hence there are $\binom{n}{k}$ elementary events in the event $[X = k]$, each occurring with probability $p^k(1 - p)^{n-k}$. The discrete density function of X is

$$f_X(x) = P[X = x] = \binom{n}{x} p^x(1 - p)^{n-x}, \quad x = 0, 1, 2, \cdots, n.$$

This collection of probabilities is referred to as the *binomial distribution.* It is easy to see that they add up to unity. If one recalls the binomial theorem which asserts that

$$(a + b)^n = \sum_{k=0}^{n} \binom{n}{k} a^k b^{n-k},$$

then one obtains

$$\sum_{x=0}^{n} \binom{n}{x} p^x(1 - p)^{n-x} = [p + (1 - p)]^n = 1.$$

The distribution function of X can be written in the following form:

$$F_X(x) = P[X \leqq x] = \sum_{k=0}^{[x]} \binom{n}{k} p^k(1 - p)^{n-k}$$

for every real number x.

Let us now consider an unending sequence of Bernoulli trials. Here the fundamental probability set consists of all infinite-tuples of letters involving S and F only. For example, $(S, F, F, S, S, F, F, F, \cdots)$ is one elementary event of Ω for this game. Let Y denote the number of trials prior to the occurrence of the first success S, i.e., Y assigns to every elementary event the number of F's standing on the left of the first S. If p denotes the probability of S in each trial, then

$$f_Y(y) = P[Y = y] = q^y p, \quad y = 0, 1, 2, \cdots.$$

We can easily check that the sum of these probabilities is unity. First one should recall that if $|x| < 1$, then $\sum_{n=0}^{\infty} x^n = (1 - x)^{-1}$. Then $\sum_{y=0}^{\infty} q^y p = p \sum_{y=0}^{\infty} q^y = p(1 - q)^{-1} = 1$. This sequence of probabilities is called the *Pascal* (or *geometric*) *distribution.*

EXERCISES

1. Prove that the distribution function of Y above may be written as

$$F_Y(y) = \begin{cases} 1 - q^{[y]+1} & \text{if } y \geqq 0, \\ 0 & \text{if } y < 0. \end{cases}$$

2. An urn contains 4 white balls and 6 black balls. A trial consists of selecting a ball at random, observing it, and replacing it. Let X denote the number of white balls selected in 14 trials. Compute $P[X \leqq 7]$. (*Hint:* it is easier to use appropriate tables of the binomial distribution found in the library than to go through the labor of computation.)

3. There are 300 men and 700 women in a small liberal arts college. Twenty-five students are selected at random, the sampling done with replacement. Let Z denote the number of women in the sample. Find $P[Z \geqq 15]$. (*Hint:* see the hint at the end of problem 2.)

4. A shipment of 1000 items contains 10 defective ones. An inspector selects an item at random, inspects it, and if it is nondefective he replaces it in the shipment. Let U denote the number of inspections he makes prior to selecting the first defective. Find $P[75 \leqq U \leqq 95]$.

5. Let X have the Pascal distribution, i.e.,

$$P[X = n] = p(1 - p)^n, \quad n = 0, 1, 2, \cdots, \quad \text{where} \quad 0 < p < 1.$$

Show that the conditional probability

$$P([X = k + n] | [X \geqq k]) = P[X = n], \quad n = 0, 1, 2, \cdots, \quad k = 0, 1, \cdots.$$

6. Prove the converse of the assertion in problem 5: Let X be a random variable whose range is the set of all nonnegative integers and which satisfies

(i) $0 < P[X = 0] < 1$

and

(ii) $P([X = k + n] | [X \geqq k]) = P[X = n]$

for all nonnegative integers n, k. Then X has the Pascal distribution where $p = P[X = 0]$.

7. An unbiased coin is tossed n times. Let X denote the number of heads among the n outcomes. Find $P[X = k]$, where $k = 0, 1, 2, \cdots, n$.

8. Let $X_1, X_2, \cdots, X_n$ be n independent random variables, each having the same distribution function, i.e., $F_{X_k}(x) = F(x)$, $k = 1, 2, \cdots, n$, $-\infty < x < \infty$. Let Y denote the number of these random variables which do not exceed x. Prove that Y is a random variable and that $P[Y = k] = \binom{n}{k}(F(x))^k(1 - F(x))^{n-k}$ for $k = 0, 1, 2, \cdots, n$.

4.3 The Hypergeometric Distribution

The hypergeometric distribution is obtained through sampling *without* replacement. Let us consider an urn which contains r red balls and b black balls. One selects k of these balls at random, either one by one (without replacing them in the urn) or all at the same time ($0 \leqq k \leqq r + b$). In this case the fundamental probability space is the set of all ordered k-tuples of letters involving R (for red) and B (for black) only, where the number of R's in each k-tuple does not exceed r and the number of B's does not exceed b. Let the random variable X denote the number of red balls obtained in this "sample of size k." The only difficulty in determining the distribution of X is in determining which values X can take (i.e., the range of X). In the first place, X cannot take any value smaller than zero. Also, if $k > b$, then the smallest value that X can take is $k - b$, i.e., there have to be at least $k - b$ red balls in the sample. We see that the smallest value of X in any case is $\max\{0, k - b\}$. The largest value of X is never greater than k, and in case $r < k$ the maximum value of X is r. The largest value of X is therefore min (k, r). In order to compute $P[X = x]$, we reason that there are $\binom{r}{x}$ ways of selecting x red balls out of r red balls, and for each way one selects x red balls there are $\binom{b}{k-x}$ ways of selecting $k - x$ black balls out of b black balls. In addition, there are $\binom{r+b}{k}$ ways of selecting k balls out of $r + b$ balls. Thus, for x an integer,

$$P[X = x] = \frac{\binom{r}{x}\binom{b}{k-x}}{\binom{r+b}{k}},$$

where max $(0, k - b) \leqq x \leqq$ min (k, r). This set of probabilities is known as the *hypergeometric distribution*.

EXERCISES

1. A shipment contains N items, among which there are d defectives. One selects $n \leqq N$ of these items without replacement. Let X denote the number of defectives in the sample. Determine the distribution of X.

2. An urn contains 2 black balls and 3 red balls. One samples three times without replacement. Let Y denote the number of red balls in the sample. Find the discrete density function and the distribution function of Y.

3. A lake contains N fish. Among them there are r tagged fish. A fisherman catches n of the N fish and discovers that X fish that he has caught are tagged. Find the discrete density function of X.

4.4 The Poisson Distribution

In Section 2.3 the Poisson distribution was deduced from a set of postulates concerning radioactive disintegration. The Poisson distribution may also be obtained as a limit of the binomial distribution in a certain sense. Let us consider n Bernoulli trials where the probability of success in each trial is p_n and $np_n = \lambda > 0$. (It should be noted that p_n does not change from trial to trial but does depend on the number of trials we *intend* to consider.) Let X_n denote the number of successes that occur in the n Bernoulli trials, where p_n is the probability of success. A random variable X is said to have a Poisson distribution with parameter $\lambda > 0$ if for every integer $x, x = 0, 1, 2, \cdots,$

$$P[X = x] = \lim_{n \to \infty} P[X_n = x].$$

Let us evaluate this limit. We have

$$\begin{aligned} P[X_n = x] &= \binom{n}{x} p_n^x (1 - p_n)^{n-x} \\ &= \binom{n}{x}\left(\frac{\lambda}{n}\right)^x\left(1 - \frac{\lambda}{n}\right)^{n-x} \\ &= \left(1 - \frac{\lambda}{n}\right)^n \frac{\lambda^x}{x!} \cdot \frac{n(n-1)\cdots(n-x+1)}{n^x}\left(1 - \frac{\lambda}{n}\right)^{-x} \\ &= \left(1 - \frac{\lambda}{n}\right)^n \frac{\lambda^x}{x!} \prod_{j=0}^{x-1}\left(\left(1 - \frac{j}{n}\right)\left(1 - \frac{\lambda}{n}\right)^{-1}\right). \end{aligned}$$

At this point the student should recall from his elementary calculus course that

$$\lim_{x \to 0} (1 + x)^{1/x} = e.$$

Using this fact, we obtain

$$\begin{aligned} \lim_{n\to\infty}\left(1 - \frac{\lambda}{n}\right)^n &= \left\{\lim_{n\to\infty}\left(1 + \frac{(-\lambda)}{n}\right)^{n/(-\lambda)}\right\}^{-\lambda} \\ &= e^{-\lambda}. \end{aligned}$$

Consequently

$$\lim_{n\to\infty} P[X_n = x] = \frac{e^{-\lambda}\lambda^x}{x!}, \quad x = 0, 1, 2, \cdots.$$

Hence we see that the Poisson distribution can be obtained as an approximation to the binomial distribution when the probability, p, of success is small and n is large. In such a case the binomial distribution is approximated by the Poisson by taking $np = \lambda$. For example, if Y denotes the number of successes in 1000 Bernoulli trials with probability of success in each trial being $p = .0015$, then the distribution of Y may be approximated by a Poisson distribution with $\lambda = 1.5$. The reader easily observes that it is easier to obtain $P[X = 5]$ by computing $e^{-1.5}(1.5)^5/5!$ than by computing $\binom{1000}{5}(.0015)^5(.9985)^{995}$.

EXERCISE

1. In the example given at the end of this section, compute $P[X \geqq 3]$.

4.5 Multivariate Discrete Densities

The joint discrete density function of n discrete random variables X_1, $X_2, \cdots, X_n$ is defined by

$$f_{X_1,\ldots,X_n}(x_1, \cdots, x_n) = P\left(\bigcap_{i=1}^{n} [X_i = x_i]\right).$$

The purpose of this section is to derive two important joint discrete density functions: the multivariate hypergeometric distribution and the multinomial distribution. But first we must introduce the notion of conditional discrete densities.

Conditional discrete densities are nothing other than conditional probabilities of events. If $X_1, X_2, \cdots, X_m, X_{m+1}, \cdots, X_n$ are n random variables, then the conditional (discrete) density of $X_1, \cdots, X_m$, given $X_{m+1}, \cdots, X_n$, is given by

$$f_{X_1,\ldots,X_m|X_{m+1},\ldots,X_n}(x_1, \cdots, x_m|x_{m+1}, \cdots, x_n)$$
$$= P\left(\bigcap_{i=1}^{m} [X_i = x_i] \middle| \bigcap_{i=m+1}^{n} [X_i = x_i]\right).$$

By the very definition of conditional probability and by the multiplication rule we have

$$\begin{aligned} f_{X_1,X_2}(x_1, x_2) &= f_{X_1|X_2}(x_1|x_2)f_{X_2}(x_2) \\ &= f_{X_1}(x_1)f_{X_2|X_1}(x_2|x_1) \end{aligned}$$

and

$$f_{X_1,X_2,X_3}(x_1, x_2, x_3) = f_{X_1}(x_1)f_{X_2|X_1}(x_2|x_1)f_{X_3|X_1,X_2}(x_3|x_1, x_2).$$

This multiplication rule for conditional densities is now used to obtain the multivariate hypergeometric distribution.

Suppose an urn contains r red balls, w white balls, and b blue balls. Let us suppose that n balls are selected *without replacement*, where $1 \leqq n \leqq r + w + b$. Let X and Y denote the number of red balls and white balls, respectively, in the "sample of size n." We now derive the joint discrete density function using the fact that

$$f_{X,Y}(x, y) = f_X(x)f_{Y|X}(y|x).$$

Clearly

$$f_X(x) = \frac{\binom{r}{x}\binom{w+b}{n-x}}{\binom{r+w+b}{n}},$$

and

$$f_{Y|X}(y|x) = \frac{\binom{w}{y}\binom{b}{n-x-y}}{\binom{w+b}{n-x}}.$$

Before performing the desired multiplication it might be instructive to enter the details of the determination of the range of X, Y. In the first place $x \leqq n$. Also $x \leqq r$. Thus $x \leqq \min(n, r)$. On the other hand, $0 \leqq x$, and in the formula for $f_X(x)$ we see that $n - x \leqq w + b$ or $x \geqq n - w - b$. Consequently, $\max\{0, n - w - b\} \leqq x$. In a similar manner, by using the formula for $f_{Y|X}(y|x)$ we obtain $y \leqq \min(n - x, w)$ and $y \geqq \max\{0, n - x - b\}$. Thus

$$f_{X,Y}(x, y) = \frac{\binom{r}{x}\binom{w}{y}\binom{b}{n-x-y}}{\binom{r+w+b}{n}},$$

where $\max\{0, n - w - b\} \leqq x \leqq \min\{n, r\}$, and $\max\{0, n - x - b\} \leqq y \leqq \min\{n - x, w\}$.

We now introduce the multinomial distribution, which can be derived using the notion of conditional density, but which can be derived much easier by a straightforward argument. Suppose that a game consists of $k + 1$ mutually exclusive (i.e., disjoint) outcomes $A_1, A_2, \cdots, A_{k+1}$, where $k \geqq 1$. We play this game n times under identical conditions. Each play of this game is called a trial, and we assume that the outcomes of each of these n trials is independent of the outcomes of the other trials. Let X_i denote the number of times the event A_i occurs in the course of n trials, $i = 1, 2, \cdots, k + 1$. One sees that $X_1 + \cdots + X_{k+1} = n$. Now we want to find the joint discrete density function of $X_1, X_2, \cdots, X_k$, i.e., $f_{X_1,\cdots,X_k}(x_1, \cdots, x_k)$. The fundamental probability set Ω for this game is the set of all ordered n-tuples involving the symbols $A_1, A_2, \cdots, A_{k+1}$. It is easy to see that Ω contains $(k + 1)^n$ elementary events. The probability of an elementary event in which the number of A_1's is x_1, the number of A_2's is x_2, $\cdots$, the number of A_k's is x_k, and the number of A_{k+1}'s is $n - x_1 - x_2 - \cdots - x_k$ is

$$p_1^{x_1}p_2^{x_2} \cdots p_k^{x_k}(1 - p_1 - \cdots - p_k)^{n-x_1-x_2-\cdots-x_k},$$

where p_i is the probability that A_i occurs in a trial. We now must determine how many such elementary events there are in the event $[X_1 = x_1][X_2 = x_2]\cdots[X_k = x_k]$. The number of ways that x_1 out of n trials can be selected for A_1 to occur is $\binom{n}{x_1}$. The number of ways in which one can select x_2 trials out of the remaining $n - x_1$ trials for A_2 to occur is $\binom{n - x_1}{x_2}$, the number of ways in which one can select x_3 trials for A_3 to occur out of the remaining $n - x_1 - x_2$ trials is $\binom{n - x_1 - x_2}{x_3}$, $\cdots$, and the number of ways that one can select x_k trials out of the remaining $n - x_1 - \cdots - x_{k-1}$ trials for A_k to occur is $\binom{n - x_1 - x_2 - \cdots - x_{k-1}}{x_k}$.

Thus

$$f_{X_1,\ldots,X_k}(x_1,\cdots,x_k)=\binom{n}{x_1}\binom{n-x_1}{x_2}\cdots\binom{n-x_1-\cdots-x_{k-1}}{x_k}\prod_{i=1}^{k+1}p_i^{x_i},$$

where $x_{k+1}=n-x_1-\cdots-x_k$. The reader can easily check (by canceling) that

$$\binom{n}{x_1}\binom{n-x_1}{x_2}\cdots\binom{n-x_1-\cdots-x_{k-1}}{x_k}=\frac{n!}{x_1!x_2!\cdots x_k!x_{k+1}!}.$$

Consequently

$$f_{X_1,\ldots,X_k}(x_1,\cdots,x_k)=n!\prod_{i=1}^{k+1}\frac{p_i^{x_i}}{x_i!},$$

where $0\leqq x_1\leqq n, 0\leqq x_2\leqq n-x_1,\cdots$, and $0\leqq x_k\leqq n-x_1-\cdots-x_{k-1}$. The probability distribution given above is called the *multinomial distribution.*

EXERCISES

1. An urn contains r red balls, w white balls, b blue balls, and g green balls. One selects n balls at random *without replacement.* Let X_1, X_2, X_3 denote, respectively, the number of red, white, and blue balls in the sample of size n. Find the joint discrete density function of X_1, X_2, X_3.

2. Solve problem 1 when the sampling is done *with replacement.*

3. Let $Y_1, Y_2, \cdots, Y_n$ denote n independent random variables, and assume that for each Y_i, $P[Y_i=k]=p_k$, $k=1,2,\cdots,m+1$, where $p_1+p_2+\cdots+p_{m+1}=1$. Let Z_k denote the number of Y_i's equal to k, $k=1,\cdots,m+1$. Find $f_{Z_1,\ldots,Z_m}(z_1,\cdots,z_m)$.

4. What distribution does the multinomial distribution become when $k=1$?

5. In the density of the multivariate hypergeometric distribution derived in this section, rewrite the range of X, Y so that the range of Y does not depend on x.

6. Prove that

$$\binom{n}{x_1}\binom{n-x_1}{x_2}\cdots\binom{n-x_1-\cdots-x_{k-1}}{x_k}=\frac{n!}{x_1!\cdots x_k!(n-x_1-\cdots-x_k)!}.$$

CHAPTER 5

Absolutely Continuous Distributions

5.1 Absolutely Continuous Distributions

In many statistics books reference is made to some distributions (or "variates") called "discrete" and to others called "continuous." It is not so stated, but some students do begin to acquire the feeling that these two expressions dichotomize the class of all probability distributions. This feeling is not true. The "discrete" distributions and the "continuous" distributions are two small disjoint classes of distributions. They are easier to handle than the others if one is not familiar with the theory of measure and the Lebesgue integral. It must be emphasized that there are many distribution functions which are not "discrete" and which are not "continuous."

Another unfortunate aspect of this false dichotomy is that the distribution functions of the so-called "continuous random variables" (whatever this expression literally means) are only a small part of those distributions with continuous distribution functions. (The student should read this last sentence again.) The main point to be brought out by the last unparenthesized sentence is that the word "continuous" is used in a particular sense here. In this text we refer to it by its regular mathematical name: *absolutely continuous.*

Definition. *A random variable X is said to have an absolutely continuous distribution if there exists a function $f_X(x)$ such that*

$$F_X(x) = \int_{-\infty}^{x} f_X(t)\,dt$$

for every real number x.

In this definition the function $f_X(x)$ is called a *density function* of the random variable X or of the distribution function $F_X(x)$. Let us consider an example. Suppose

$$F_X(x) = \begin{cases} 0 & \text{if } x \leqq 0 \\ x/2 & \text{if } 0 < x < 2 \\ 1 & \text{if } x \geqq 2. \end{cases}$$

Then X certainly possesses an absolutely continuous distribution, because if we take

$$f_X(x) = \begin{cases} 0 & \text{if } x \leqq 0 \text{ or } x \geqq 2 \\ \frac{1}{2} & \text{if } 0 < x < 2, \end{cases}$$

then one may easily verify that for every real number x,

$$F_X(x) = \int_{-\infty}^{x} f_X(t)\, dt.$$

Definition. *The random variables* $X_1, \cdots, X_n$ *are said to have a joint absolutely continuous distribution if there exists a function* $f_{X_1,\ldots,X_n}(x_1, \cdots, x_n)$ *such that*

$$F_{X_1,\ldots,X_n}(x_1, \cdots, x_n) = \int_{-\infty}^{x_1} \cdots \int_{-\infty}^{x_n} f_{X_1,\ldots,X_n}(t_1, \cdots, t_n)\, dt_1 \cdots dt_n$$

for every n-tuple of real numbers $(x_1, \cdots, x_n)$.

The function $f_{X_1,\ldots,X_n}(x_1, \cdots, x_n)$ is called a joint density function of the random variables $X_1, \cdots, X_n$. At this point we recall for the student the Fundamental Theorem of Calculus: *if a real-valued function* g *is Riemann-integrable over the interval* $[a, b]$, *then the function* G *defined by* $G(x) = \int_a^x g(t)\, dt$ *for all* $x \in [a, b]$ *is continuous over* $[a, b]$, *and if* g *is continuous at* $x_0 \in [a, b]$, *then* G *is differentiable at* x_0 *and* $G'(x_0) = g(x_0)$. Using this theorem, one easily sees that at every value of x at which a density $f_X(x)$ is continuous, $F'_X(x) = f_X(x)$. In the multivariate case, at every point $(x_1, \cdots, x_n)$ in n-dimensional Euclidian space at which $f_{X_1,\ldots,X_n}(x_1, \cdots, x_n)$ is continuous,

$$\frac{\partial^n}{\partial x_1 \cdots \partial x_n} F_{X_1,\ldots,X_n}(x_1, \cdots, x_n) = f_{X_1,\ldots,X_n}(x_1, \cdots, x_n).$$

The following theorem will not be stated and proved in all its generality because the general statement and proof provides more difficulties than we care to introduce in the text now. We instead state and prove a particular case; the student should be able to "feel" the general case.

1. Theorem. *If* X_1, X_2, X_3 *have a joint absolutely continuous distribution, then so does* X_1, X_3, *and a joint density of* X_1, X_3 *may be written as*

$$f_{X_1,X_3}(x_1, x_3) = \int_{-\infty}^{+\infty} f_{X_1,X_2,X_3}(x_1, x_2, x_3)\, dx_2.$$

Proof. By Theorem 2 in Section 3.5, the definition of density, and the usual properties of integrals,

$$\begin{aligned} F_{X_1,X_3}(x_1, x_3) &= \lim_{x_2\to\infty} F_{X_1,X_2,X_3}(x_1, x_2, x_3) \\ &= \lim_{x_2\to\infty} \int_{-\infty}^{x_1}\int_{-\infty}^{x_2}\int_{-\infty}^{x_3} f_{X_1,X_2,X_3}(t_1, t_2, t_3)\, dt_1\, dt_2\, dt_3 \\ &= \int_{-\infty}^{x_1}\int_{-\infty}^{x_3}\left\{\lim_{x_2\to\infty}\int_{-\infty}^{x_2} f_{X_1,X_2,X_3}(t_1, t_2, t_3)\, dt_2\right\} dt_1\, dt_3 \\ &= \int_{-\infty}^{x_1}\int_{-\infty}^{x_3}\left\{\int_{-\infty}^{\infty} f_{X_1,X_2,X_3}(t_1, t_2, t_3)\, dt_2\right\} dt_1\, dt_3. \end{aligned}$$

Thus by the definition of joint density function of X_1 and X_3 we may take

$$f_{X_1,X_3}(x_1, x_3) = \int_{-\infty}^{+\infty} f_{X_1,X_2,X_3}(x_1, x_2, x_3)\, dx_2.$$

This proves the theorem.

The joint density $f_{X_1,X_3}(x_1, x_3)$ just obtained is called a "marginal" or "marginal density" of the joint density $f_{X_1,X_2,X_3}(x_1, x_2, x_3)$. In general we see that when we want to find a joint density of a certain (finite) number of random variables, and if we are given a joint density of a finite set of random variables which includes them, then we integrate out the extraneous variables. As an example, suppose X, Y are random variables with joint density as follows:

$$f_{X,Y}(x, y) = \begin{cases} e^{-(x+y)} & \text{if } \min\{x, y\} \geqq 0, \\ 0 & \text{otherwise.} \end{cases}$$

Let us find a density $f_Y(y)$ of Y. From the theorem just proved we obtain

$$\begin{aligned} f_Y(y) &= \int_{-\infty}^{+\infty} f_{X,Y}(x, y)\, dx \\ &= \begin{cases} \int_0^{\infty} e^{-(x+y)}\, dx = e^{-y} & \text{if } y \geqq 0, \\ 0 & \text{otherwise.} \end{cases} \end{aligned}$$

If random variables have a joint absolutely continuous distribution, then it is easy to tell if they are independent. This is accomplished by the following theorem.

2. Theorem. *If $X_1, X_2, \cdots, X_n$ have a joint absolutely continuous distribution, then a necessary and sufficient condition that they be independent is that a joint density of $X_1, X_2, \cdots, X_n$ is*

$$f_{X_1,\ldots,X_n}(x_1, \cdots, x_n) = \prod_{j=1}^{n} f_{X_j}(x_j).$$

Proof. We first prove that the condition is sufficient. Assuming the above factorization to be true, we obtain

$$F_{X_1,\ldots,X_n}(x_1, \cdots, x_n) = \int_{-\infty}^{x_1} \cdots \int_{-\infty}^{x_n} f_{X_1,\ldots,X_n}(t_1, \cdots, t_n)\, dt_1 \cdots dt_n$$

$$= \int_{-\infty}^{x_1} \cdots \int_{-\infty}^{x_n} \left\{\prod_{j=1}^{n} f_{X_j}(t_j)\, dt_j\right\}$$

$$= \prod_{j=1}^{n} \int_{-\infty}^{x_j} f_{X_j}(t_j)\, dt_j = \prod_{j=1}^{n} F_{X_j}(x_j).$$

Independence of $X_1, \cdots, X_n$ follows from Theorem 4 in Section 3.5. We now prove the condition is necessary. Assuming the random variables to be independent we find that for every $(x_1, \cdots, x_n)$

$$F_{X_1,\ldots,X_n}(x_1, \cdots, x_n) = \prod_{j=1}^{n} F_{X_j}(x_j)$$

$$= \prod_{j=1}^{n} \int_{-\infty}^{x_j} f_{X_j}(t_j)\, dt_j = \int_{-\infty}^{x_1} \cdots \int_{-\infty}^{x_n} \left\{\prod_{j=1}^{n} f_{X_j}(t_j)\right\} dt_1 \cdots dt_n.$$

By the very definition of a joint density, the integrand of the last multiple integral above is a joint density, and the theorem is proved.

Conditional distributions are needed in much work in probability and statistics, and the remainder of this section is devoted to these.

Definition. *The conditional distribution function of a random variable X given that a random variable $Y = y$ is defined by*

$$F_{X|Y}(x|y) = \lim_{\epsilon\to 0+} P([X \leqq x] \mid [y - \epsilon < Y \leqq y + \epsilon]),$$

provided that such a limit exists. If $F_{X|Y}(x|y)$ exists, then a conditional density of X given Y, $f_{X|Y}(x|y)$, is defined as a function such that

$$F_{X|Y}(x|y) = \int_{-\infty}^{x} f_{X|Y}(t|y)\, dt$$

for every real x.

3. Theorem. *If X and Y are two random variables which have a joint absolutely continuous distribution, then, at every point (x, y) at which $f_{X,Y}(x, y)$ is continuous and at which $f_Y(y) > 0$ and is continuous, a conditional density of X, given Y exists, and one such conditional density may be written as*

$$f_{X|Y}(x|y) = \frac{f_{X,Y}(x, y)}{f_Y(y)}.$$

Proof. By the definition of conditional distribution function we obtain

$$F_{X|Y}(x|y) = \lim_{\epsilon\to 0+} \frac{P([X \leqq x][y - \epsilon < Y \leqq y + \epsilon])}{P[y - \epsilon < Y \leqq y + \epsilon]}$$

$$= \lim_{\epsilon\to 0+} \frac{\int_{u=-\infty}^{x} \int_{v=y-\epsilon}^{y+\epsilon} f_{X,Y}(u, v)\, du\, dv}{\int_{v=y-\epsilon}^{y+\epsilon} f_Y(v)\, dv}$$

$$= \frac{\lim_{\epsilon\to 0+} \int_{u=-\infty}^{x} \left\{\frac{1}{2\epsilon} \int_{v=y-\epsilon}^{y+\epsilon} f_{X,Y}(u, v)\, dv\right\} du}{\lim_{\epsilon\to 0+} \frac{1}{2\epsilon} \int_{v=y-\epsilon}^{y+\epsilon} f_Y(v)\, dv}$$

$$= \frac{\int_{u=-\infty}^{x} f_{X,Y}(u, y)\, du}{f_Y(y)}$$

$$= \int_{-\infty}^{x} (f_{X,Y}(u, y)/f_Y(y))\, du.$$

By the previous definition the assertion of the theorem follows.

EXERCISES

1. Prove: If $X_1, \cdots, X_n$ have a joint absolutely continuous distribution, then so do $X_1, \cdots, X_{n-1}$ and

$$f_{X_1,\ldots,X_{n-1}}(x_1, \cdots, x_{n-1}) = \int_{-\infty}^{\infty} f_{X_1,\ldots,X_n}(x_1, \cdots, x_n)\, dx_n.$$

2. Using problem 1, prove the Theorem: If $X_1, \cdots, X_n$ have a joint absolutely continuous distribution, and if $\{i_1, i_2, \cdots, i_k\} \subset \{1, 2, \cdots, n\}$, then so does $X_{i_1}, \cdots, X_{i_k}$, and

$$f_{X_{i_1},\ldots,X_{i_k}}(x_{i_1}, \cdots, x_{i_k})$$
$$= \int_{x_{i_{k+1}}=-\infty}^{\infty} \cdots \int_{x_{i_n}=-\infty}^{\infty} f_{X_1,\ldots,X_n}(x_1, \cdots, x_n)\, dx_{i_{k+1}} \cdots dx_{i_n},$$

where $\{i_{k+1}, \cdots, i_n\}$ are the integers in $\{1, 2, \cdots, n\}$ which are not in $\{i_1, \cdots, i_k\}$.

3. If $F_X(x)$ has a derivative at every x, and if $F'_X(x)$ is continuous at all values of x, then $F'_X(x)$ is a density of X, i.e.,

$$F_X(x) = \int_{-\infty}^{x} F'_X(t)\, dt \quad \text{for all } x.$$

4. Let

$$f_{X,Y}(x, y) = \begin{cases} 0 & \text{if } \min\{x, y\} < 0 \\ xye^{-x-y} & \text{if } \min\{x, y\} \geqq 0. \end{cases}$$

Find $F_{X,Y}(x, y)$, $F_X(x)$, $F_Y(y)$, $f_X(x)$, and $f_Y(y)$.

5. Let $f_{X,Y}(x, y) = 1/\pi^2(1 + x^2)(1 + y^2)$ for all real x, y. Do the same as in problem 4.

6. Let

$$f_{X,Y}(x, y) = \begin{cases} 1/\pi^2(xy(1-x)(1-y))^{1/2} & \text{if } 0 < x < 1, \ 0 < y < 1, \text{ and} \\ 0 & \text{otherwise.} \end{cases}$$

Do the same as in problem 4.

7. Let $f_{X,Y}(x, y) = 1$ if $0 \leqq x \leqq 2$ and $\max\{0, x-1\} \leqq y \leqq \min\{1, x\}$, and $f_{X,Y}(x, y) = 0$ for all other values of x and y. Do the same as in problem 4.

8. If

$$F_X(x) = \begin{cases} 0 & \text{if } x < 0 \\ 1 - e^{-x} & \text{if } x \geqq 0, \end{cases}$$

find a density of X.

9. If

$$F_X(x) = \begin{cases} 0 & \text{if } x < 0 \\ (2/\pi) \operatorname{Arcsin} x & \text{if } 0 \leqq x < 1 \\ 1 & \text{if } x \geqq 1, \end{cases}$$

find $f_X(x)$.

5.2 Densities of Functions of Random Variables

Let us consider n random variables $X_1, X_2, \cdots, X_n$ which have a joint absolutely continuous distribution. Very often it is desired to find a density for a random variable Y which is some function of $X_1, \cdots, X_n$. For example, Y might be the sum of these random variables, or the sum of their squares, or the ratio of X_1 to X_2. In this section a technique for obtaining a density for such a Y is explained. In order to do this we must state two theorems whose proofs will be omitted. The first theorem as stated can be proved by a long, tortuous argument; the student should try to prove it on his own, at least in the case when $n = 2$. The second theorem is usually given in an advanced calculus course.

We now state the first of these two theorems. Let $X_1, \cdots, X_n$ be n random variables with a joint absolutely continuous distribution. Let $u_1 = u_1(x_1, \cdots, x_n), \cdots, u_n = u_n(x_1, \cdots, x_n)$ be a continuous mapping (i.e., function) of n-dimensional Euclidian space $E^{(n)}$ into itself. Let $S \subset E^{(n)}$ be a set defined by

$$S = \{(x_1, \cdots, x_n) | u_1(x_1, \cdots, x_n) \leqq a_1, \cdots, u_n(x_1, \cdots, x_n) \leqq a_n\},$$

where $a_1, \cdots, a_n$ are constants. Then

$$P[(X_1, \cdots, X_n) \in S] = \int \underset{S}{\cdots} \int f_{X_1, \ldots, X_n}(x_1, \cdots, x_n)\, dx_1 \cdots dx_n.$$

A more general form of this theorem, which we shall subsequently use, states the following: If S is a set in n-dimensional Euclidian space $E^{(n)}$ for which

$$\{\omega | (X_1(\omega), \cdots, X_n(\omega)) \in S\} = [(X_1, \cdots, X_n) \in S] \in \mathcal{A}$$

is an event), then

$$P[(X_1, \cdots, X_n) \in S] = \int \underset{S}{\cdots} \int f_{X_1, \ldots, X_n}(x_1, \cdots, x_n)\, dx_1 \cdots dx_n,$$

provided the integral on the right exists.

The second theorem that we state without proof deals with multiple integrals. Let $H(x_1, \cdots, x_n)$ be a continuous real-valued function for $a_1 \leqq x_1 \leqq b_1, a_2 \leqq x_2 \leqq b_2, \cdots, a_n \leqq x_n \leqq b_n$. Suppose $u_1 = u_1(x_1, \cdots, x_n), \cdots, u_n = u_n(x_1, \cdots, x_n)$ is a one-to-one mapping of $E^{(n)}$ into itself, i.e., there exists the inverse transformation $x_1 = x_1(u_1, \cdots, u_n), \cdots, x_n = x_n(u_1, \cdots, u_n)$ defined over the range of the transformation. Second, we assume that both the mapping and its inverse are continuous. Third, we assume that the n^2 partial derivatives $\partial x_i/\partial u_j$, $1 \leqq i \leqq n, 1 \leqq j \leqq n$, exist and are continuous. Fourth, we assume that the Jacobian

$$\frac{\partial(x_1, \cdots, x_n)}{\partial(u_1, \cdots, u_n)} = \begin{vmatrix} \frac{\partial x_1}{\partial u_1} & \frac{\partial x_1}{\partial u_2} & \cdots & \frac{\partial x_1}{\partial u_n} \\ \frac{\partial x_2}{\partial u_1} & \frac{\partial x_2}{\partial u_2} & \cdots & \frac{\partial x_2}{\partial u_n} \\ \cdot & \cdot & & \cdot \\ \cdot & \cdot & & \cdot \\ \cdot & \cdot & & \cdot \\ \frac{\partial x_n}{\partial u_1} & \frac{\partial x_n}{\partial u_2} & \cdots & \frac{\partial x_n}{\partial u_n} \end{vmatrix}$$

does not vanish for $(u_1, \cdots, u_n) \in R$, where

$$R = \{(u_1, \cdots, u_n) | a_i \leqq x_i(u_1, \cdots, u_n) \leqq b_i,\ 1 \leqq i \leqq n\}.$$

Then

$$\int_{a_1}^{b_1} \cdots \int_{a_n}^{b_n} H(x_1, \cdots, x_n)\, dx_1 \cdots dx_n$$

$$= \int \underset{R}{\cdots} \int H(x_1(u_1, \cdots, u_n), \cdots, x_n(u_1, \cdots, u_n))|J|\, du_1 \cdots du_n,$$

where

$$J = \frac{\partial(x_1, \cdots, x_n)}{\partial(u_1, \cdots, u_n)}.$$

The student has already used this second theorem in the case of polar coordinates. In this case $n = 2$, $u_1 = r$, $u_2 = \theta$, $x_1 = x$, $x_2 = y$, and $x = r \cos \theta$, $y = r \sin \theta$. Since $\partial x/\partial r = \cos \theta$, $\partial x/\partial \theta = -r \sin \theta$, $\partial y/\partial r = \sin \theta$, $\partial y/\partial \theta = r \cos \theta$, the Jacobian is

$$\frac{\partial(x, y)}{\partial(r, \theta)} = \begin{vmatrix} \cos \theta & -r \sin \theta \\ \sin \theta & r \cos \theta \end{vmatrix} = r.$$

Since the absolute value of the Jacobian is r, we have

$$\int_{a_1}^{b_1}\int_{a_2}^{b_2} H(x, y)\,dx\,dy = \iint_R H(r\cos\theta, r\sin\theta)r\,dr\,d\theta,$$

where

$$R = \{(r, \theta)|a_1 \leqq r\cos\theta \leqq b_1, a_2 \leqq r\sin\theta \leqq b_2\}.$$

This is the familiar formula for change of variable to polar coordinates in double integrals. We now prove the basic theorem for this section.

1. Theorem. *Let $X_1, \cdots, X_n$ be n random variables with a joint absolutely continuous distribution. Let $u_1(x_1, \cdots, x_n), \cdots, u_n(x_1, \cdots, x_n)$ be a mapping of E^n into E^n with the properties stated above in the theorem on change of variables for multiple integrals. Let $U_i = u_i(X_1, \cdots, X_n)$, $1 \leqq i \leqq n$. Then $U_1, \cdots, U_n$ have a joint absolutely continuous distribution, and*

$$f_{U_1,\ldots,U_n}(u_1, \cdots, u_n)$$
$$= f_{X_1,\ldots,X_n}(x_1(u_1, \cdots, u_n), \cdots, x_n(u_1, \cdots, u_n))\left|\frac{\partial(x_1, \cdots, x_n)}{\partial(u_1, \cdots, u_n)}\right|.$$

Proof. For $(v_1, \cdots, v_n) \in E^n$, let

$$R = \{(x_1, \cdots, x_n)|u_i(x_1, \cdots, x_n) \leqq v_i, 1 \leqq i \leqq n\}.$$

Then by the two theorems stated above,

$$F_{U_1,\ldots,U_n}(v_1, \cdots, v_n) = P[(X_1, \cdots, X_n) \in R]$$
$$= \int \underset{R}{\cdots} \int f_{X_1,\ldots,X_n}(x_1, \cdots, x_n)\,dx_1 \cdots dx_n$$
$$= \int_{-\infty}^{v_1} \cdots \int_{-\infty}^{v_n} f_{X_1,\ldots,X_n}(x_1(u_1, \cdots, u_n), \cdots, x_n(u_1, \cdots, u_n))$$
$$\cdot \left|\frac{\partial(x_1, \cdots, x_n)}{\partial(u_1, \cdots, u_n)}\right| du_1 \cdots du_n.$$

By the definition of joint density we obtain the conclusion of the theorem.

We now show how this theorem can be applied.

Example 1. Suppose

$$f_{X,Y}(x, y) = \begin{cases} 1 & \text{if } \; 0 < x < 1, \; 0 < y < 1 \\ 0 & \text{otherwise.} \end{cases}$$

The problem is to find a density of $U = X + Y$. We shall do this by finding first a joint density of U and V, where $V = Y$. We consider the transformation $u = x + y$, $v = y$ from which we obtain $x = u - v$, $y = v$. The Jacobian of this transformation is 1. By Theorem 1 we may therefore write

$$f_{U,V}(u, v) = \begin{cases} 1 & \text{if } \; 0 < v < 1 \; \text{ and } \; 0 < u - v < 1 \\ 0 & \text{otherwise.} \end{cases}$$

The inequalities $0 < v < 1$, $0 < u - v < 1$ are equivalent to $0 < v < 1$, $u > v > u - 1$. In order to obtain $f_U(u)$ we must perform the integration $\int_{-\infty}^{+\infty} f_{U,V}(u, v)\, dv$. When $0 < u \leqq 1$, then $0 < v < u$ (by the above inequalities), and when $1 < u < 2$, then $u - 1 < v < 1$. Thus we obtain

$$f_U(u) = \begin{cases} \int_0^u 1\, dv = u & \text{if } 0 < u \leqq 1, \\ \int_{u-1}^1 1\, dv = 2 - u & \text{if } 1 < u < 2, \\ 0 & \text{if } u \leqq 0 \text{ or } u \geqq 2. \end{cases}$$

Example 2. Suppose

$$f_{X,Y}(x, y) = \begin{cases} 4xy & \text{if } 0 < x < 1, \quad 0 < y < 1 \\ 0 & \text{otherwise.} \end{cases}$$

The problem is to find a joint density of X^2, Y^2. In this case $u = x^2$, $v = y^2$, and $x = \sqrt{u}$, $y = \sqrt{v}$. The Jacobian of the transformation is

$$\frac{\partial(x, y)}{\partial(u, v)} = \begin{vmatrix} 1/2\sqrt{u} & 0 \\ 0 & 1/2\sqrt{v} \end{vmatrix} = 1/4\sqrt{uv}.$$

By Theorem 1 we obtain

$$f_{U,V}(u, v) = \begin{cases} 1 & \text{if } 0 < u < 1, \quad 0 < v < 1 \\ 0 & \text{otherwise.} \end{cases}$$

Example 3. Let

$$f_{X,Y}(x, y) = \begin{cases} 3x & \text{if } 0 < y < x, \quad 0 < x < 1 \\ 0 & \text{otherwise.} \end{cases}$$

The problem is to find a density of $Z = X - Y$. In this case we consider the transformation $z = x - y$, $w = y$, from which we obtain $x = z + w$, $y = w$. The Jacobian of the transformation is easily seen to be unity. The inequalities $0 < y < x$, $0 < x < 1$ are equivalent to $0 < w < w + z$, $0 < z + w < 1$. These two inequalities imply that $0 < w < 1 - z$. Using Theorem 1 we obtain

$$f_Z(z) = \int_0^{1-z} f_{Z,W}(z, w)\, dw = \int_0^{1-z} 3(z + w)\, dw$$

$$= \begin{cases} 3(1 - z^2)/2 & \text{if } 0 < z < 1 \\ 0 & \text{otherwise.} \end{cases}$$

Example 4. Suppose

$$f_{X,Y,Z}(x, y, z) = \begin{cases} e^{-(x+y+z)} & \text{if } x > 0, \quad y > 0, \quad z > 0, \\ 0 & \text{otherwise.} \end{cases}$$

The problem is to find a density of $U = (X + Y + Z)/3$. We consider the transformation $u = (x + y + z)/3$, $v = y$, $w = z$, from which we obtain $x = 3u - v - w$, $y = v$, $z = w$. The Jacobian is easily seen to be equal to 3. By Theorem 1, a joint density of U, V, W is

$$f_{U,V,W}(u, v, w) = \begin{cases} 3e^{-3u} & \text{if} \quad 3u - v - w > 0, \quad v > 0, \quad w > 0 \\ 0 & \text{otherwise.} \end{cases}$$

The two inequalities $w > 0$, $3u - v - w > 0$ imply that $0 < w < 3u - v$. Thus

$$f_{U,V}(u, v) = \begin{cases} \displaystyle\int_0^{3u-v} 3e^{-3u}\, dw & \text{if} \quad 3u - v > 0, \quad v > 0 \\ 0 & \text{otherwise.} \end{cases}$$

Finally

$$f_U(u) = \begin{cases} \displaystyle\int_0^{3u} dv \int_0^{3u-v} 3e^{-3u}\, dw = \frac{27}{2} u^2 e^{-3u} & \text{if} \quad u > 0, \\ 0 & \text{otherwise.} \end{cases}$$

We conclude this section with an application of Theorem 1 which is important and useful.

2. Theorem. *Let $X_1, X_2, \cdots, X_n$ be n independent random variables, each with an absolutely continuous distribution, and let $r_1, r_2, \cdots, r_k$ be k positive integers such that $r_1 + r_2 + \cdots + r_k = n$. Then the k random variables*

$$X_1 + \cdots + X_{r_1}, X_{r_1+1} + \cdots + X_{r_1+r_2}, \cdots, X_{n-r_k+1} + \cdots + X_n,$$

are independent.

Proof. We shall prove this theorem only in the case $k = 2$. The proof is the same for $k > 2$ and only involves more complicated notation. Let us first consider only the r_1 random variables $X_1, \cdots, X_{r_1}$. By Theorem 2 in Section 5.1 their joint density is

$$f_{X_1,\cdots,X_{r_1}}(x_1, \cdots, x_{r_1}) = \prod_{i=1}^{r_1} f_{X_i}(x_i).$$

Let us consider the transformation

$$\begin{aligned} u_1 &= x_1 + x_2 + \cdots + x_{r_1} \\ u_2 &= x_2 \\ &\cdot \\ &\cdot \\ &\cdot \\ u_{r_1} &= x_{r_1}, \end{aligned}$$

from which we obtain

$$\begin{aligned} x_1 &= u_1 - u_2 - \cdots - u_{r_1} \\ x_2 &= u_2 \\ &\ \cdot \\ &\ \cdot \\ &\ \cdot \\ x_{r_1} &= u_{r_1}. \end{aligned}$$

The Jacobian of this transformation is

$$\frac{\partial(x_1, \cdots, x_{r_1})}{\partial(u_1, \cdots, u_{r_1})} = \begin{vmatrix} 1 & -1 & \cdots & -1 & -1 \\ 0 & 1 & \cdots & 0 & 0 \\ \cdot & \cdot & & \cdot & \cdot \\ \cdot & \cdot & & \cdot & \cdot \\ \cdot & \cdot & & \cdot & \cdot \\ 0 & 0 & \cdots & 1 & 0 \\ 0 & 0 & \cdots & 0 & 1 \end{vmatrix} = 1.$$

If we consider the new random variables $U_1, \cdots, U_{r_1}$ defined by $U_1 = X_1 + \cdots + X_{r_1}$, $U_2 = X_2, \cdots, U_{r_1} = X_{r_1}$, then by Theorem 1,

$$\begin{aligned} f_{U_1,\cdots,U_{r_1}}(u_1, \cdots, u_{r_1}) &= f_{X_1,\cdots,X_{r_1}}(u_1 - u_2 - \cdots - u_{r_1}, u_2, \cdots, u_{r_1}) \\ &= f_{X_1}(u_1 - u_2 - \cdots - u_{r_1}) \prod_{i=2}^{r_1} f_{X_i}(u_i). \end{aligned}$$

Using Theorem 1 in Section 5.1,

$$f_{U_1}(u_1) = \int_{-\infty}^{\infty} \cdots \int_{-\infty}^{\infty} f_{X_1}(u_1 - u_2 - \cdots - u_{r_1}) \prod_{i=2}^{r_1} f_{X_i}(u_i)\, du_2 \cdots du_{r_1}.$$

If we let $U_{r_1+1} = X_{r_1+1} + \cdots + X_n$, $U_{r_1+2} = X_{r_1+2}, \cdots, U_n = X_n$, then in the same way we obtain

$$\begin{aligned} &f_{U_{r_1+1}}(u_{r_1+1}) \\ &= \int_{-\infty}^{\infty} \cdots \int_{-\infty}^{\infty} f_{X_{r_1+1}}(u_{r_1+1} - u_{r_1+2} - \cdots - u_n) \prod_{i=r_1+2}^{n} f_{X_i}(u_i)\, du_{r_1+2} \cdots du_n. \end{aligned}$$

We now make use of the independence of $X_1, \cdots, X_n$, which implies that

$$f_{X_1,\cdots,X_n}(x_1, \cdots, x_n) = \prod_{i=1}^{n} f_{X_i}(x_i).$$

We consider the transformation

$$\begin{aligned} u_1 &= x_1 + x_2 + \cdots + x_{r_1} \\ u_2 &= x_2 \\ &\ \cdot \\ &\ \cdot \\ &\ \cdot \\ u_{r_1} &= x_{r_1} \end{aligned}$$

$$\begin{aligned} u_{r_1+1} &= x_{r_1+1} + x_{r_1+2} + \cdots + x_n \\ u_{r_1+2} &= x_{r_1+2} \\ &\cdot \\ &\cdot \\ &\cdot \\ u_n &= x_n. \end{aligned}$$

The Jacobian is easily computed, and again

$$\frac{\partial(x_1, \cdots, x_n)}{\partial(u_1, \cdots, u_n)} = 1.$$

If we now let $U_1, \cdots, U_n$ be defined as above, then

$$f_{U_1,\cdots,U_n}(u_1, \cdots, u_n)$$
$$= f_{X_1}(u_1 - u_2 - \cdots - u_{r_1}) \left\{ \prod_{i=2}^{r_1} f_{X_i}(u_i) \right\} f_{X_{r_1+1}}(u_{r_1+1} - u_{r_1+2} - \cdots - u_n)$$
$$\cdot \left\{ \prod_{i=r_1+2}^{n} f_{X_i}(u_i) \right\}.$$

By Theorem 1 in Section 5.1 we may integrate both sides with respect to $u_2, \cdots, u_{r_1}, u_{r_1+2}, \cdots, u_n$ and finally obtain

$$f_{U_1, U_{r_1+1}}(u_1, u_{r_1+1}) = f_{U_1}(u_1) f_{U_{r_1+1}}(u_{r_1+1}).$$

Theorem 2 in Section 5.1 then implies that $U_1 = X_1 + \cdots + X_{r_1}$ and $U_{r_1+1} = X_{r_1+1} + \cdots + X_n$ are independent.

EXERCISES

1. Let $f_{X,Y}(x, y)$ be as in example 1. Let $U = X$, $V = X - Y$. Find $f_{U,V}(u, v)$ and $f_V(v)$.

2. Let

$$f_{X,Y}(x, y) = \begin{cases} 9x^2y^2 & \text{if } 0 < x < 1, \quad 0 < y < 1, \\ 0 & \text{otherwise.} \end{cases}$$

Let $U = X^3$, $V = Y^3$. Find $f_{U,V}(u, v)$ and $f_U(u)$.

3. Let

$$f_{X,Y}(x, y) = \begin{cases} 3x/2 & \text{if } 0 < x < 1, \quad -x < y < x \\ 0 & \text{otherwise.} \end{cases}$$

Find the density of $X - Y$.

4. Let

$$f_{X,Y,Z,W}(x, y, z, w) = \begin{cases} e^{-(x+y+z+w)} & \text{if } x > 0, \quad y > 0, \quad z > 0, \text{ and } w > 0 \\ 0 & \text{otherwise.} \end{cases}$$

Find a density of $X + Y + Z + W$.

5. Write a proof of Theorem 2 for arbitrary k.

CHAPTER 6

Some Special Absolutely Continuous Distributions

6.1 The Gamma and Beta Functions

In a course in advanced calculus one learns that the integral

$$\Gamma(p) = \int_0^\infty x^{p-1}e^{-x}\,dx$$

converges for all real $p > 0$. (See problem 1 in the exercises.) This integral as a function defined for all $p \in (0, \infty)$ is called the gamma function. Upon integrating by parts, one obtains

$$\Gamma(p+1) = -x^p e^{-x}\Big|_0^\infty + p\int_0^\infty x^{p-1}e^{-x}\,dx.$$

One easily sees that

$$0 \leqq \lim_{x\to\infty} x^p e^{-x} \leqq \lim_{x\to\infty} \frac{x^{[p]+1}}{e^x}.$$

If we evaluate this last limit by applying L'Hospital's rule $[p] + 1$ times, we finally obtain:

$$0 \leqq \lim_{x\to\infty} x^p e^{-x} \leqq 0 \quad \text{or} \quad \lim_{x\to\infty} x^p e^{-x} = 0.$$

Thus $\Gamma(p+1) = p\Gamma(p)$ for all $p > 0$. When $p = 1$,

$$\Gamma(1) = \int_0^\infty e^{-x}\,dx = 1,$$

and hence for p any positive integer we obtain $\Gamma(p+1) = p!$.

Of particular interest is $\Gamma(\frac{1}{2}) = \int_0^\infty x^{-1/2}e^{-x}\,dx$, which we now evaluate. We first make the substitution $x = z^2 (z > 0)$ and obtain

$$\Gamma(\tfrac{1}{2}) = 2\int_0^\infty \exp(-z^2)\,dz.$$

We note now that $\Gamma(\frac{1}{2}) > 0$, so $\Gamma(\frac{1}{2})$ is the positive square root of $\Gamma^2(\frac{1}{2})$. But

$$\begin{aligned}\Gamma^2(\tfrac{1}{2}) &= 4 \int_0^\infty \exp(-x^2)\, dx \int_0^\infty \exp(-y^2)\, dy \\ &= 4 \int_0^\infty \int_0^\infty \exp(-(x^2 + y^2))\, dx\, dy.\end{aligned}$$

We next consider the transformation

$$x = r \cos \theta, \quad y = r \sin \theta.$$

The Jacobian of the transformation is r, and we see that

$$\{(x, y)|0 < x < \infty, 0 < y < \infty\} = \{(r, \theta)|0 < r < \infty, 0 < \theta < \pi/2\}.$$

Thus

$$\Gamma^2(\tfrac{1}{2}) = 4 \int_0^{\pi/2} d\theta \int_0^\infty \exp(-r^2) r\, dr = \pi,$$

and $\Gamma(\frac{1}{2}) = \sqrt{\pi}$.

The gamma function may also be written in the form

$$\Gamma(\alpha + 1) = \int_0^\infty (x/\beta)^\alpha e^{-x/\beta}\, dx/\beta,$$

for $\alpha > -1$, $\beta > 0$. Thus the function

$$f(x) = \begin{cases} \dfrac{1}{\Gamma(\alpha + 1)\beta^{\alpha+1}} x^\alpha e^{-x/\beta} & \text{if } \quad x > 0 \\ 0 & \text{otherwise,} \end{cases}$$

could serve as a density function for a random variable. If a random variable does have such a density, it is said to have the *gamma distribution*. We shall soon discover that particular cases of the gamma distribution arise in a very natural way.

The beta function, $B(p, q)$, is defined by the integral

$$B(p, q) = \int_0^1 x^{p-1}(1 - x)^{q-1}\, dx,$$

for p and q any positive real numbers. If $0 < p < 1$ or $0 < q < 1$, then this integral is a Cauchy (or improper) integral. (See exercises 4–6.) This function has an intimate connection with the gamma function which is exhibited in the following theorem.

1. Theorem. *If* $p > 0$, $q > 0$, *then* $B(p, q) = \Gamma(p)\Gamma(q)/\Gamma(p + q) = B(q, p)$.

Proof. In the definition of $\Gamma(p)$,

$$\Gamma(p) = \int_0^\infty x^{p-1} e^{-x}\, dx,$$

if we make a change of variable $x = y^2$, then we obtain

$$\Gamma(p) = 2\int_0^\infty y^{2p-1}\exp(-y^2)\,dy.$$

Thus we may write

$$\begin{aligned}\Gamma(p)\Gamma(q) &= 4\int_0^\infty u^{2p-1}\exp(-u^2)\,du\int_0^\infty v^{2q-1}\exp(-v^2)\,dv\\ &= 4\int_0^\infty\int_0^\infty u^{2p-1}v^{2q-1}\exp[-(u^2+v^2)]\,du\,dv.\end{aligned}$$

We consider the transformation $u = r\cos\theta$, $v = r\sin\theta$, and in the same way that we computed $\Gamma^2(\frac{1}{2})$ we obtain

$$\begin{aligned}\Gamma(p)\Gamma(q) &= 4\int_0^\infty dr\int_0^{\pi/2}(r\cos\theta)^{2p-1}(r\sin\theta)^{2q-1}\exp(-r^2)r\,d\theta\\ &= 4\int_0^\infty r^{2p+2q-1}\exp(-r^2)\,dr\int_0^{\pi/2}(\cos\theta)^{2p-1}(\sin\theta)^{2q-1}\,d\theta.\end{aligned}$$

In the first integral we make the substitution $r^2 = x$, and in the second integral we let $\sin^2\theta = y$. We then obtain

$$\begin{aligned}\Gamma(p)\Gamma(q) &= \int_0^\infty x^{p+q-1}e^{-x}\,dx\int_0^1 y^{q-1}(1-y)^{p-1}\,dy\\ &= \Gamma(p+q)B(q,p),\end{aligned}$$

which proves the theorem.

If $p > 0$, $q > 0$, a function g defined by

$$g(x) = \begin{cases}0 & \text{if } x \leqq 0 \text{ or } x \geqq 1\\ x^{p-1}(1-x)^{q-1}/B(p,q) & \text{if } 0 < x < 1\end{cases}$$

could serve as a density function for a random variable. If a random variable does have such a density, it is said to have the *beta distribution*.

EXERCISES

1. Prove that the Cauchy (or improper) integral $\int_0^1 x^{p-1}e^{-x}\,dx$ exists for $1 > p > 0$. (*Hint:* First prove that $\int_0^1 x^{p-1}e^{-x}\,dx \leqq \int_0^1 x^{p-1}\,dx$.)

2. Prove that for every positive integer n the Cauchy (or improper) integral $\int_1^\infty x^n e^{-x}\,dx$ converges. (*Hint:* Use induction, integration by parts, and L'Hospital's rule.)

3. Use problems 1 and 2 to prove that the Cauchy integral $\Gamma(p) = \int_0^\infty x^{p-1}e^{-x}\,dx$ exists for all $p > 0$.

4. Prove that the Cauchy (or improper) integral $\int_0^{1/2} x^{p-1}(1-x)^{q-1}\,dx$ exists for $1 > p > 0$, $q > 0$. (*Hint:* First prove that $\int_0^{1/2} x^{p-1}(1-x)^{q-1}\,dx \leqq 2\int_0^{1/2} x^{p-1}\,dx$.)

5. Prove that the Cauchy (or improper) integral $\int_{1/2}^{1} x^{p-1}(1-x)^{q-1}\,dx$ exists for $p > 0$, $1 > q > 0$.

6. Prove that the integral $\int_0^1 x^{p-1}(1-x)^{q-1}\,dx$ exists for all $p > 0$, $q > 0$.

6.2 The Normal Distribution

If a random variable X has a density

$$f_X(x) = \frac{1}{\sqrt{2\pi\sigma^2}} \exp -\frac{(x-\mu)^2}{2\sigma^2}, \qquad -\infty < x < \infty,$$

where μ and σ^2 are fixed constants, $-\infty < \mu < \infty$, $\sigma^2 > 0$, then X is said to have a *normal distribution* or is said to be *normally distributed.* Other ways of saying this is to say that the distribution of X is $N(\mu, \sigma^2)$ or that X has the $N(\mu, \sigma^2)$ distribution. (In many references this distribution is referred to as the Gaussian, Laplace, or bell-shaped distribution.) This distribution arises in a very natural way, and the student will learn about this later when he learns the central limit theorem.

At this point we should check that the above density function can be a density function by verifying that $\int_{-\infty}^{\infty} f_X(x)\,dx = 1$. If we consider the substitution $t = (x-\mu)/\sqrt{2\sigma^2}$, then

$$\int_{-\infty}^{\infty} f_X(x)\,dx = \frac{1}{\sqrt{\pi}} \int_{-\infty}^{\infty} \exp(-t^2)\,dt = \frac{2}{\sqrt{\pi}} \int_0^{\infty} \exp(-t^2)\,dt.$$

In Section 6.1 we proved that $2\int_0^{\infty} \exp(-t^2)\,dt = \sqrt{\pi}$, and with this we have completed our check.

Values of the normal distribution function in the case when $\mu = 0$ and $\sigma^2 = 1$ are tabulated in Table I in the tables at the end of the book, i.e., values of the function

$$\Phi(x) = \frac{1}{\sqrt{2\pi}} \int_{-\infty}^{x} \exp\left(-\frac{t^2}{2}\right) dt$$

are given. In this table one finds, for example, that $\Phi(1.09) = .8621$ and $\Phi(2.35) = .9906$. If a random variable X has a distribution which is $N(\mu, \sigma^2)$, the values of its distribution function can be found by means of the following theorem.

1. Theorem. *If the distribution of a random variable X is $N(\mu, \sigma^2)$, then*

$$F_X(x) = \Phi\left(\frac{x-\mu}{\sigma}\right).$$

Proof. Since

$$F_X(x) = \frac{1}{\sqrt{2\pi\sigma^2}} \int_{-\infty}^{x} \exp\left(-\frac{(t-\mu)^2}{2\sigma^2}\right) dt,$$

if the substitution $s = (t-\mu)/\sigma$ or $t = \sigma s + \mu$ is made, we finally obtain

$$F_X(x) = \frac{1}{\sqrt{2\pi}} \int_{-\infty}^{(x-\mu)/\sigma} \exp\left(-\frac{s^2}{2}\right) ds = \Phi\left(\frac{x-\mu}{\sigma}\right).$$

The theorem just stated and proved is actually the same as the next theorem.

2. Theorem. *If the distribution of a random variable X is $N(\mu, \sigma^2)$, then the distribution of $(X-\mu)/\sigma$ is $N(0, 1)$.*

Proof. Let $Y = (X-\mu)/\sigma$ or $X = \sigma Y + \mu$. Then by Theorem 1 in Section 5.2

$$f_Y(y) = f_X(\sigma y + \mu)\sigma = \frac{1}{\sqrt{2\pi}} \exp -\frac{y^2}{2},$$

which proves the theorem.

We conclude this section by deriving a density of X^2 when X is a random variable whose distribution is $N(0, 1)$. The method we shall use is that of finding the distribution function of X^2 directly which we then differentiate to obtain the density desired. Clearly,

$$\begin{aligned} P[X^2 \leqq x] &= P[-\sqrt{x} \leqq X \leqq \sqrt{x}] \\ &= \frac{1}{\sqrt{2\pi}} \int_{-\sqrt{x}}^{\sqrt{x}} \exp\left(-\frac{t^2}{2}\right) dt \\ &= \frac{2}{\sqrt{2\pi}} \int_{0}^{\sqrt{x}} \exp\left(-\frac{t^2}{2}\right) dt. \end{aligned}$$

Now, making use of the fundamental theorem of calculus and the chain rule for differentiating, we obtain

$$f_{X^2}(x) = \begin{cases} x^{-1/2}e^{-x/2}/\sqrt{2\pi} & \text{if} \quad x > 0 \\ 0 & \text{if} \quad x \leqq 0, \end{cases}$$

which is easily recognized as the density of the gamma distribution (see Section 6.1) with $\alpha = -\frac{1}{2}$, $\beta = 2$. Thus we have established a relationship between the gamma and the normal distributions.

EXERCISES

1. Let $X_1, X_2, \cdots, X_n$ be n independent random variables, each with the same $N(\mu, \sigma^2)$ distribution. Prove that $X_1 + X_2 + \cdots + X_n$ has a distribution which is $N(n\mu, n\sigma^2)$. (*Hint:* use the transformation $u_1 = x_1 + x_2 + \cdots + x_n$, $u_2 = x_2 + x_3 + \cdots + x_n$, $u_3 = x_3 + \cdots + x_n$, $\cdots$, $u_n = x_n$.)

2. Let X, Y be two independent random variables, each with a distribution which is $N(0, 1)$. Find $f_Z(z)$, where $Z = X/Y$. (The distribution of Z is called the *Cauchy distribution.*)

3. Prove: If X is a random variable whose distribution is $N(\mu, \sigma^2)$, and if K is a constant, then the distribution of KX is $N(K\mu, K^2\sigma^2)$.

4. Prove: If X is a random variable whose distribution is $N(\mu, \sigma^2)$, and if a is a constant, then the distribution of $X + a$ is $N(\mu + a, \sigma^2)$.

5. Prove: If $X_1, \cdots, X_n$ are independent random variables, each having the same $N(\mu, \sigma^2)$ distribution, and if $\overline{X}_n = (X_1 + \cdots + X_n)/n$, then the distribution of $\sqrt{n}(\overline{X}_n - \mu)/\sigma$ is $N(0, 1)$. (*Hint:* use problems 1, 3, and 4.)

6. If the distribution of X is $N(2, 9)$, use Table I to find $P[X \leqq 5.21]$.

7. If the distribution of X is $N(-1, 4)$, use Table I to find the value of x_0 in order that $P[X \leqq x_0] = .66$.

8. If the distribution of X is $N(0, 1)$, prove that $P[|X| \geqq x_0] = p$ if and only if $P[X \leqq x_0] = (2 - p)/2$.

9. If the distribution of X is $N(0, 1)$, use Table I to find $P[|X| \geqq 1.12]$.

10. If the distribution of X is $N(0, 1)$, use Table I to find the value of x_0 such that $P[|X| \geqq x_0] = .5$.

11. If the distribution of X is $N(0, 1)$, and if $x < 0$, prove that $P[X \leqq x] = 1 - P[X \leqq -x]$.

12. If X is a random variable whose distribution is $N(2, 16)$, use Table I to find $P[X \leqq -1]$, $P[X \leqq -2.5]$, and $P[X \leqq .5]$.

6.3 The Negative Exponential Distribution

A random variable X is said to have a negative exponential distribution if

$$f_X(x) = \begin{cases} \alpha e^{-\alpha(x-\beta)} & \text{if } x > \beta \\ 0 & \text{if } x \leqq \beta, \end{cases}$$

where α and β are fixed constants, $\alpha > 0$, $-\infty < \beta < \infty$. The student can easily check for himself that $\int_{-\infty}^{\infty} f_X(x)\,dx = 1$. The negative exponential distribution is very useful in problems of waiting times and arises in a most natural way (see problem 1 in the exercises).

Let $X_1, X_2, \cdots, X_n$ be n independent random variables, where for each i, X_i has a negative exponential distribution with $\beta = 0$ and fixed $\alpha > 0$

which does not depend on i. We now derive a density of the sum $X_1 + \cdots + X_n$. First we note that

$$f_{X_1,\cdots,X_n}(x_1, \cdots, x_n) = \begin{cases} \alpha^n e^{-\alpha(x_1+\cdots+x_n)} & \text{if } \min\{x_1, \cdots, x_n\} > 0 \\ 0 & \text{otherwise.} \end{cases}$$

Let us consider the transformation $u_1 = x_1 + x_2 + \cdots + x_n$, $u_2 = x_2, \cdots, u_n = x_n$. The inverse transformation is $x_1 = u_1 - u_2 - \cdots - u_n$, $x_2 = u_2, \cdots, x_n = u_n$, and the Jacobian of the transformation is unity. Thus, a joint density of $U_1 = X_1 + \cdots + X_n$, $U_2 = X_2, \cdots, U_n = X_n$ is, by Theorem 1 in Section 5.2,

$$f_{U_1,U_2,\cdots,U_n}(u_1, \cdots, u_n) = \begin{cases} \alpha^n e^{-\alpha u_1} & \text{if } u_1 - u_2 - \cdots - u_n > 0 \\ & \quad u_2 > 0, \cdots, u_n > 0, \\ 0 & \text{otherwise.} \end{cases}$$

We now find the marginal density for U_1. If we first integrate the above density with respect to u_n between the limits 0 and $u_1 - u_2 - \cdots - u_{n-1}$, then with respect to u_{n-1} between 0 and $u_1 - u_2 - \cdots - u_{n-2}, \cdots$, and finally with respect to u_2 between 0 and u_1, we obtain

$$f_{U_1}(u_1) = \begin{cases} \dfrac{\alpha^n}{(n-1)!} u_1^{n-1} e^{-\alpha u_1} & \text{if } u_1 > 0 \\ 0 & \text{if } u_1 \leqq 0. \end{cases}$$

If one compares this with the gamma distribution given in Section 6.1 one sees that this is the gamma distribution where the α in Section 6.1 is a nonnegative integer.

EXERCISES

1. In the problem of radioactive decay given in Section 2.3, let T_1 denote the time that the first alpha particle is emitted. Find $F_{T_1}(x)$ and $f_{T_1}(x)$.

2. In the problem considered in problem 1, let T_n denote the time at which the nth alpha particle is emitted. Find $F_{T_n}(x)$ and $f_{T_n}(x)$.

3. Let $X_1, \cdots, X_n$ be n independent random variables. Assume that the distribution of each X_i is negative exponential with α, β not depending on i. Find a density of $X_1 + \cdots + X_n$.

4. If g is a function defined by

$$g(x) = \begin{cases} \alpha e^{-\alpha(x-\beta)} & \text{if } x > \beta \\ 0 & \text{if } x \leqq \beta \end{cases}$$

where α and β are fixed constants, $\alpha > 0$, $-\infty < \beta < \infty$, prove that

$$\int_{-\infty}^{\infty} g(x)\, dx = 1.$$

5. Let X have a negative exponential distribution with $\beta = 0$. If $t > 0$, $x > 0$, prove that

$$P([X > t + x]|[X > t]) = P[X > x].$$

6. Prove the converse to problem 5: If X is a random variable with an absolutely continuous distribution such that $P[X > 0] = 1$ and $P[X > x] > 0$ for all $x > 0$, and if

$$P([X > t + x]|[X > t]) = P[X > x]$$

for all $t > 0$ and all $x > 0$, then X has a negative exponential distribution. (*Hint:* use Cauchy's theorem which states: if f is a function defined over $(-\infty, \infty)$ which is continuous at 0 and satisfies the equation $f(x + y) = f(x) + f(y)$ identically in x and y, then there is a constant α such that $f(x) = \alpha x$ for all x.)

6.4 The Chi-Square Distribution

Let $X_1, X_2, \cdots, X_n$ be n independent random variables, each having a normal distribution with $\mu = 0$ and $\sigma^2 = 1$ (i.e., each X_i being $N(0, 1)$). The problem that we consider in this section is the derivation of a density of the random variable $\chi^2 = X_1^2 + X_2^2 + \cdots + X_n^2$. The distribution of χ^2 is called the *chi-square* (or χ^2) *distribution with n degrees of freedom.*

A joint density of $X_1, \cdots, X_n$ is given by

$$f_{X_1,\cdots,X_n}(x_1, \cdots, x_n) = (2\pi)^{-n/2} \exp -\sum_{i=1}^{n} \frac{x_i^2}{2},$$

where $-\infty < x_i < \infty$ for $i = 1, 2, \cdots, n$. Let us consider the transformation:

$$\begin{aligned}
x_1 &= \rho \cos \theta_1 \cos \theta_2 \cdots \cos \theta_{n-3} \cos \theta_{n-2} \cos \theta_{n-1} \\
x_2 &= \rho \cos \theta_1 \cos \theta_2 \cdots \cos \theta_{n-3} \cos \theta_{n-2} \sin \theta_{n-1} \\
x_3 &= \rho \cos \theta_1 \cos \theta_2 \cdots \cos \theta_{n-3} \sin \theta_{n-2} \\
&\cdot \\
&\cdot \\
&\cdot \\
x_n &= \rho \sin \theta_1
\end{aligned}$$

where $\rho > 0$, $0 \leqq \theta_{n-1} \leqq \pi, \cdots, 0 \leqq \theta_2 \leqq \pi$, $0 \leqq \theta_1 < 2\pi$. One easily notes that $x_1^2 + x_2^2 + \cdots + x_n^2 = \rho^2$. Also, the Jacobian of the transformation is easily seen to be

$$\frac{\partial(x_1, \cdots, x_n)}{\partial(\rho, \theta_1, \cdots, \theta_{n-1})} = \rho^{n-1} D(\theta_1, \cdots, \theta_{n-1}),$$

where $D(\theta_1, \cdots, \theta_{n-1})$ is some function of $\theta_1, \theta_2, \cdots, \theta_{n-1}$ only. (The phrase "easily seen" in the last sentence applies to students who know that a common factor of a column can be factored out of a determinant. See Theorem 24 in Chapter 9.)

Let us now consider random variables $\chi, \Theta_1, \Theta_2, \cdots, \Theta_{n-1}$, which are defined by replacing ρ by χ, θ_i by Θ_i, and x_i by X_i in the above transformation. Using Theorem 1 in Section 5.2 we obtain a joint density of $\chi, \Theta_1, \cdots, \Theta_{n-1}$ by the formula

$$f_{X,\Theta_1,\cdots,\Theta_{n-1}}(\rho, \theta_1, \cdots, \theta_{n-1})$$
$$= \begin{cases} (2\pi)^{-n/2} \exp(-\rho^2/2)\rho^{n-1}|D(\theta_1, \cdots, \theta_{n-1})| \\ \quad \text{for } \rho > 0, \quad 0 \leqq \theta_1 < 2\pi, \quad 0 \leqq \theta_2 \leqq \pi, \cdots, 0 \leqq \theta_{n-1} \leqq \pi, \\ 0 \quad \text{otherwise.} \end{cases}$$

We obtain, as a marginal density for X,

$$f_X(\rho) = \int_0^{2\pi} d\theta_1 \int_0^{\pi} d\theta_2 \cdots \int_0^{\pi} f_{X,\Theta_1,\cdots,\Theta_{n-1}}(\rho, \theta_1, \cdots, \theta_{n-1})\, d\theta_{n-1}$$
$$= \begin{cases} K(2\pi)^{-n/2} \exp(-\rho^2/2)\rho^{n-1} & \text{if } \rho > 0 \\ 0 & \text{if } \rho \leqq 0 \end{cases}$$

where

$$K = \int_0^{2\pi} d\theta_1 \int_0^{\pi} d\theta_2 \cdots \int_0^{\pi} |D(\theta_1, \cdots, \theta_{n-1})|\, d\theta_{n-1}.$$

The easiest way to evaluate K is *not* to compute the Jacobian but to make use of the fact that

$$\int_{-\infty}^{\infty} f_X(\rho)\, d\rho = \int_0^{\infty} K(2\pi)^{-n/2} \exp\left(-\frac{\rho^2}{2}\right) \rho^{n-1}\, d\rho = 1.$$

From this we obtain

$$K = (2\pi)^{n/2} \Big/ \int_0^{\infty} \rho^{n-1} \exp\left(-\frac{\rho^2}{2}\right) d\rho.$$

In order to evaluate the integral in the denominator, let $z = \rho^2/2$, or $\rho = \sqrt{2z}$. Then

$$K = (2\pi)^{n/2} \Big/ \int_0^{\infty} 2^{(n-1)/2} z^{(n-1)/2} e^{-z} 2^{-1/2} z^{-1/2}\, dz$$
$$= (2\pi)^{n/2}/2^{(n-2)/2}\Gamma(n/2).$$

Thus

$$f_X(\rho) = \begin{cases} \rho^{n-1} \exp(-\rho^2/2)/2^{(n-2)/2}\Gamma(n/2) & \text{if } \rho > 0 \\ 0 & \text{if } \rho \leqq 0. \end{cases}$$

In order to find a density of χ^2, we note that $f_{\chi^2}(x) = 0$ if $x \leqq 0$ and, if $x > 0$,

$$f_{\chi^2}(x) = \frac{d}{dx} P[\chi^2 \leqq x] = \frac{d}{dx} P[\chi \leqq \sqrt{x}]$$
$$= \frac{d}{dx} \int_0^{\sqrt{x}} \rho^{n-1} \exp\left(-\frac{\rho^2}{2}\right) d\rho / 2^{(n-2)/2}\Gamma(n/2)$$
$$= x^{(n-1)/2} e^{-x/2} 2^{-1} x^{-1/2} / 2^{(n-2)/2}\Gamma(n/2).$$

Thus

$$f_{\chi^2}(x) = \begin{cases} (2\Gamma(n/2))^{-1} e^{-x/2} (x/2)^{(n-2)/2} & \text{if } x > 0 \\ 0 & \text{if } x \leqq 0. \end{cases}$$

Upon comparing with Section 6.1, one notices that this is the gamma distribution in the particular case where $\alpha = (n-2)/2$, $\beta = 2$.

At this time we should also record densities for random variables χ^2/n and $\chi/\sqrt{n}$. The student can easily derive the following two formulas:

$$f_{\chi^2/n}(y) = \begin{cases} n^{n/2}e^{-ny/2}(y/2)^{(n-2)/2}/2\Gamma(n/2) & \text{if } y > 0 \\ 0 & \text{if } y \leqq 0, \end{cases}$$

$$f_{\chi/\sqrt{n}}(z) = \begin{cases} 2(n/2)^{n/2}\exp(-nz^2/2)z^{n-1}/\Gamma(n/2) & \text{if } z > 0 \\ 0 & \text{if } z \leqq 0. \end{cases}$$

A very important property of the chi-square distribution is one called the *reproductive property* which we prove in the following theorem.

1. Theorem. *If $X_1, \cdots, X_m$ are independent random variables, and if X_i has a chi-square distribution with n_i degrees of freedom for $1 \leqq i \leqq m$, then $X_1 + \cdots + X_m$ has a chi-square distribution with $n_1 + n_2 + \cdots + n_m$ degrees of freedom.*

Proof. It is clearly sufficient to prove this theorem in the case $m = 2$. In this case

$$f_{X_1,X_2}(x_1, x_2) = \begin{cases} \dfrac{e^{-\frac{1}{2}(x_1+x_2)}}{4\Gamma(n_1/2)\Gamma(n_2/2)}\left(\dfrac{x_1}{2}\right)^{\frac{1}{2}n_1-1}\left(\dfrac{x_2}{2}\right)^{\frac{1}{2}n_2-1} & \\ & \text{if } x_1 > 0, \quad x_2 > 0 \\ 0 & \text{if } \min\{x_1, x_2\} \leqq 0. \end{cases}$$

We consider the transformation $u_1 = x_1 + x_2$, $u_2 = x_2$ or $x_1 = u_1 - u_2$, $x_2 = u_2$. The Jacobian is seen to be 1. If we let $U_1 = X_1 + X_2$, $U_2 = X_2$, then by Theorem 1 in Section 5.2 we obtain

$$f_{U_1,U_2}(u_1, u_2) = \begin{cases} \dfrac{e^{-u_1/2}}{4\Gamma(n_1/2)\Gamma(n_2/2)}\left(\dfrac{u_1-u_2}{2}\right)^{\frac{1}{2}n_1-1}\left(\dfrac{u_2}{2}\right)^{\frac{1}{2}n_2-1} & \\ \qquad \text{if } 0 < u_2 < u_1, \quad 0 < u_1 < \infty & \\ 0 \qquad \text{otherwise.} & \end{cases}$$

Now, for $u_1 > 0$,

$$f_{U_1}(u_1) = \int_{-\infty}^{\infty} f_{U_1,U_2}(u_1, u_2)\, du_2$$

$$= \frac{e^{-u_1/2}}{4\Gamma(n_1/2)\Gamma(n_2/2)}\int_0^{u_1}\left(\frac{u_1-u_2}{2}\right)^{\frac{1}{2}n_1-1}\left(\frac{u_2}{2}\right)^{\frac{1}{2}n_2-1} du_2.$$

In this integral let us make the substitution $x = u_2/u_1$, and we obtain for $u_1 > 0$

$$f_{U_1}(u_1) = \frac{e^{-u_1/2}}{2\Gamma(n_1/2)\Gamma(n_2/2)}\left(\frac{u_1}{2}\right)^{\frac{1}{2}(n_1+n_2)-1} B\left(\frac{n_1}{2}, \frac{n_2}{2}\right)$$

where

$$B\left(\frac{n_1}{2}, \frac{n_2}{2}\right) = \int_0^1 x^{\frac{1}{2}n_1 - 1}(1 - x)^{\frac{1}{2}n_2 - 1}\, dx.$$

Making use of Theorem 1 in Section 6.1 we finally obtain

$$f_{U_1}(u_1) = \begin{cases} \left(2\Gamma\left(\dfrac{n_1 + n_2}{2}\right)\right)^{-1} e^{-u_1/2}\left(\dfrac{u_1}{2}\right)^{\frac{1}{2}(n_1+n_2)-1} & \text{if} \quad u_1 > 0 \\ 0 & \text{if} \quad u_1 \leqq 0, \end{cases}$$

which is the density of the chi-square distribution with $n_1 + n_2$ degrees of freedom.

The chi-square distribution is tabulated in Table II in the tables at the end of this book. In this table there are recorded values of x corresponding to given values of n (the number of degrees of freedom) and to given values of $F_{\chi^2}(x)$. For example, the table tells us that if X is a random variable which has a chi-square distribution with 12 degrees of freedom, then $P[X \leqq 18.5] = .90$, and if Y is a random variable which has a chi-square distribution with 21 degrees of freedom, then $P[Y \leqq 10.3] = .025$.

EXERCISES

1. Derive the formula for $f_{\chi^2/n}(y)$ given in this section.

2. Derive the formula for $f_{X/\sqrt{n}}(z)$ given in this section.

3. Why does it suffice to prove Theorem 1 only in the case $m = 2$?

4. If X is a random variable whose distribution is chi-square with 5 degrees of freedom, use Table II to find x so that $P[X \leqq x] = .995$.

5. If Y is a random variable whose distribution is chi-square with 20 degrees of freedom, find y so that $P[Y \leqq y] = .01$.

6.5 The *F*-Distribution and the *t*-Distribution

The two distributions obtained in this section are among the most important in practical applications of mathematical statistics.

In order to obtain the F-distribution we consider two independent random variables X, Y, where X has a chi-square distribution with m degrees of freedom, and Y has a chi-square distribution with n degrees of freedom. Our problem is to find a density of the random variable

$$U = \frac{X/m}{Y/n}.$$

The distribution of the random variable U is called the F-distribution with (m, n) degrees of freedom. We now derive a density function of U.

A joint density of X, Y is

$$f_{X,Y}(x, y) = \begin{cases} \dfrac{e^{-(x+y)/2}}{4\Gamma(m/2)\Gamma(n/2)}\left(\dfrac{x}{2}\right)^{\frac{1}{2}m-1}\left(\dfrac{y}{2}\right)^{\frac{1}{2}n-1} & \text{if} \quad x > 0, \quad y > 0 \\ 0 & \text{if} \quad \min\{x, y\} \leqq 0. \end{cases}$$

We consider the transformation $u = nx/my$, $v = y$ or $x = muv/n$, $y = v$. The Jacobian of the transformation is

$$\frac{\partial(x, y)}{\partial(u, v)} = \begin{vmatrix} \dfrac{mv}{n} & \dfrac{mu}{n} \\ 0 & 1 \end{vmatrix} = \frac{m}{n}v.$$

By Theorem 1 in Section 5.2 we obtain

$$f_{U,V}(u, v) = \begin{cases} \dfrac{\exp -\dfrac{v}{2}\left(\dfrac{mu}{n} + 1\right)}{2^{(m+n)/2}\Gamma(m/2)\Gamma(n/2)}\left(\dfrac{muv}{n}\right)^{\frac{1}{2}m-1} v^{\frac{1}{2}n-1}\dfrac{m}{n}v & \\ & \text{if} \quad u > 0, \quad v > 0, \\ 0 & \text{if} \quad \min(u, v) \leqq 0. \end{cases}$$

Now, if $u > 0$,

$$f_U(u) = \int_{-\infty}^{\infty} f_{U,V}(u, v)\, dv$$

$$= \frac{(m/n)^{m/2}u^{\frac{1}{2}m-1}}{2^{(m+n)/2}\Gamma(m/2)\Gamma(n/2)}\int_0^{\infty} \exp\left(-\frac{v}{2}\left(\frac{mu}{n} + 1\right)\right) v^{\frac{1}{2}(m+n)-1}\, dv.$$

In the integral we make the substitution $y = (v/2n)(mu + n)$, and we finally obtain

$$f_U(u) = \begin{cases} \dfrac{m^{m/2}n^{n/2}\Gamma((m+n)/2)}{\Gamma(m/2)\Gamma(n/2)} \dfrac{u^{\frac{1}{2}m-1}}{(mu+n)^{(m+n)/2}} & \text{if} \quad u > 0 \\ 0 & \text{if} \quad u \leqq 0. \end{cases}$$

Any random variable with this density is said to have the F-distribution with (m, n) degrees of freedom.

The F-distribution is tabulated in Table III in the tables at the end of this book. Given pairs of positive integers (m, n) and given probabilities p, the table records the numbers x for which

$$P[X \leqq x] = p,$$

when X has the F-distribution with (m, n) degrees of freedom. For example, if $(m, n) = (8, 4)$ and $p = .975$, then $x = 8.98$, and if one is given that $(m, n) = (4, 8)$ and $p = .95$, then $x = 3.84$. It should be noticed that the only values of p considered in the tables are the large values. However, one can easily use the tables for small values of p by noting that if X has the F-distribution with (m, n) degrees of freedom, then

$$P[X \leqq x] = 1 - P[Y \leqq 1/x],$$

where Y is a random variable with the F-distribution with (n, m) degrees of freedom. For example, suppose one wants to find the value of x for which $P[X \leqq x] = .05$, where X has the F-distribution with (10, 5) degrees of freedom. In this problem we look in the tables for the value of $1/x$ for which $P[Y \leqq 1/x] = .95$, where Y has the F-distribution with (5, 10) degrees of freedom. Thus $1/x = 3.33$, and $x = 1/3.33 = .300$.

The second density that we seek is that of the t-distribution. Let X, Y be two independent random variables, the distribution of X being $N(0, 1)$ and the distribution of Y being chi-square with n degrees of freedom. We shall say that a random variable has a t-distribution with n degrees of freedom if it has the same distribution function (or density function) as

$$T = X/\sqrt{Y/n}.$$

We now derive the density of T.

In Section 6.4 we found the density of $Z = \sqrt{Y/n}$ to be

$$f_Z(z) = f_{X/\sqrt{n}}(z)$$
$$= \begin{cases} 2(n/2)^{n/2} \exp(-nz^2/2) z^{n-1}/\Gamma(n/2) & \text{if } z > 0 \\ 0 & \text{if } z \leqq 0. \end{cases}$$

Hence the joint density of X and Z is

$$f_{X,Z}(x, z) = f_X(x) f_Z(z)$$
$$= \begin{cases} \dfrac{2(n/2)^{n/2}}{\sqrt{2\pi}\,\Gamma(n/2)} z^{n-1} \exp -\dfrac{(x^2 + nz^2)}{2} & \\ \qquad\qquad \text{if } -\infty < x < \infty \text{ and } z > 0 \\ 0 \qquad\qquad \text{otherwise.} \end{cases}$$

We now consider the transformation $t = x/z$, $s = z$, from which we obtain $x = ts$, $z = s$. The Jacobian is easily computed, and

$$\frac{\partial(x, z)}{\partial(t, s)} = s.$$

Thus

$$f_{T,S}(t, s) = f_{X,Z}(ts, s)s$$
$$= \begin{cases} \dfrac{2(n/2)^{n/2}}{\sqrt{2\pi}\,\Gamma(n/2)} s^n \exp -\dfrac{s^2(t^2 + n^2)}{2} & \\ \qquad\qquad \text{if } -\infty < t < \infty, \quad 0 < s < \infty \\ 0 \qquad\qquad \text{otherwise.} \end{cases}$$

If we integrate both sides with respect to s from $s = 0$ to ∞, and if we remember the integral definition of $\Gamma((n + 1)/2)$, we obtain

$$f_T(t) = (n\pi)^{-1/2}\frac{\Gamma((n+1)/2)}{\Gamma(n/2)}\left(1+\frac{t^2}{n}\right)^{-(n+1)/2}$$

for $-\infty < t < \infty$. Thus we have found a density of the t-distribution with n degrees of freedom.

The t-distribution is tabulated in Table IV in the tables at the end of this book. If a random variable X has the t-distribution with n degrees of freedom, then this table records values of x for which

$$P[X \leqq x] = p,$$

for select large values of p. For example, if $n = 11$ and $p = .975$, then $x = 2.201$, i.e., $P[X \leqq 2.201] = .975$. If p is a small probability, we can still use the table by making use of the following easily verified identity for the t-distribution:

$$P[X \leqq x] = 1 - P[X \leqq -x].$$

For example, if $n = 20$ and $p = .01$, we notice that since

$$P[X \leqq 2.528] = .99,$$

then $x = -2.528$, i.e.,

$$P[X \leqq -2.528] = .01.$$

For large values of n, say, $n \geqq 50$, the t-distribution with n degrees of freedom is close to the $N(0, 1)$ distribution. Thus for large values of n one can use Table I as an approximation for what is left out of Table IV.

EXERCISES

1. Prove: If X has the F-distribution with (m, n) degrees of freedom, and if Y has the F-distribution with (n, m) degrees of freedom, then, for every $x > 0$,

$$P[X \leqq x] = 1 - P[Y \leqq 1/x].$$

2. If X has the F-distribution with (m, n) degrees of freedom, use Table III to find the value of x for which

(a) $P[X \leqq x] = .99$, when $m = 7$, $n = 3$,
(b) $P[X \leqq x] = .95$, when $m = 2$, $n = 9$,
(c) $P[X \leqq x] = .10$, when $m = 10$, $n = 6$,
(d) $P[X \leqq x] = .005$, when $m = 20$, $n = 30$.

3. Prove that if X has the t-distribution with n degrees of freedom, then the distribution of X is symmetric, i.e.,

$$P[X \leqq x] = 1 - P[X \leqq -x].$$

4. Prove: If X has the t-distribution with n degrees of freedom, then

$$P[|X| \leqq x] = 1 - 2(1 - P[X \leqq x]).$$

5. If X has a t-distribution with n degrees of freedom, use Table IV to find the value of x such that

(a) $P[X \leqq x] = .99$ when $n = 17$,
(b) $P[X \leqq x] = .05$ when $n = 6$,
(c) $P[|X| \leqq x] = .90$ when $n = 12$,
(d) $P[|X| \geqq x] = .05$ when $n = 8$.

6. Let T be a random variable which has a t-distribution with n degrees of freedom. Prove that T^2 has an F-distribution with $(1, n)$ degrees of freedom.

7. Let Z be a random variable with the Cauchy distribution, i.e., Z has an absolutely continuous distribution with a density function

$$f_Z(z) = 1/\pi(1 + z^2), \quad -\infty < z < \infty.$$

Prove that Z^2 has an F-distribution with $(1, 1)$ degrees of freedom.

CHAPTER 7

Expectation and Limit Theorems

7.1 Definition of Expectation

We begin this chapter and this section with the following definition.

Definition. *Let X be a random variable with distribution function $F_X(x)$. The expectation EX of X is defined by*

$$EX = \int_0^\infty (1 - F_X(x))\,dx - \int_{-\infty}^0 F_X(x)\,dx,$$

provided that both integrals are finite. When at least one of these integrals is infinite we shall say that the expectation of X does not exist.

Graphically speaking, EX is the area above $y = F_X(x)$, to the right of the y-axis, and below the line $y = 1$, minus the area below $y = F_X(x)$, to the left of the y-axis, and above the line $y = 0$. It will turn out that the number EX is nothing else than the center of gravity (or centroid) of the spread of unit (probability) mass over $(-\infty, +\infty)$ as determined by $F_X(x)$. We shall prove two theorems showing this: one for the discrete case and one for the absolutely continuous case.

First we shall need a lemma.

1. Lemma. *If $\{a_n\}$ is a sequence of nonnegative numbers, and if $Q_n = \sum_{j=n}^\infty a_j$, then $\sum_{n=1}^\infty Q_n = \sum_{n=1}^\infty na_n$.*

Proof. By direct computation,

$$\begin{aligned}\sum_{n=1}^\infty Q_n = a_1 + a_2 + a_3 + a_4 + \cdots \\ + a_2 + a_3 + a_4 + \cdots \\ + a_3 + a_4 + \cdots \\ + a_4 + \cdots \\ \cdots \\ = a_1 + 2a_2 + 3a_3 + 4a_4 + \cdots,\end{aligned}$$

which completes the proof.

2. Theorem. *Let X be a random variable with a discrete distribution, i.e., there exists a finite or denumerable set of numbers $\{x_n\}$ and probabilities $\{p_n\}$ such that $P[X = x_n] = p_n$ and $\sum_{n=1}^{\infty} p_n = 1$. Then the expectation of X exists, and*

$$EX = \sum_{n=1}^{\infty} x_n p_n,$$

if and only if the series is absolutely convergent.

Proof. Let

$$I_1 = \int_0^{\infty} P[X > x]\,dx \quad \text{and} \quad I_2 = \int_{-\infty}^{0} P[X \leqq x]\,dx.$$

We shall make use of the fact that $P[X > x]$ is nonincreasing in x, i.e., if $x_1 < x_2$, then $P[X > x_1] \geqq P[X > x_2]$. Because of the definition of the Cauchy (or improper) integral, we may write

$$I_1 = \sum_{k=1}^{\infty} \int_{(k-1)/n}^{k/n} P[X > x]\,dx.$$

Because of the nonincreasing property of $P[X > x]$ mentioned above, the inequality

$$\frac{1}{n} P\left[X > \frac{k}{n}\right] \leqq \int_{(k-1)/n}^{k/n} P[X > x]\,dx \leqq \frac{1}{n} P\left[X > \frac{k-1}{n}\right]$$

is true. Thus, if we denote

$$L_n = \sum_{k=1}^{\infty} \frac{1}{n} P\left[X > \frac{k}{n}\right],$$

$$U_n = \sum_{k=1}^{\infty} \frac{1}{n} P\left[X > \frac{k-1}{n}\right],$$

we easily see because of the above inequality that

$$L_n \leqq I_1 \leqq U_n$$

for every positive integer n. However, we may write

$$L_n = \frac{1}{n} \sum_{k=1}^{\infty} \sum_{j=k}^{\infty} P\left[\frac{j}{n} < X \leqq \frac{j+1}{n}\right].$$

If we let $a_j = P[j/n < X \leqq (j+1)/n]$, then we may apply Lemma 1 and obtain

$$L_n = \sum_{k=1}^{\infty} \frac{k-1}{n} P\left[\frac{k-1}{n} < X \leqq \frac{k}{n}\right]$$

$$= \sum_{k=1}^{\infty} \frac{k}{n} P\left[\frac{k-1}{n} < X \leqq \frac{k}{n}\right]$$

$$- \sum_{k=1}^{\infty} \frac{1}{n} P\left[\frac{k-1}{n} < X \leqq \frac{k}{n}\right].$$

However,

$$\frac{k}{n} P\left[\frac{k-1}{n} < X \leqq \frac{k}{n}\right] = \frac{k}{n} \sum_{\{j|(k-1)/n < x_j \leqq k/n\}} p_j$$
$$\geqq \sum_{\{j|(k-1)/n < x_j \leqq k/n\}} x_j p_j.$$

Hence

$$L_n \geqq \sum_{k=1}^{\infty} \sum_{\{j|(k-1)/n < x_j \leqq k/n\}} x_j p_j - \frac{1}{n} P[X > 0]$$
$$\geqq \sum_{\{m|x_m > 0\}} p_m x_m - \frac{1}{n}.$$

In a similar fashion one can prove that

$$U_n \leqq \sum_{\{m|x_m > 0\}} x_m p_m + \frac{1}{n}.$$

Thus, for every positive integer n,

$$\sum_{\{m|x_m > 0\}} x_m p_m - \frac{1}{n} \leqq I_1 \leqq \sum_{\{m|x_m > 0\}} x_m p_m + \frac{1}{n},$$

from which there follows, by taking the limit as $n \to \infty$, that

$$I_1 = \sum_{\{m|x_m > 0\}} x_m p_m.$$

In an entirely similar manner, one can prove that

$$I_2 = - \sum_{\{m|x_m \leqq 0\}} x_m p_m.$$

Thus, absolute convergence of the series

$$\sum_n x_n p_n$$

is necessary and sufficient for the integrals I_1, I_2 to exist, and we obtain

$$EX = I_1 - I_2 = \sum_n x_n p_n,$$

which proves the theorem.

3. Theorem. *Let X be a random variable with an absolutely continuous distribution. The expectation of X exists and*

$$EX = \int_{-\infty}^{\infty} x f_X(x)\, dx$$

if and only if this integral exists (as an improper integral).

The proof of this theorem is the same as the proof of Theorem 2 except that

$$\sum_{\{j \mid (k-1)/n < x_j \leqq k/n\}} p_j$$

is replaced by $\int_{(k-1)/n}^{k/n} f_X(x)\,dx$,

$$\sum_{\{j \mid (k-1)/n < x_j \leqq k/n\}} x_j p_j$$

is replaced by $\int_{(k-1)/n}^{k/n} x f_X(x)\,dx$, and

$$\sum_{\{m \mid x_m > 0\}} x_m p_m$$

is replaced by $\int_0^\infty x f_X(x)\,dx$.

We now give some examples of expectations of random variables.

Example 1. *The Binomial Distribution.* Let X have a binomial distribution with parameters p and n, i.e.,

$$P[X = x] = \begin{cases} \binom{n}{x} p^x (1-p)^{n-x} & \text{if } x = 0, 1, \cdots, n, \\ 0 & \text{otherwise.} \end{cases}$$

In this case of a discrete distribution we have

$$\begin{aligned} EX &= \sum_{k=0}^{n} kP[X = k] = \sum_{k=0}^{n} k \binom{n}{k} p^k (1-p)^{n-k} \\ &= np \sum_{k=1}^{n} \binom{n-1}{k-1} p^{k-1} (1-p)^{n-k} \\ &= np \sum_{j=0}^{n-1} \binom{n-1}{j} p^j (1-p)^{n-1-j} \\ &= np(p + (1-p))^{n-1} = np. \end{aligned}$$

Example 2. *Poisson Distribution.* In this discrete case,

$$P[X = n] = e^{-\lambda}\lambda^n/n!, \quad n = 0, 1, 2, \cdots.$$

Then

$$\begin{aligned} EX &= \sum_{n=0}^{\infty} n e^{-\lambda} \frac{\lambda^n}{n!} = \lambda e^{-\lambda} \sum_{n=1}^{\infty} \frac{\lambda^{n-1}}{(n-1)!} \\ &= \lambda e^{-\lambda} e^{\lambda} = \lambda. \end{aligned}$$

Example 3. *Pascal Distribution.* In this discrete case,

$$P[X = n] = q^n p, \quad n = 0, 1, 2, \cdots, \quad 0 < p = 1 - q < 1.$$

Then by Lemma 1 and the formula $\sum_{n=0}^{\infty} x^n = (1-x)^{-1}$ if $|x| < 1$, we obtain

$$\begin{aligned} EX &= \sum_{n=0}^{\infty} nq^n p = p \sum_{n=1}^{\infty} \left(\sum_{j=n}^{\infty} q^j \right) \\ &= p \sum_{n=1}^{\infty} q^n (1-q)^{-1} = q(1-q)^{-1} = q/p. \end{aligned}$$

Example 4. *Normal Distribution.* In this absolutely continuous case,

$$f_X(x) = (2\pi\sigma^2)^{-1/2} \exp\{-(x-\mu)^2/2\sigma^2\}, \quad -\infty < x < \infty.$$

Using Theorem 3 we obtain

$$EX = \int_{-\infty}^{\infty} x(2\pi\sigma^2)^{-1/2} \exp\left\{-\frac{(x-\mu)^2}{2\sigma^2}\right\} dx.$$

If we let $y = (x - \mu)/\sigma$, we obtain

$$EX = (2\pi)^{-1/2} \int_{-\infty}^{\infty} \sigma\, y \exp\left(-\frac{y^2}{2}\right) dy + \mu(2\pi)^{-1/2} \int_{-\infty}^{\infty} \exp\left(-\frac{y^2}{2}\right) dy = 0 + \mu = \mu.$$

EXERCISES

1. Find the expectation of a random variable X having the gamma distribution as defined in Section 6.1.

2. Find the expectation of a random variable having a negative exponential distribution as defined in Section 6.3.

3. Find the expectation of a random variable having a χ^2 distribution with n degrees of freedom as defined in Section 6.4.

4. Find the expectation of the discrete random variable X, where

$$P[X = n] = \begin{cases} q^{n-1}p, & n = 1, 2, \cdots, \quad 0 < p = 1 - q < 1 \\ 0 & \text{otherwise.} \end{cases}$$

5. If X has a Cauchy distribution, i.e., if $f_X(x) = (\pi(1 + x^2))^{-1}$, $-\infty < x < \infty$, show that X does *not* have an expectation.

6. Write out the details of the proof of the inequality

$$U_n \leqq \sum_{\{m|x_m>0\}} x_m p_m + \frac{1}{n}$$

given in the proof of Theorem 2.

7. Write out the details of the proof of the equality

$$I_2 = -\sum_{\{m|x_m \leqq 0\}} x_m p_m$$

given in the proof of Theorem 2.

8. Write out a complete proof of Theorem 3.

9. If X is a random variable with an absolutely continuous distribution and whose density is

$$f_X(x) = \begin{cases} 1/\theta & \text{if } \ 0 < x < \theta \\ 0 & \text{if } \ x \leqq 0 \ \text{ or } \ x \geqq \theta, \end{cases}$$

where $\theta > 0$, find EX.

10. Let X be a random variable with a discrete distribution, its density function being

$$f_X(x) = 6/(\pi x)^2, \quad x = 1, 2, 3, \cdots.$$

Prove that the expectation of X does not exist.

11. Compute the expectation of a random variable having a beta distribution as defined in Section 6.1.

7.2 Expectation of Functions of Random Variables

Let g be a real-valued function defined over $(-\infty, +\infty)$, and let X be a random variable. The function g is not assumed to be arbitrary; it is assumed that g has the property that $g(X)$ is a random variable. [*Remember:* $g(X)$ is a function defined over Ω which assigns to every $\omega \in \Omega$ the number $g(X(\omega))$, and the assumption that $g(X)$ is a random variable means that for every real number t, the collection of elementary events $[g(X) \leqq t] = \{\omega \in \Omega | g(X(\omega)) \leqq t\}$ is an event, i.e., is an element of $\mathcal{A}$.] The purpose of this section is to show how to compute $Eg(X)$ in the cases when X has a discrete distribution and when X has an absolutely continuous distribution. In addition, functions of several random variables will also be considered.

1. Theorem. *If X is a discrete random variable whose range is a sequence $\{x_n\}$ real numbers, then $Eg(X)$ exists and*

$$Eg(X) = \sum_n g(x_n) f_X(x_n)$$

if and only if this series is absolutely convergent.

Proof. Since X is discrete, it follows that $g(X)$ is discrete. However, a small amount of care must be taken in this proof. Let T denote the set of all real numbers of the form $g(x_n)$. Then T is finite or denumerable and, by Theorem 2 in Section 7.1,

$$\begin{aligned} Eg(X) &= \sum_{t \in T} t \sum_{\{x_n | g(x_n) = t\}} f_X(x_n) \\ &= \sum_{t \in T} \sum_{\{x_n | g(x_n) = t\}} t f_X(x_n) \\ &= \sum_n g(x_n) f_X(x_n), \end{aligned}$$

which proves the theorem.

We now state a theorem which is a special case of the more general form of the first unproved theorem of Section 5.2.

2. Theorem. *Let $X_1, \cdots, X_n$ be n random variables with a joint absolutely continuous distribution. Let $g_1, g_2, \cdots, g_m$ be m real-valued functions of n arguments such that $g_i(X_1, \cdots, X_n)$ is a random variable for $i = 1, 2, \cdots, m$. If $-\infty \leqq a_i < b_i \leqq \infty$ for $1 \leqq i \leqq m$, and if*

$$B = \{(x_1, \cdots, x_n) | a_i < g_i(x_1, \cdots, x_n) \leqq b_i, 1 \leqq i \leqq m\},$$

then

$$P\left\{\bigcap_{i=1}^{m} [a_i < g_i(X_1, \cdots, X_n) \leqq b_i]\right\}$$
$$= \int \underset{B}{\cdots} \int f_{X_1,\cdots,X_n}(x_1, \cdots, x_n)\, dx_1 \cdots dx_n.$$

3. Theorem. *If the random variable X has an absolutely continuous distribution, then the expectation of g(X) exists and*

$$Eg(X) = \int_{-\infty}^{\infty} g(x)f_X(x)\, dx$$

if and only if

$$\int_{-\infty}^{\infty} |g(x)|f_X(x)\, dx < \infty.$$

Proof. The proof of this theorem is very similar to the proof of Theorem 3 in Section 7.1. If we let

$$I_1 = \int_0^{\infty} P[g(X) > x]\, dx \quad \text{and} \quad I_2 = \int_{-\infty}^{0} P[g(X) \leqq x]\, dx,$$

then the expectation of $g(X)$ exists if and only if I_1 and I_2 are finite, in which case $Eg(X) = I_1 - I_2$. Now let

$$\pi(x) = \{t \in (-\infty, +\infty) | g(t) > x\}.$$

It is easy to see that if $x' < x''$, then $\pi(x') \supset \pi(x'')$. If we define $h(x) = P[g(X) > x]$, then by Theorem 2,

$$h(x) = \int_{\pi(x)} f_X(t)\, dt$$

is a nonincreasing function of x, i.e., if $x' < x''$, then $h(x') \geqq h(x'')$. If we denote

$$L_n = \sum_{k=1}^{\infty} \frac{1}{n} \int_{\pi(k/n)} f_X(t)\, dt,$$

$$U_n = \sum_{k=1}^{\infty} \frac{1}{n} \int_{\pi((k-1)/n)} f_X(t)\, dt,$$

then (just as in the proof of Theorem 3 in Section 7.1), $L_n \leqq I_1 \leqq U_n$ for every positive integer n. But, just as in the proof of Theorem 3 in Section 7.1,

$$L_n = \sum_{k=1}^{\infty} \frac{k-1}{n} \int_{\{x|((k-1)/n) < g(x) \leqq k/n\}} f_X(x)\, dx$$

$$= \sum_{k=1}^{\infty} \frac{k}{n} \int_{\{x|((k-1)/n) < g(x) \leqq k/n\}} f_X(x)\, dx$$

$$- \sum_{k=1}^{\infty} \frac{1}{n} \int_{\{x|((k-1)/n) < g(x) \leqq k/n\}} f_X(x)\, dx$$

$$\geqq \sum_{k=1}^{\infty} \int_{\{x|((k-1)/n) < g(x) \leqq k/n\}} g(x) f_X(x)\, dx$$

$$- \frac{1}{n} \int_{\{x|g(x) > 0\}} f_X(x)\, dx$$

$$\geqq \int_{\{x|g(x) > 0\}} g(x) f_X(x)\, dx - \frac{1}{n}.$$

In the same way one arrives at the inequality

$$U_n \leqq \int_{\{x|g(x)>0\}} g(x) f_X(x)\, dx + \frac{1}{n}.$$

Consequently,

$$\int_{\{x|g(x)>0\}} g(x) f_X(x)\, dx - \frac{1}{n} \leqq I_1 \leqq \int_{\{x|g(x)>0\}} g(x) f_X(x)\, dx + \frac{1}{n},$$

or, what amounts to the same thing,

$$\left| I_1 - \int_{\{x|g(x)>0\}} g(x) f_X(x)\, dx \right| \leqq \frac{1}{n}$$

for every positive integer n. Since the left-hand side of this inequality does not depend on n, it vanishes, and thus

$$I_1 = \int_{\{x|g(x)>0\}} g(x) f_X(x)\, dx.$$

In the same way one can prove that

$$I_2 = - \int_{\{x|g(x) \leqq 0\}} g(x) f_X(x)\, dx,$$

from which the theorem is established.

Now let us consider two random variables X and Y. Let $h(\cdot, \cdot)$ denote a function of two real arguments for which $h(X, Y)$ is a random variable, i.e.,

$$[h(X, Y) \leqq x] = \{\omega \in \Omega | h(X(\omega), Y(\omega)) \leqq x\} \in \mathfrak{A}$$

for every real number x.

4. Theorem. *If X, Y have a joint discrete distribution, then the expectation of $h(X, Y)$ exists and*

$$Eh(X, Y) = \sum_{i,j} h(x_i, y_j) f_{X,Y}(x_i, y_j)$$

(where the set of x_i's is the range of X and the set of y_j's is the range of Y) if and only if the double series is absolutely convergent.

The proof of this theorem is the same as that of Theorem 2 in Section 7.1 and is left to the student to perform.

5. Theorem. *If X and Y have a joint absolutely continuous distribution, then the expectation of $h(X, Y)$ exists and*

$$Eh(X, Y) = \int_{-\infty}^{\infty} \int_{-\infty}^{\infty} h(x, y) f_{X,Y}(x, y)\, dx\, dy$$

if and only if

$$\int_{-\infty}^{\infty} \int_{-\infty}^{\infty} |h(x, y)| f_{X,Y}(x, y)\, dx\, dy < \infty.$$

The proof of this theorem is the same as that of Theorem 3 in Section 7.1 and is left to the student. It should be noticed that Theorem 5 can be stated and proved for h a function of any finite number of random variables.

We now apply the theorems given in this section. The statements made in the following theorems can be made more general, but the proofs of the more general statements are beyond the scope of this course.

6. Theorem. *If X, Y either have a discrete joint distribution or an absolutely continuous joint distribution, and if EX and EY exist, then $E(X + Y)$ exists and $E(X + Y) = E(X) + E(Y)$.*

Proof. In either case let $h(\cdot, \cdot)$ be defined by $h(u, v) = u + v$. Then in the discrete case we apply Theorem 4 and get

$$\begin{aligned} EX + EY &= \sum_i x_i f_X(x_i) + \sum_j y_j f_Y(y_j) \\ &= \sum_i x_i \sum_j f_{X,Y}(x_i, y_j) + \sum_j y_j \sum_i f_{X,Y}(x_i, y_j) \\ &= \sum_i \sum_j (x_i + y_j) f_{X,Y}(x_i, y_j) = E(X + Y). \end{aligned}$$

In the absolutely continuous case,

$$\begin{aligned} EX + EY &= \int_{-\infty}^{\infty} x f_X(x)\, dx + \int_{-\infty}^{\infty} y f_Y(y)\, dy \\ &= \int_{-\infty}^{\infty} x \int_{-\infty}^{\infty} f_{X,Y}(x, y)\, dy\, dx + \int_{-\infty}^{\infty} y \int_{-\infty}^{\infty} f_{X,Y}(x, y)\, dx\, dy \\ &= \int_{-\infty}^{\infty} \int_{-\infty}^{\infty} (x + y) f_{X,Y}(x, y)\, dx\, dy = E(X + Y). \end{aligned}$$

The theorem is proved.

7. Theorem. *For any random variable X for which EX exists and for any constant c, $EcX = cEX$.*

Proof. We prove the theorem only in the case $c > 0$. (The case $c \leqq 0$ is left to the student.) In this case,

$$
\begin{aligned}
EX &= \int_0^\infty P[X > x]\,dx - \int_{-\infty}^0 P[X \leqq x]\,dx \\
&= \frac{1}{c}\left\{\int_0^\infty P\left[X > \frac{x}{c}\right]dx - \int_{-\infty}^0 P\left[X \leqq \frac{x}{c}\right]dx\right\} \\
&= \frac{1}{c}\left\{\int_0^\infty P[cX > x]\,dx - \int_{-\infty}^0 P[cX \leqq x]\,dx\right\} \\
&= \frac{1}{c}\,E(cX),
\end{aligned}
$$

which proves the theorem.

8. Theorem. *If X, Y either have a joint discrete distribution or a joint absolutely continuous distribution, and if a and b are constants, then $E(aX + bY) = aEX + bEY$.*

This theorem is a direct consequence of Theorems 6 and 7.

EXERCISES

1. In the proof of Theorem 3, prove the inequality

$$U_n \leqq \int_{\{x|g(x)>0\}} g(x)f_X(x)\,dx + \frac{1}{n}$$

2. In the proof of Theorem 3, prove that

$$I_2 = -\int_{\{x|g(x)\leqq 0\}} g(x)f_X(x)\,dx.$$

3. Prove Theorem 4.

4. Write out a proof for Theorem 7 when $c \leqq 0$.

7.3 Moments and Central Moments

The purpose of this section is to define moments, central moments and mixed moments of random variables and to derive some of their properties.

Definition. *If r is a positive integer, we define the rth moment of a random variable X to be $\mu'_r = E(X^r)$, provided such expectation exists.*

Definition. *If r is a positive integer we define the rth central moment of a random variable X to be $\mu_r = E(X - EX)^r$, provided the two expectations involved exist. The second central moment μ_2 of X is called the variance of X and is denoted by* Var (X) *or* Var X.

1. Theorem. *If X is a random variable which has a discrete or absolutely continuous distribution, and if EX^2 exists, then* Var $X = EX^2 - (EX)^2$.

Proof.

$$\text{Var}(X) = E(X - EX)^2$$
$$= E(X^2 - 2(EX)X + (EX)^2) = EX^2 - 2(EX)^2 + (EX)^2 = EX^2 - (EX)^2.$$

Definition. *The covariance of two random variables X and Y is defined to be*

$$\text{Cov}(X, Y) = E\{(X - EX)(Y - EY)\},$$

provided the expectations exist.

2. Theorem. *If X and Y have a joint discrete or joint absolutely continuous distribution, then* $\text{Cov}(X, Y) = E(XY) - (EX)(EY)$, *provided the expectations exist.*

Proof.

$$\text{Cov}(X, Y) = E((X - EX)(Y - EY))$$
$$= E(XY - XEY - YEX + (EX)(EY))$$
$$= E(XY) - (EX)(EY) - (EY)(EX) + (EX)(EY) = E(XY) - EXEY.$$

3. Lemma. *If X is a random variable such that $P[X \geqq 0] = 1$, $P[X > 0] > 0$, and EX exists, then $EX > 0$.*

Proof. The student can easily verify that for any sequence of positive real numbers $\{\epsilon_n\}$ for which $\epsilon_n \to 0$ as $n \to \infty$, we have the identity

$$[X > 0] = \bigcup_{n=1}^{\infty} [X > \epsilon_n].$$

By Boole's inequality,

$$P[X > 0] \leqq \sum_{n=1}^{\infty} P[X > \epsilon_n].$$

Since $P[X > 0] > 0$, then for at least one value of n, $P[X > \epsilon_n] > 0$. Hence there exists an $\epsilon > 0$ and a $\delta > 0$ such that $P[X > \epsilon] = \delta$, or $F_X(x) \leqq F_X(\epsilon) = 1 - \delta$ for all $x \in [0, \epsilon]$. The hypothesis $P[X \geqq 0] = 1$ implies that $F_X(x) = 0$ for all $x < 0$. If we let g be a function defined by $g(x) = \delta$ if $x \in [0, \epsilon]$ and $= 0$ if $x \notin [0, \epsilon]$, then $1 - F_X(x) \geqq g(x)$ for all $x > 0$. Thus

$$EX = \int_0^{\infty} (1 - F_X(x))\, dx \geqq \int_0^{\infty} g(x)\, dx = \delta\epsilon > 0,$$

which proves the lemma.

4. Theorem. (Schwarz' Inequality). *If X and Y are two random variables with a joint discrete or joint absolutely continuous distribution, and if they have finite second moments, then*

$$E^2(XY) \leq E(X^2)E(Y^2),$$

and equality holds if and only if there exists a real number t such that $P[tX + Y = 0] = 1$ *or* $P[X + tY = 0] = 1$.

Proof. The student should recall that the quadratic equation $ax^2 + 2bx + c = 0$, has two distinct real roots if and only if $b^2 - ac > 0$, one double real root if and only if $b^2 - ac = 0$, and no real roots if and only if $b^2 - ac < 0$. For any real t, $P[(tX + Y)^2 \geqq 0] = 1$, and this implies that

$$E(tX + Y)^2 = t^2EX^2 + 2tEXY + EY^2 \geqq 0.$$

This quadratic has either no real roots or one double real root, and hence $E^2(XY) - EX^2EY^2 \leqq 0$, which gives the inequality. Strict equality holds if and only if there exists a t such that $E(tX + Y)^2 = 0$. By Lemma 3, this implies that $P[tX + Y = 0] = 1$. Conversely, if $P[tX + Y = 0] = 1$ for some t, $E(tX + Y)^2 = 0$, and thus the proof is complete.

Definition. *If the random variable X has a finite second moment, then the standard deviation of X,* s.d.(X), *is defined to be* s.d.$(X) = \sqrt{\text{Var}(X)}$.

Definition. *Let X, Y be two random variables with finite second moments. The correlation coefficient $\rho(X, Y)$ of X and Y is defined to be*

$$\rho(X, Y) = \frac{\text{Cov}(X, Y)}{\text{s.d.}(X)\text{s.d.}(Y)}.$$

provided s.d.$(X) > 0$ *and* s.d.$(Y) > 0$. *If one of these standard deviations is equal to zero, then the correlation coefficient of X and Y is not defined.*

5. Theorem. *If X and Y are random variables with a joint discrete or joint absolutely continuous distribution, with finite second moments, and with positive standard deviations, then $-1 \leqq \rho(X, Y) \leqq 1$. The equality $\rho(X, Y) = 1$ holds if and only if there is a positive number β such that $Y - EY = \beta(X - EX)$. The equality $\rho(X, Y) = -1$ holds if and only if there exists a negative number γ such that $Y - EY = \gamma(X - EX)$.*

Proof. By Schwarz' inequality,

$$E^2(X - EY)(Y - EY) \leqq E(X - EX)^2E(Y - EY)^2,$$

which implies that $\rho^2(X, Y) \leqq 1$, which in turn implies $-1 \leqq \rho(X, Y) \leqq 1$. By Schwarz' inequality, one of the two equal signs holds if and only if there exists a constant t such that $Y - EY = t(X - EX)$. Suppose $t < 0$. Then, multiplying both sides by $X - EX$ and taking expectations, we get Cov $(X, Y) = t$ Var (X). Hence Cov $(X, Y) < 0$, which implies that $\rho(X, Y) < 0$, and consequently $\rho(X, Y) = -1$. The student can easily show that when $t > 0$, $\rho(X, Y) = +1$. This ends the proof.

The next theorem gives a very useful property of independence.

6. Theorem. *Let $X_1, X_2, \cdots, X_n$ be n independent random variables for which expectations exist. If they have a joint absolutely continuous distribution or a joint discrete distribution, then the expectation of $\prod_{i=1}^n X_i$ exists, and*

$$E\left(\prod_{i=1}^n X_i\right) = \prod_{i=1}^n EX_i.$$

Proof. We give the proof only in the absolutely continuous case and leave the proof for the discrete case to the student. By Theorem 5 in Section 7.2 in the case where h is a function of n arguments and $h(x_1, x_2, \cdots, x_n) = \prod_{i=1}^n x_i$, we have

$$\begin{aligned} E\left(\prod_{k=1}^n X_k\right) &= \int_{-\infty}^{\infty} \cdots \int_{-\infty}^{\infty} x_1x_2 \cdots x_n f_{X_1,\dots,X_n}(x_1, \cdots, x_n)\, dx_1 \cdots dx_n \\ &= \int_{-\infty}^{\infty} \cdots \int_{-\infty}^{\infty} x_1 \cdots x_n f_{X_1}(x_1) f_{X_2}(x_2) \cdots f_{X_n}(x_n)\, dx_1 \cdots dx_n \\ &= \prod_{j=1}^n \int_{-\infty}^{\infty} x_j f_{X_j}(x_j)\, dx_j = \prod_{j=1}^n EX_j, \end{aligned}$$

which proves the assertion.

7. Theorem. *If X and Y are two independent random variables with discrete or absolutely continuous distributions, with finite second moments and with positive standard deviations, then* Cov $(X, Y) = 0$ *and* $\rho(X, Y) = 0$.

Proof. By Theorems 2 and 6, we have Cov $(X, Y) = EXY - EXEY = EXEY - EXEY = 0$. Then, trivially, $\rho(X, Y) = 0$.

At this point it should be emphasized that the converse of Theorem 7 is not necessarily true. As an example of this fact, let X be any random variable of which EX and EX^3 exist and which has an absolutely continuous distribution. Assume that X has a density $f_X(x)$ which is an even function, i.e., $f_X(x) = f_X(-x)$ for every real x. Let $Y = X^2$. Then Cov $(X, Y) = EX^3 - EXEX^2$. Since $f_X(x)$ is an even function the student can easily verify that $EX = EX^3 = 0$. Hence Cov $(X, Y) = 0$, which implies that $\rho(X, Y) = 0$. Intuitively, X and Y are not independent despite the fact that they have zero correlation, because for any value that X takes, the value of Y is strictly determined as the square of the value that X takes. The student can easily prove that X and Y are not independent using the definition of independence of random variables (see exercise 9). Thus we have here a case of two random variables which have zero correlation and yet are highly dependent.

Before completing this section we need two further results on variance.

8. Theorem. *If $X_1, \cdots, X_n$ are n independent random variables, all having discrete or absolutely continuous distributions, and all having finite second moments, then*

$$\operatorname{Var} \sum_{k=1}^{n} X_k = \sum_{k=1}^{n} \operatorname{Var} X_k.$$

Proof. First note that $E(X_1 + \cdots + X_n) = EX_1 + \cdots + EX_n$. Then

$$\begin{aligned}\operatorname{Var}\left(\sum_{k=1}^{n} X_k\right) &= E\left(\sum_{k=1}^{n} X_k - E\left(\sum_{k=1}^{n} X_k\right)\right)^2 \\ &= E\left(\sum_{k=1}^{n} (X_k - EX_k)\right)^2 \\ &= E\left\{\sum_{k=1}^{n} (X_k - EX_k)^2 + \sum_{i \neq j} (X_i - EX_i)(X_j - EX_j)\right\} \\ &= \sum_{k=1}^{n} \operatorname{Var} X_k + \sum_{i \neq j} \operatorname{Cov}(X_i, X_j).\end{aligned}$$

For $i \neq j$, X_i and X_j are independent and, by Theorem 7, $\operatorname{Cov}(X_i, X_j) = 0$. This proves the theorem.

9. Theorem. *If X is a random variable with finite second moment and if K is any constant, then* $\operatorname{Var}(KX) = K^2 \operatorname{Var} X$.

The proof of this theorem is an easy consequence of Theorem 7 in Section 7.2 and the definition of variance.

EXERCISES

1. Prove: If $P[X \leqq 0] = 1$, and if the expectation of X exists, then $EX \leqq 0$.

2. Prove: If $P[X \geqq 0] = 1$, and if the expectation of X exists, then $EX \geqq 0$.

3. Prove: If X, Y are two random variables whose expectations exist, and if $P[X \leqq Y] = 1$, then $EX \leqq EY$.

4. Prove: If $a < b$ are two real numbers, and if $P[a \leqq X \leqq b] = 1$, then the expectation of X exists, and $a \leqq EX \leqq b$.

5. Prove: If X is a random variable, then $P[X^2 \geqq 0] = 1$.

6. Prove: If X is any random variable, and if $\{\epsilon_n\}$ is a sequence of positive numbers which converges to zero, then

$$[X > 0] = \bigcup_{n=1}^{\infty} [X > \epsilon_n].$$

7. Complete the proof of Theorem 5 for the case $t > 0$.

8. Prove Theorem 6 in the discrete case.

9. In the example given after Theorem 7, show that X and Y are not independent. (*Hint:* Let t be such that $\frac{3}{4} = F_X(t)$, and consider the events $[0 < X \leqq t]$ and $[t^2 < Y < \infty]$.)

10. Prove Theorem 9.

7.4 Convergence in Probability

In this section we deal with the definition and properties of convergence in probability.

Definition. *Let $\{X_n\}$ denote a sequence of random variables. We say that this sequence converges in probability to a random variable X, or in symbols we write $X_n \xrightarrow{P} X$, if for every $\epsilon > 0$, $P[|X_n - X| \geqq \epsilon] \to 0$ as $n \to \infty$.*

1. Theorem. *If $X_n \xrightarrow{P} X$, then $X_n - X \xrightarrow{P} 0$.*

The proof of this theorem is trivial and is left to the reader.

2. Theorem. *If $X_n \xrightarrow{P} X$ and if $Y_n \xrightarrow{P} Y$, then $X_n + Y_n \xrightarrow{P} X + Y$.*

Proof. Let $\epsilon > 0$ be arbitrary. Then by hypothesis, $P[|X_n - X| \geqq \epsilon/2] \to 0$ and $P[|Y_n - Y| \geqq \epsilon/2] \to 0$ as $n \to \infty$. We now make use of the fact that if the sum of two numbers is not less than ϵ, then at least one of them is not less than $\epsilon/2$. Using the triangle inequality (i.e., $|a + b| \leqq |a| + |b|$), we obtain

$$\begin{aligned}[|(X_n + Y_n) - (X + Y)| \geqq \epsilon] &= [|(X_n - X) + (Y_n - Y)| \geqq \epsilon] \\ &\subset [|X_n - X| + |Y_n - Y| \geqq \epsilon] \\ &\subset [|X_n - X| \geqq \epsilon/2] \cup [|Y_n - Y| \geqq \epsilon/2].\end{aligned}$$

We then take probabilities and use Boole's inequality to obtain

$$\begin{aligned}0 &\leqq P[|(X_n + Y_n) - (X + Y)| \geqq \epsilon] \\ &\leqq P[|X_n - X| \geqq \epsilon/2] + P[|Y_n - Y| \geqq \epsilon/2].\end{aligned}$$

Since each of these last two terms tends to zero as $n \to \infty$, we have the conclusion of the theorem.

Remember: a constant is a random variable which takes only one value with probability one.

3. Theorem. *If $X_n \xrightarrow{P} X$ and if K is a constant, then $KX_n \xrightarrow{P} KX$.*

Proof. If $K = 0$, the theorem is trivial. If $K \neq 0$, let $\epsilon > 0$ be arbitrary, and note that the hypothesis implies that $P[|X_n - X| \geqq \epsilon/|K|] \to 0$ as $n \to \infty$. Since

$$P[|KX_n - KX| \geqq \epsilon] = P[|X_n - X| \geqq \epsilon/|K|],$$

the conclusion of the theorem follows.

4. Theorem. *If $X_n \xrightarrow{P} 0$, then $X_n^2 \xrightarrow{P} 0$.*

Proof. Let $\epsilon > 0$ be arbitrary. By hypothesis, $P[|X_n| \geqq \sqrt{\epsilon}] \to 0$ as $n \to \infty$. But $P[|X_n| \geqq \sqrt{\epsilon}] = P[|X_n^2| \geqq \epsilon]$, from which the conclusion of the theorem follows.

5. Theorem. *If* $X_n \xrightarrow{P} K$, *where* K *is a constant, then* $X_n^2 \xrightarrow{P} K^2$.

Proof. By Theorem 1, $X_n - K \xrightarrow{P} 0$. By Theorem 4, $(X_n - K)^2 \xrightarrow{P} 0$, or $X_n^2 - 2KX_n + K^2 \xrightarrow{P} 0$. By hypothesis and Theorem 3, $2KX_n \xrightarrow{P} 2K^2$, or $2KX_n - K^2 \to K^2$. We obtain the conclusion by applying Theorem 2.

6. Theorem. *If* $X_n \xrightarrow{P} a$ *and* $Y_n \xrightarrow{P} b$, *where* a *and* b *are constants, then* $X_nY_n \xrightarrow{P} ab$.

Proof. By Theorems 2 and 3, $X_n + Y_n \xrightarrow{P} a + b$ and $X_n - Y_n \xrightarrow{P} a - b$. By the same theorems and Theorem 5 we obtain

$$X_nY_n = \tfrac{1}{4}\{(X_n + Y_n)^2 - (X_n - Y_n)^2\} \xrightarrow{P} \tfrac{1}{4}\{(a + b)^2 - (a - b)^2\} = ab,$$

which proves the theorem.

7. Lemma. *If* $X_n \xrightarrow{P} K$, *where* K *is a constant, and if* $\epsilon > 0$, *then* $P[X_n < K - \epsilon] \to 0$ *and* $P[X_n > K + \epsilon] \to 0$ *as* $n \to \infty$.

Proof. The proof easily follows from the fact that probabilities are nonnegative and

$$[X_n \geqq K + \epsilon] + [X_n \leqq K - \epsilon] = [|X_n - K| \geqq \epsilon].$$

8. Lemma. *If* $X_n \xrightarrow{P} 1$, *then* $1/X_n \xrightarrow{P} 1$.

Proof. We repeatedly use the previous lemma. First, $P[X_n \leqq 0] = P[1/X_n \leqq 0] \to 0$ as $n \to \infty$. Let $\epsilon > 0$ be arbitrary, but $0 < \epsilon < 1$. Then by hypothesis,

$$P\left[0 < X_n \leqq 1 - \frac{\epsilon}{1 + \epsilon}\right] = P\left[\frac{1}{X_n} \geqq 1 + \epsilon\right] \to 0 \quad \text{as} \quad n \to \infty.$$

Also

$$P\left[X_n \geqq 1 + \frac{\epsilon}{1 - \epsilon}\right] = P\left[0 < \frac{1}{X_n} \leqq 1 - \epsilon\right] \to 0 \quad \text{as} \quad n \to \infty.$$

Hence

$$P\left[\left|\frac{1}{X_n} - 1\right| \geqq \epsilon\right] = P\left[\frac{1}{X_n} \leqq 0\right] + P\left[0 < \frac{1}{X_n} \leqq 1 - \epsilon\right] + P\left[\frac{1}{X_n} \geqq 1 + \epsilon\right] \to 0 \quad \text{as} \quad n \to \infty,$$

and the lemma is proved.

9. Theorem. *If $X_n \xrightarrow{P} a$ and $Y_n \xrightarrow{P} b \neq 0$, where a and b are constants, then $X_n/Y_n \xrightarrow{P} a/b$.*

Proof. Making use of the previous theorems, we have $Y_n/b \xrightarrow{P} 1$, and hence $b/Y_n \xrightarrow{P} 1$. Thus $X_n b/Y_n \xrightarrow{P} a$, from which we obtain $X_n/Y_n \xrightarrow{P} a/b$, the conclusion of the theorem.

We now see that finite sums, products, and quotients of sequences of random variables which converge in probability to constants converge in probability to the corresponding sum, product, and quotient of these constants.

EXERCISES

1. Prove Theorem 1.

2. Let $\{X_n\}$ be a sequence of independent, identically distributed random variables, where X_n has an absolutely continuous distribution with density

$$f_{X_n}(x_n) = \begin{cases} e^{-(x_n-\alpha)} & \text{if} \quad x_n \geqq \alpha \\ 0 & \text{if} \quad x_n < \alpha. \end{cases}$$

Let $Y_n = \min\{X_1, X_2, \cdots, X_n\}$ for each n. Prove that $Y_n \xrightarrow{P} \alpha$. (*Hint:* compute $P[|Y_n - \alpha| \geqq \epsilon]$ directly.)

3. Let $\{U_n\}$ be a sequence of independent, identically distributed random variables with a common absolutely continuous distribution whose density is

$$f_{U_n}(u_n) = \begin{cases} 1/\beta & \text{if} \quad 0 \leqq u_n \leqq \beta \\ 0 & \text{if} \quad u_n < 0 \quad \text{or} \quad u_n > \beta, \end{cases}$$

where $\beta > 0$. Let $V_n = \max\{U_1, U_2, \cdots, U_n\}$. Prove that $V_n \xrightarrow{P} \beta$. (*Hint:* See the hint after exercise 2.)

(*Hint for problems 4 and 5:* Suppose $\{z_n\}$ is a sequence of positive real numbers such that $z_n \to \infty$ as $n \to \infty$. Since

$$\int_{-\infty}^{\infty} \frac{1}{\sqrt{2\pi}} \exp\left(-\frac{x^2}{2}\right) dx = 1,$$

then by the definition of this Cauchy (or improper) integral,

$$\lim_{n\to\infty} \int_{-z_n}^{z_n} \frac{1}{\sqrt{2\pi}} \exp\left(-\frac{x^2}{2}\right) dx = 1,$$

or

$$\lim_{n\to\infty} 1 - \int_{-z_n}^{z_n} \frac{1}{\sqrt{2\pi}} \exp\left(-\frac{x^2}{2}\right) dx = 0.)$$

4. Let $\{X_n\}$ be a sequence of random variables, where the distribution of X_n is $N(\mu, \sigma^2/n)$, and where μ and $\sigma^2 > 0$ are fixed constants which do not depend on n. Prove that $X_n \xrightarrow{P} \mu$. (*Hint:* Prove $X_n - \mu \xrightarrow{P} 0$.)

5. Let $\{X_n\}$ be a sequence of independent random variables, each having the distribution $N(\mu, \sigma^2)$, where μ and $\sigma^2 > 0$ are fixed constants not depending on n. Let $Y_n = (1/n) \sum_{k=1}^n X_k$. Prove that $Y_n \xrightarrow{P} \mu$. (*Hint:* Use problem 1, Section 6.2, and problem 4 above.)

6. Complete the proof of Lemma 7.

7.5 Limit Theorems

The law of large numbers and the central limit theorem are perhaps the two most important theorems in probability and statistics. This section is devoted to these two theorems.

1. Theorem. (Chebishev's Inequality.) *If X is any random variable with finite expectation and second moment, then*

$$P[|X - EX| \geqq \epsilon] \leqq \text{Var}(X)/\epsilon^2$$

for every $\epsilon > 0$.

Proof. Let $\delta > 0$ be arbitrarily selected such that $0 < \delta < \epsilon$. Then

$$EX^2 = \int_0^\infty P[X^2 > x]\,dx \geqq \int_0^{(\epsilon-\delta)^2} P[X^2 > x]\,dx$$
$$\geqq (\epsilon - \delta)^2 P[X^2 > (\epsilon - \delta)^2] \geqq (\epsilon - \delta)^2 P[|X| \geqq \epsilon].$$

Because of arbitrariness of $\delta > 0$, we obtain

$$EX^2 \geqq \epsilon^2 P[|X| \geqq \epsilon].$$

Now, if we replace X by $X - EX$, we obtain the desired inequality.

Definition. *A sequence $\{X_n\}$ of random variables is said to be an independent, identically distributed sequence of random variables if they are independent and if all have the same distribution function.*

2. Theorem. (Law of Large Numbers.) *Let $\{X_n\}$ be a sequence of independent, identically distributed random variables, all having the same absolutely continuous distribution or discrete distribution. Assume that they have finite common expectation μ and finite common variance σ^2. Then the sequence of arithmetic means converges in probability to μ, i.e., if $\overline{X}_n = (X_1 + \cdots + X_n)/n$, then*

$$P[|\overline{X}_n - \mu| \geqq \epsilon] \to 0 \quad \text{as} \quad n \to \infty$$

for every $\epsilon > 0$.

Proof. It is easy to see that

$$E\overline{X}_n = \frac{1}{n} \sum_{k=1}^n EX_k = \frac{1}{n} n\mu = \mu.$$

Also, by Theorems 8 and 9 in Section 7.3

$$\operatorname{Var}(\overline{X}_n) = \frac{1}{n^2}\operatorname{Var}(X_1 + \cdots + X_n) = \frac{1}{n^2}\sum_{k=1}^{n}\operatorname{Var}(X_k)$$

$$= \frac{1}{n^2}n\sigma^2 = \frac{\sigma^2}{n}.$$

Hence by Chebishev's inequality,

$$0 \leqq P[|\overline{X}_n - \mu| \geqq \epsilon] \leqq \sigma^2/n\epsilon^2.$$

But $\sigma^2/n\epsilon^2 \to 0$ as $n \to \infty$. This finishes the proof.

A particular case of the law of large numbers is a famous theorem called Bernoulli's theorem. This was first proved by J. Bernoulli and was published posthumously in his book "Ars Conjectandi" in 1713.

3. Theorem. (Bernoulli's Theorem.) *Let S_n denote the number of successes in n Bernoulli trials, where p denotes the probability of success in a trial. Then $S_n/n \xrightarrow{P} p$.*

Proof. Let X_k be a random variable which denotes the number of successes in the kth Bernoulli trial. Then $P[X_k = 1] = p$ and $P[X_k = 0] = 1 - p$. One easily verifies that $EX_k = p$ and $\operatorname{Var}(X_k) = pq$ for all k. It is easy to see that the random variables $\{X_n\}$ are independent and identically distributed. Also, one easily verifies that $S_n = X_1 + X_2 + \cdots + X_n$. Applying the law of large numbers we obtain $\overline{X}_n = S_n/n \xrightarrow{P} p$, which is the assertion of the theorem.

Before we proceed to further applications of the law of large numbers we must prove three important lemmas.

4. Lemma. *If m and n are integers with $0 < m < n$, if X is a random variable with either an absolutely continuous or discrete distribution, and if $E(X^n)$ exists, then $E(X^m)$ exists.*

Proof. We first observe that we may write

$$X^m = X^m I_{[|X| \leqq 1]} + X^m I_{[|X| > 1]}.$$

Since $P[-1 \leqq X^m I_{[|X| \leqq 1]} \leqq 1] = 1$, then by exercise 4, Section 7.3, we obtain that $E(X^m I_{[|X| \leqq 1]})$ exists. Now let

$$U = X^m I_{[|X| > 1]} \quad \text{and} \quad V = X^n I_{[|X| > 1]}.$$

The reader can easily check that when $x > 1$, $P[U > x] \leqq P[V > x]$, and when $x < -1$, $P[U \leqq x] \leqq P[V \leqq x]$. Applying the definition of expectation, and using the hypothesis that EV exists, we obtain that EU exists. We obtain the conclusion of the theorem by applying Theorem 6 in Section 7.2.

This lemma guarantees the existence of all integer moments of lesser order when one specific moment of a random variable is known to exist.

5. Lemma. *If x is any real number, then*

$$P[X < x] = \underset{t<x}{\text{l.u.b.}}\, F_X(t).$$

Proof. The student will recall that if S is any nonempty set of real numbers, then l.u.b. S (the least upper bound of S) is a number s_0 such that (i) $s \leqq s_0$ for every $s \in S$, and (ii) for every $\epsilon > 0$ there exists an $s \in S$ such that $s > s_0 - \epsilon$. In order to show that $P[X < x]$ satisfies (i), we note that if $t < x$, then

$$[X \leqq t] \subset [X < x].$$

Taking probabilities establishes that $F_X(t) \leqq P[X < x]$ for all $t < x$. In order to verify property (ii) for $P[X < x]$ it is sufficient to show that if $\{y_n\}$ is any sequence of real numbers such that $y_n < y_{n+1} < x$, and $y_n \to x$ as $n \to \infty$, then $P[X < x] = \lim_{n\to\infty} F_X(y_n)$. In order to show this we note that

$$[X < x] = [X \leqq y_1] + \sum_{n=1}^{\infty} [y_n < X \leqq y_{n+1}].$$

Taking probabilities of both sides we obtain

$$\begin{aligned} P[X < x] &= P[X \leqq y_1] + \sum_{n=1}^{\infty} P[y_n < X \leqq y_{n+1}] \\ &= \lim_{n\to\infty} \left\{ P[X \leqq y_1] + \sum_{k=1}^{n-1} P[y_k < X \leqq y_{k+1}] \right\} \\ &= \lim_{n\to\infty} P\left\{ [X \leqq y_1] + \sum_{k=1}^{n-1} [y_k < X \leqq y_{k+1}] \right\} \\ &= \lim_{n\to\infty} P[X \leqq y_n] = \lim_{n\to\infty} F_X(y_n). \end{aligned}$$

This establishes the lemma.

6. Lemma. *Let $\{X_n\}$ be a sequence of independent, identically distributed random variables, and let k be any positive integer. Then the sequence of kth powers $\{X_n^k\}$ is also a sequence of independent, identically distributed random variables.*

Proof. We first prove independence by Theorem 4 in Section 3.5. All we need do is show that, for every integer n, the random variables $X_1^k, \cdots, X_n^k$ are independent. If k is odd, then

$$F_{X_1^k,\cdots,X_n^k}(x_1, \cdots, x_n) = P\left(\bigcap_{i=1}^n [X_i^k \leqq x_i]\right)$$
$$= P\left(\bigcap_{i=1}^n [X_i \leqq x_i^{1/k}]\right) = \prod_{i=1}^n P[X_i \leqq x_i^{1/k}]$$
$$= \prod_{i=1}^n P[X_i^k \leqq x_i] = \prod_{i=1}^n F_{X_i^k}(x_i).$$

If k is even, then for all $x_i \geqq 0$,

$$P\left(\bigcap_{i=1}^n [X_i^k \leqq x_i]\right) = P\left(\bigcap_{i=1}^n [-x_i^{1/k} \leqq X_i \leqq x_i^{1/k}]\right)$$
$$= \prod_{i=1}^n P[-x_i^{1/k} \leqq X_i \leqq x_i^{1/k}]$$
$$= \prod_{i=1}^n P[X_i^k \leqq x_i].$$

(In the case k is even and if one or more $x_k < 0$, then the equation is trivially true.) In order to prove that these random variables are identically distributed we need only prove that $F_{X_n^k}(x)$ does not depend on n. If k is even and $x < 0$, then $F_{X_n^k}(x) = 0$ for all n. If k is even and $x \geqq 0$, then by Lemma 5,

$$\begin{aligned} F_{X_n^k}(x) &= P[X_n^k \leqq x] = P[-x^{1/k} \leqq X_n \leqq x^{1/k}] \\ &= P[X_n \leqq x^{1/k}] - P[X_n < -x^{1/k}] \\ &= F_{X_n}(x^{1/k}) - \underset{t<-x^{1/k}}{\text{l.u.b.}}\, F_{X_n}(t) \\ &= F_{X_1}(x^{1/k}) - \underset{t<-x^{1/k}}{\text{l.u.b.}}\, F_{X_1}(t) \\ &= F_{X_1^k}(x). \end{aligned}$$

If k is odd, then

$$F_{X_n^k}(x) = F_{X_n}(x^{1/k}) = F_{X_1}(x^{1/k}) = F_{X_1^k}(x),$$

and the lemma is proved.

We are now ready to prove two important consequences of the law of large numbers.

7. Theorem. *Let $\{X_n\}$ be a sequence of independent, identically distributed random variables for which $E(X_1^{2k})$ exists, where k is a positive integer, each with discrete or absolutely continuous distribution. Then*

$$\frac{1}{n}\sum_{j=1}^n X_j^k \xrightarrow{P} E(X_1^k).$$

Proof. By Lemma 6, the random variables $X_1^k, X_2^k, \cdots, X_n^k, \cdots$ are independent and identically distributed. The conclusion follows by the law of large numbers.

8. Theorem. *Let $\{X_n\}$ be a sequence of independent, identically distributed random variables with finite common fourth moment EX_1^4 and common variance σ^2, each with discrete or absolutely continuous distribution. Then*

$$\hat{\sigma}_n^2 = \frac{1}{n} \sum_{k=1}^{n} (X_k - \overline{X}_n)^2 \xrightarrow{P} \sigma^2.$$

Proof. From a little algebra we obtain

$$\frac{1}{n} \sum_{k=1}^{n} (X_k - \overline{X}_n)^2 = \frac{1}{n} \sum_{k=1}^{n} X_k^2 - \overline{X}_n^2.$$

By the law of large numbers,

$$\frac{1}{n} \sum_{k=1}^{n} X_k^2 \xrightarrow{P} EX_1^2,$$

and

$$\overline{X}_n \xrightarrow{P} EX_1.$$

By the theorems of Section 7.4 we obtain

$$\frac{1}{n} \sum_{k=1}^{n} (X_k - \overline{X}_n)^2 \xrightarrow{P} EX_1^2 - (EX_1)^2 = \sigma^2,$$

which proves the assertion.

Now we must state a theorem without proof. We must omit any of its proofs because these depend on some rather deep results in analysis.

9. Theorem. (Central Limit Theorem.) *Let $\{X_n\}$ be a sequence of independent, identically distributed random variables with finite common expectation μ and variance σ^2. Let*

$$Y_n = (X_1 + \cdots + X_n - n\mu)/\sigma\sqrt{n}.$$

Then

$$F_{Y_n}(x) \to \frac{1}{\sqrt{2\pi}} \int_{-\infty}^{x} \exp\left(-\frac{t^2}{2}\right) dt$$

as $n \to \infty$ uniformly in x.

The important thing to notice in this theorem is that the limiting distribution of Y_n does not depend on the common distribution of X_n's. This theorem will find important uses in the last chapters of this book. We conclude this section by proving an important but easy corollary to the central limit theorem.

10. Theorem. (Laplace-DeMoivre Theorem.) *Let S_n denote the number of successes in n Bernoulli trials, where p denotes the probability of success. Let*

$$Y_n = (S_n - np)/\sqrt{np(1-p)}.$$

Then

$$F_{Y_n}(x) \to \frac{1}{\sqrt{2\pi}} \int_{-\infty}^{x} \exp\left(-\frac{t^2}{2}\right) dt$$

as $n \to \infty$ *uniformly in* x.

Proof. Let X_n denote the number of successes in the nth trial. Then $P[X_n = 1] = p$ and $P[X_n = 0] = 1 - p$. From this it is easy to compute $EX_n = p$ and $\text{Var } X_n = p(1 - p)$. The conclusion of this theorem immediately follows from the central limit theorem.

EXERCISES

1. Let $\{X_n\}$ be the same as in problem 2, Section 7.4. Prove that $\overline{X}_n - 1 \xrightarrow{P} \alpha$.

2. Let $\{X_n\}$ be a sequence of independent, identically distributed random variables, and assume that EX_1^{2r} exists for r a positive integer. Then

$$\frac{1}{n} \sum_{i=1}^{n} (X_i - \overline{X}_n)^r \xrightarrow{P} E(X_1 - EX_1)^r$$

as $n \to \infty$. (*Hint:* use the binomial theorem on r.)

CHAPTER 8

Point Estimation

8.1 Sampling

In this section we set up the mathematical model for sampling with replacement in the physical world. This is one of the most important sections of this book. In fact, this section constitutes one long definition.

Sampling in the physical world deals with a "population." One might be dealing with a population of an hour's production of light bulbs in a certain factory. One might consider the population of oranges harvested from a certain orchard in one season. Also, one frequently deals with a population of bottles of a specific drug. We may also consider a certain population of people, but here, as before, population does not refer to a number (or count) but to a specific collection or set of people; for example, we might consider the population of students (not to be confused with the number of them) currently enrolled at the University of California, Riverside.

Whatever the population with which we are concerned, let it be denoted by Ω. Let us denote an arbitrary element or individual in this population by ω. Usually in dealing with a population we intend to select an individual or element from it at random and to determine some specific numerical characteristic of this individual. For example, if the population Ω consists of an hour's production of light bulbs, we might select a light bulb at random and measure its length of life; if Ω consists of the oranges harvested from a certain orchard, we might select an orange at random and determine its sugar content; and if Ω consists of the students currently enrolled at the University of California, Riverside, we might select a student at random and compute his grade-point average. In other words, for each situation we have a population Ω consisting of many an individual or element, ω, and we consider a function X which assigns to every individual ω in Ω a number $X(\omega)$, which is some numerical characteristic under consideration. We shall consider Ω as a fundamental probability set associated with a sigma-field of events $\mathcal{A}$ and a probability P, and we shall assume that X is a random variable defined over Ω.

Suppose we want to "sample n times with replacement." By this we mean we shall select an individual at random from Ω, call it ω_1, replace it, again select an individual at random from Ω, call it ω_2, replace it, and continue until we select element ω_n at random from Ω. The outcome of our activity is the ordered n-tuple $(\omega_1, \omega_2, \cdots, \omega_n)$ of individuals or elements of Ω. However, we are now considering a new fundamental probability set when we "sample n times with replacement." This new fundamental probability set, which we shall denote by $\Omega^{(n)}$, is the collection or set of all possible ordered n-tuples of elementary events or individuals in Ω, with repetition allowed. In other words, $\Omega^{(n)}$ consists of *all possible* n-tuples $(\omega_1, \omega_2, \cdots, \omega_n)$, for all possible selections of $\omega_1, \omega_2, \cdots, \omega_n$ in Ω. For example, in the case that Ω consists of the outcome of the toss of a coin, i.e., $\Omega = \{H, T\}$, then $\Omega^{(2)}$ is the fundamental probability set consisting of the four elementary events, or ordered pairs, (H, H), (H, T), (T, H), and (T, T). Also, $\Omega^{(3)}$ is the fundamental probability set whose elementary events are the following eight ordered triples:

$$\begin{array}{cccc} (H, H, H) & (H, H, T) & (H, T, H) & (H, T, T) \\ (T, H, H) & (T, H, T) & (T, T, H) & (T, T, T). \end{array}$$

In general we shall denote an arbitrary point in $\Omega^{(n)}$ by $\omega^{(n)}$.

We shall need to define a sigma-field $\mathcal{A}^{(n)}$ of events composed of elementary events of this new fundamental probability set $\Omega^{(n)}$. For every $A_1 \in \mathcal{A}$, $A_2 \in \mathcal{A}, \cdots, A_n \in \mathcal{A}$ let us define

$$A_1 \times A_2 \times \cdots \times A_n = \{\omega^{(n)} \in \Omega^{(n)} | \omega_1 \in A_1, \omega_2 \in A_2, \cdots, \omega_n \in A_n\}.$$

This event is the compound event: A_1 occurs in the first trial, A_2 occurs in the second trial, $\cdots$, A_n occurs in the nth trial. We shall call such an event a rectangular event. We shall require that $\mathcal{A}^{(n)}$ contain all such rectangular events. Let $\mathcal{R}^{(n)}$ denote the set of all such rectangular events. We shall define $\mathcal{A}^{(n)}$ to be the *smallest sigma-field of subsets* of $\Omega^{(n)}$ which contains $\mathcal{R}^{(n)}$. By this we mean that $\mathcal{A}^{(n)}$ is the intersection of all sigma-fields of subsets of $\Omega^{(n)}$ which contain $\mathcal{R}^{(n)}$. In order to give this definition substance, two things must be proved: (i) the intersection of any collection of sigma-fields of subsets of $\Omega^{(n)}$ is a sigma-field, and (ii) the collection of sigma-fields which contain $\mathcal{R}^{(n)}$ is nonempty. We prove (i) with the following lemma.

1. Lemma. *Let $\{\mathcal{B}_\lambda, \lambda \in \Lambda\}$ be a nonempty collection of sigma-fields of subsets of $\Omega^{(n)}$. Then*

$$\bigcap_{\lambda \in \Lambda} \mathcal{B}_\lambda$$

is a sigma-field.

Proof. Let $B \in \bigcap_{\lambda\in\Lambda}\mathcal{B}_\lambda$. Then $B \in \mathcal{B}_\lambda$ for each $\lambda \in \Lambda$. Since each $\mathcal{B}_\lambda$ is a sigma-field, $B \in \mathcal{B}_\lambda$ implies that $B^c \in \mathcal{B}_\lambda$ for every $\lambda \in \Lambda$. Hence $B^c \in \bigcap_{\lambda\in\Lambda}\mathcal{B}_\lambda$, and thus $\bigcap_{\lambda\in\Lambda}\mathcal{B}_\lambda$ is closed under complementation. In order to prove that $\bigcap_{\lambda\in\Lambda}\mathcal{B}_\lambda$ is closed under denumerable unions, let $B_n \in \bigcap_{\lambda\in\Lambda}\mathcal{B}_\lambda$ for $n = 1, 2, \cdots$. Then for every $\lambda \in \Lambda$, every $B_n \in \mathcal{B}_\lambda$. Since every $\mathcal{B}_\lambda$ is a sigma-field, every $B_n \in \mathcal{B}_\lambda$ implies that $\bigcup_{n=1}^{\infty} B_n \in \mathcal{B}_\lambda$ for every $\lambda \in \Lambda$, which in turn implies that $\bigcup_{n=1}^{\infty} B_n \in \bigcap_{\lambda\in\Lambda}\mathcal{B}_\lambda$. Also, since $\phi \in \mathcal{B}_\lambda$ for all $\lambda \in \Lambda$, then $\phi \in \bigcap_{\lambda\in\Lambda}\mathcal{B}_\lambda$. Since the three requirements for a sigma-field have been satisfied, the lemma is proved.

Now that we have proved that the intersection of a nonempty collection of sigma-fields is a sigma-field, we must show that the collection of sigma-fields which contain $\mathcal{R}^{(n)}$ is nonempty. This is trivial, since certainly the set of all subsets of $\Omega^{(n)}$ is a sigma-field, and it does contain $\mathcal{R}^{(n)}$. Hence $\mathcal{A}^{(n)}$ is well defined when we define it as the intersection of all sigma-fields which contain $\mathcal{R}^{(n)}$.

We have yet to define a probability over $\mathcal{A}^{(n)}$, and we do this now. We denote this probability by $P^{(n)}$, and for each rectangular event $A_1 \times \cdots \times A_n$ in $\mathcal{A}^{(n)}$ we define

$$P^{(n)}(A_1 \times \cdots \times A_n) = \prod_{i=1}^{n} P(A_i).$$

The reason we do so is not difficult. In the first place we keep in mind the definition given above of $A_1 \times A_2 \times \cdots \times A_n$. With respect to $\Omega^{(n)}$ the event "A_1 occurs in the first trial" is

$$A_{1,1}^{(n)} = A_1 \times \Omega \times \cdots \times \Omega,$$

the event "A_2 occurs in the second trial" is

$$A_{2,2}^{(n)} = \Omega \times A_2 \times \Omega \times \cdots \times \Omega,$$

$\cdots$, and the event "A_n occurs in the nth trial" is

$$A_{n,n}^{(n)} = \Omega \times \cdots \times \Omega \times A_n.$$

Thus it is easy to verify that

$$A_1 \times A_2 \times \cdots \times A_n = \bigcap_{i=1}^{n} A_{i,i}^{(n)}.$$

In sampling with replacement the intent is to consider whatever occurs in different trials to be independent and to have $P^{(n)}(A_{i,i}^{(n)}) = P(A_i)$. Consequently we want

$$P^{(n)}(A_1 \times \cdots \times A_n) = \prod_{i=1}^{n} P^{(n)}(A_{i,i}^{(n)}) = \prod_{i=1}^{n} P(A_i).$$

So far we have defined $P^{(n)}$ over $\mathcal{R}^{(n)}$, and $\mathcal{R}^{(n)}$ is a proper subset of $\mathcal{A}^{(n)}$ (unless $\mathcal{A}$ is the trivial sigma-field $\{\phi, \Omega\}$). We need to extend (or enlarge) the domain of $P^{(n)}$ from $\mathcal{R}^{(n)}$ to $\mathcal{A}^{(n)}$. The method by which this is done is beyond the scope of this book. However, in advanced probability theory and measure theory there is a theorem which states that there does exist *one and only one* probability defined over $\mathcal{A}^{(n)}$ which agrees with $P^{(n)}$ over $\mathcal{R}^{(n)}$, i.e., $P^{(n)}$ can be *extended uniquely over* $\mathcal{A}^{(n)}$. There will be no confusion resulting if we denote this probability over $\mathcal{A}^{(n)}$ by P.

In sampling these n times with replacement (or, equivalently, in performing these n trials), let X_1 denote the numerical observation made on the first trial, let X_2 denote the numerical observation made on the second trial, $\cdots$, and let X_n denote the numerical observation made on the nth trial. More precisely, for every

$$\omega^{(n)} = (\omega_1, \omega_2, \cdots, \omega_n) \in \Omega^{(n)},$$

we define

$$\begin{aligned} X_1(\omega^{(n)}) &= X(\omega_1), \\ X_2(\omega^{(n)}) &= X(\omega_2), \\ &\;\cdot \\ &\;\cdot \\ &\;\cdot \\ X_n(\omega^{(n)}) &= X(\omega_n). \end{aligned}$$

We now prove a fundamental property of $X_1, X_2, \cdots, X_n$.

2. Theorem. *The above functions $X_1, \cdots, X_n$ defined over $\Omega^{(n)}$ are random variables which are independent, and each has the same distribution function that X has.*

Proof. It is easy to verify that

$$\begin{aligned} [X_1 \leqq x_1] &= [X \leqq x_1] \times \Omega \times \cdots \times \Omega \in \mathcal{A}^{(n)}, \\ [X_2 \leqq x_2] &= \Omega \times [X \leqq x_2] \times \Omega \times \cdots \times \Omega \in \mathcal{A}^{(n)}, \\ &\;\cdot \\ &\;\cdot \\ &\;\cdot \\ [X_n \leqq x_n] &= \Omega \times \cdots \times \Omega \times [X \leqq x_n] \in \mathcal{A}^{(n)}, \end{aligned}$$

thus proving that $X_1, X_2, \cdots, X_n$ are random variables. From the above definition of $P^{(n)}$ we obtain

$$P^{(n)}[X_i \leqq x] = P[X \leqq x]$$

for each i, thus proving that each X_i has the same distribution function that X has. Finally,

$$\begin{aligned} P^{(n)}\left(\bigcap_{i=1}^{n} [X_i \leqq x_i]\right) &= P^{(n)}\left([X \leqq x_1] \times \cdots \times [X \leqq x_n]\right) \\ &= \prod_{i=1}^{n} P[X \leqq x_i] = \prod_{i=1}^{n} P^{(n)}[X_i \leqq x_i], \end{aligned}$$

which proves the independence of $X_1, \cdots, X_n$, and concludes the proof of the theorem.

Thus, $X_1, \cdots, X_n$ are random variables which are independent and identically distributed. The term "identically distributed" means that they all have the same distribution function. These random variables $X_1, \cdots, X_n$ will be called, or referred to, as "*n independent observations on* X," and X_i will be called the ith observation on X.

As an example, let us consider the sampling procedure where we sample three times with replacement from a population Ω of two equally likely elementary events or individuals, H and T, i.e., we toss an unbiased coin three times. The fundamental probability set $\Omega^{(3)}$ was listed earlier in this section. Let X be defined over Ω by $X(H) = 1$, $X(T) = 0$, i.e., for each $\omega \in \Omega$, $X(\omega)$ denotes the number of heads in ω. Now let X_1 denote the number of heads obtained on the first trial, let X_2 denote the number of heads obtained on the second trial, and let X_3 denote the number of heads obtained on the third trial. Thus we have, for example, $X_1(H, H, T) = X(H) = 1$, $X_2(H, H, T) = X(H) = 1$, and $X_3(H, H, T) = X(T) = 0$. It is easy to see that X_1, X_2, X_3 are independent and that each has the same distribution as X.

We note that in each ordered n-tuple $\omega^{(n)} = (\omega_1, \omega_2, \cdots, \omega_n) \in \Omega^{(n)}$ it is possible to have duplication of the elements from Ω. However, if we were to sample *without replacement*, each n-tuple $\omega^{(n)}$ would consist of n different elements or individuals from the original population Ω, and $\Omega^{(n)}$ would consist of all such n-tuples. For practical purposes, in the equally likely case, if the number of individuals in Ω is large compared to n, we might consider that the sampling done was with replacement and use the mathematical model discussed in this section.

Finally, it is theoretically possible to consider sampling with replacement an infinite (denumerable) number of times. This gives rise to a fundamental probability set $\Omega^{(\infty)}$, the set of all possible ordered infinite-tuples

$$\omega^{(\infty)} = (\omega_1, \omega_2, \cdots, \omega_n, \cdots)$$

of elements or individuals in Ω. The sigma-field of events, $\mathcal{A}^{(\infty)}$, is defined to be the smallest sigma-field of subsets of $\Omega^{(\infty)}$ which contains all subsets of $\Omega^{(\infty)}$ of the form

$$A_1 \times A_2 \times \cdots \times A_n \times \Omega \times \Omega \times \cdots,$$

where $A_1 \in \mathcal{A}, \cdots, A_n \in \mathcal{A}$, and where n is any positive integer. The collection of all sets of the form

$$A_1 \times A_2 \times \cdots \times A_n \times \Omega \times \Omega \times \cdots$$

is denoted by $\mathcal{R}^{(\infty)}$, and a probability $P^{(\infty)}$ is defined over $\mathcal{R}^{(\infty)}$ by

$$P^{(\infty)}(A_1 \times \cdots \times A_n \times \Omega \times \Omega \times \cdots) = \prod_{i=1}^{n} P(A_i).$$

As we mentioned above, a theorem in advanced probability theory and measure theory states that $P^{(\infty)}$ can be uniquely extended from $\mathcal{R}^{(\infty)}$ to $\mathcal{A}^{(\infty)}$. Now we can consider an infinite sequence $X_1, X_2, \cdots, X_n, \cdots$ of random variables which are called "independent observations on X." In other words, for every $\omega^{(\infty)} = (\omega_1, \omega_2, \cdots, \omega_n, \cdots) \in \Omega^{(\infty)}$ we define

$$X_n(\omega^{(\infty)}) = X(\omega_n)$$

for every integer n. As before one can show that the random variables $X_1, \cdots, X_n, \cdots$ are independent and identically distributed. Further, any n of these random variables constitutes n independent observations on X.

EXERCISES

1. Prove that $A_1 \times A_2 \times \cdots \times A_n = \bigcap_{i=1}^{n} A_{i,i}^{(n)}$, where $A_{i,i}^{(n)}$ is as defined in this section.

2. Prove the assertion made in this section: $\mathcal{R}^{(n)}$ is a proper subset of $\mathcal{A}^{(n)}$ unless $\mathcal{A}$ is the trivial sigma-field $\{\phi, \Omega\}$.

3. In the proof of Theorem 2, supply the details of the proof that

$$[X_1 \leqq x_1] = [X \leqq x_1] \times \Omega \times \cdots \times \Omega.$$

4. Let $\Omega = \{1, 2, 3\}$, and assume that these elementary events are equally likely. Let X be a random variable defined over Ω by $X(i) = i$, $i = 1, 2, 3$. One then samples twice with replacement, and X_1, X_2 denotes two independent observations on X.

(a) List all $\omega^{(2)}$'s in $\Omega^{(2)}$.
(b) List the elementary events of $\Omega^{(2)}$ which are in $[X_1 \leqq 2]$ and in $[X_2 \leqq 1]$.
(c) Verify that X_1 and X_2 are independent and each has the same distribution as X.
(d) Give examples of subsets of $\Omega^{(2)}$ which are rectangular events and of subsets which are not.

5. In the last example given in this section, verify the assertion made that X_1, X_2, X_3 are independent and that each has the same distribution as X.

6. In the case of sampling an infinite number of times with replacement, prove that the random variables $X_1, X_2, \cdots, X_n, \cdots$ are independent and identically distributed.

7. Prove that the set of all subsets of $\Omega^{(n)}$ is a sigma-field.

8.2 Unbiased and Consistent Estimates

In mathematical statistics there are two synonyms used for the word "random variable." One is the word "estimate," and the other is the word "statistic." By traditional usage the word "estimate" is used in problems of estimation, and the word "statistic" is used in problems of hypothesis testing. This section will deal with two properties of estimates, those of unbiasedness and consistency.

Consider a population Ω with a random variable X defined over it. Let θ denote a fixed constant associated with Ω. Suppose one samples n times and then considers a random variable U defined over $\Omega^{(n)}$.

Definition. *The random variable U is called an* **unbiased** *estimate of θ if the expectation of U exists and if $EU = \theta$, whatever be the value of θ.* (Another way of writing this second requirement is: $E(U|\theta) \equiv \theta$.)

Example. Let Ω denote a population of electric fuses. We want an estimate of the proportion p of defectives among them, i.e., $p =$ the number of defectives divided by the total number of fuses. Let X be defined over Ω as follows: if $\omega \in \Omega$, then

$$X(\omega) = \begin{cases} 1 & \text{if} \quad \omega \text{ is defective,} \\ 0 & \text{if} \quad \omega \text{ is not defective.} \end{cases}$$

One easily computes $EX = p$. Suppose we sample n times with replacement, and let $X_1, X_2, \cdots, X_n$ denote the n independent observations on X. Let $U = (X_1 + \cdots + X_n)/n$ be defined over $\Omega^{(n)}$. Then one easily computes that $EU = p$, whatever be the value of p. Thus, U is an unbiased estimate of p. Note that U is the relative frequency of the number of defectives in a sample of size n.

In any sampling experiment one can physically sample only a finite number of times. Yet, as was noted in Section 8.1, we may consider $\Omega^{(n)}$ as "part" of $\Omega^{(\infty)}$, i.e., an n-dimensional subspace of a space with infinitely many dimensions. Over the fundamental probability set $\Omega^{(\infty)}$ one can consider a sequence of random variables, $U_1, U_2, \cdots, U_n, \cdots$ each of which depends on only a finite number of coordinates for all points in $\Omega^{(\infty)}$. In other words, each U_n can be observed after a finite number of trials.

Definition. *We say that the sequence $\{U_n\}$ is a consistent sequence of estimates of the constant θ if $U_n \xrightarrow{P} \theta$, whatever be θ. Other ways of writing this are: $P[|U_n - \theta| \geqq \epsilon] \to 0$ as $n \to \infty$, for every $\epsilon > 0$, whatever be θ, or $P([|U_n - \theta| \geqq \epsilon]|\theta) \to 0$ as $n \to \infty$, for every $\epsilon > 0$, whatever be θ.*

Example. In the previous example, let $U_n = (X_1 + \cdots + X_n)/n$. By Bernoulli's theorem, $U_n \xrightarrow{P} p$, whatever be p. Hence the sequence $\{U_n\}$ is a consistent sequence of estimates of p.

In some books and research articles the author might simply say that U_n is a consistent estimate (or estimator) of θ. We might do the same too, but the student should understand what is meant, namely, that $\{U_n\}$ is a consistent sequence of estimates of θ.

1. Theorem. *Let Ω denote a population, and let X denote an observable random variable defined over Ω with discrete or absolutely continuous distribution and with finite second moment. If $X_1, X_2, \cdots, X_n$ are n independent observations on X, and if $\overline{X}_n = (X_1 + \cdots + X_n)/n$, then $\overline{X}_n$ is an unbiased and consistent estimate of EX.*

This theorem has been proved before with different words. Unbiasedness follows from a simple application of the linear properties of expectation. The assertion about consistency is merely a restatement of the law of large numbers.

Let Ω denote a population, and let X be an observable random variable defined over it with discrete or absolutely continuous distribution and for which the fourth moment exists. Let $X_1, X_2, \cdots, X_n$ denote n independent observations on X, and let us denote

$$\hat{\sigma}_n^2 = \frac{1}{n}\sum_{k=1}^{n}(X_k - \overline{X}_n)^2,$$

$$s_n^2 = \frac{1}{n-1}\sum_{k=1}^{n}(X_k - \overline{X}_n)^2.$$

2. Theorem. *Both $\hat{\sigma}_n^2$ and s_n^2 are consistent estimates of* Var (X), *s_n^2 is an unbiased estimate of* Var (X), *but $\hat{\sigma}_n^2$ is not an unbiased estimate of* Var (X).

Proof. One can easily verify that $s_n^2 = n\hat{\sigma}_n^2/(n-1)$. In Theorem 8 in Section 7.5 we have already proved that $\hat{\sigma}_n^2 \xrightarrow{P} \operatorname{Var}(X)$. Since $n/(n-1) \to 1$ as $n \to \infty$, and since $n/(n-1)$ can be considered as a random variable which is constant with probability one, then it trivially follows that $s_n^2 \xrightarrow{P} \operatorname{Var}(X)$. A little algebra shows that

$$\hat{\sigma}_n^2 = \frac{1}{n}\sum_{k=1}^{n} X_k^2 - \overline{X}_n^2,$$

and one easily computes

$$E(\hat{\sigma}_n^2) = E(X^2) - E(\overline{X}_n^2).$$

But

$$\begin{aligned} E(\overline{X}_n^2) &= E\left\{\left(\frac{X_1 + \cdots + X_n}{n}\right)^2\right\} = \frac{1}{n^2}E\left\{\sum_{i=1}^{n} X_i^2 + \sum_{i\neq j} X_iX_j\right\} \\ &= \frac{1}{n^2}\left\{nE(X^2) + \sum_{i\neq j} E(X_i)E(X_j)\right\} \\ &= \frac{1}{n^2}\left\{nE(X^2) + n(n-1)(EX)^2\right\}. \\ &= \frac{1}{n}E(X^2) + \frac{(n-1)(EX)^2}{n}. \end{aligned}$$

Hence

$$E(\hat{\sigma}_n^2) = \frac{n-1}{n}(E(X^2) - (EX)^2) = \frac{n-1}{n}\operatorname{Var}(X).$$

Thus $\hat{\sigma}_n^2$ is not an unbiased estimate of Var (X). However, s_n^2 is an unbiased estimate of Var (X), since

$$E(s_n^2) = E\left(\frac{n}{n-1}\hat{\sigma}_n^2\right) = \operatorname{Var}(X).$$

This concludes our proof.

It should be apparent to the student that a consistent sequence of estimates of an unknown constant is very desirable if one wants to find the value of this constant. However, why is one interested in unbiasedness? Some assert that the only claim for unbiasedness as a good criterion is that it forces the distribution of the estimator to be centered (in the center-of-gravity sense) at the true parameter value. An equally strong, if not stronger, claim for unbiasedness is that if one has an unbiased estimate of a constant θ, then one can construct a consistent sequence of estimates of θ. We prove this in the next theorem.

3. Theorem. *Let U_m be a random variable defined on $\Omega^{(m)}$, suppose that U_m is an unbiased estimate of θ, and assume that $E(U_m^2) < \infty$. Let $V_1, V_2, \cdots$ denote a sequence of independent observations on U_m, and let $Z_n = (V_1 + \cdots + V_n)/n$ for every n. Then the sequence of random variables $\{Z_n\}$ is a consistent sequence of estimates of θ.*

Proof. Clearly, the random variables $\{V_n\}$ are independent, identically distributed random variables with common finite second moment $E(U_m^2)$ and common finite expectation θ. The conclusion follows from the law of large numbers.

EXERCISES

In the problems below, X is a random variable defined over a population Ω, and $\{X_n\}$ is a sequence of independent observations on X.

1. If X is uniformly distributed over $[0, \beta]$, i.e., if

$$f_X(x) = \begin{cases} 1/\beta & \text{if } 0 \leqq x \leqq \beta \\ 0 & \text{if } x < 0 \text{ or } x > \beta \end{cases}$$

for $\beta > 0$, and if $Y_n = \max\{X_1, \cdots, X_n\}$, verify that Y_n is a consistent estimate of β, and discover whether it is an unbiased estimate of β.

2. In problem 1, let $Z_n = 2\overline{X}_n$. Is Z_n an unbiased estimate of β? Is Z_n a consistent estimate of β?

3. In problem 1 let U_n = twice the sample median of $X_1, X_2, \cdots, X_{2n+1}$, i.e., for every $\omega^{(2n+1)} = (\omega_1, \omega_2, \cdots, \omega_{2n+1}) \in \Omega^{(2n+1)}$, let $U_n(\omega^{(2n+1)})$ be the $(n+1)$st largest of the numbers $2X(\omega_1), 2X(\omega_2), \cdots, 2X(\omega_{2n+1})$. Is U_n an unbiased estimate of β? Is it a consistent estimate of β?

4. Suppose the distribution of X is Poisson with parameter λ. Is $\overline{X}_n$ an unbiased and consistent estimate of λ? Is s_n^2 an unbiased estimate of λ? Is it consistent?

5. Suppose $E(X^{2k}) < \infty$, and denote, for fixed positive integer k,

$$\mu_{k,n} = \frac{1}{n}\sum_{i=1}^{n} (X_i - \overline{X}_n)^k.$$

Prove that $\mu_{k,n}$ is a consistent estimate of $\mu_k = E(X - EX)^k$.

8.3 The Method of Moments

Let Ω denote a population, and let us suppose that there are certain constants, say $\theta_1, \theta_2, \cdots, \theta_k$, of this population whose values we want to know. It might occur that these constants can be measured directly, in which case there is no further problem. However, if they cannot be measured directly it might be possible to do the next best thing, namely, to estimate them. In other words, it might happen that we can define an observable random variable X over Ω whose distribution function is completely known as a function of these constants. For example, if $k = 2$, it might occur that one can define a random variable X whose distribution is $N(\theta_1, \theta_2)$. In this case one can obtain consistent estimates of θ_1 and θ_2 by taking n independent observations on X, denoted by $X_1, X_2, \cdots, X_n$, and then evaluating $\overline{X}_n$ and s_n^2. This example is the simplest example of the *method of moments*. We now develop this method in general for the case $k = 2$.

The problem, formally, is this. X is a random variable defined over a population Ω, and $\{X_n\}$ is a sequence of independent observations on X. The distribution of X is assumed to be known except for the value of the two unknown constants θ_1, θ_2. (In this case we might denote the distribution function of X by $F_X(x|\theta_1, \theta_2)$.) The problem is to construct a sequence of consistent estimates of θ_1 and a consistent estimate of θ_2.

The method of moments is applicable in such a case when the following additional conditions occur. Suppose first that $E(X^4) < \infty$. Suppose one computes the first two moments of X, call them m_1 and m_2, and suppose that they are functions of θ_1, θ_2, i.e., $m_1 = m_1(\theta_1, \theta_2)$ and $m_2 = m_2(\theta_1, \theta_2)$. Suppose further that θ_1 and θ_2 can be solved in terms of m_1 and m_2, i.e., $\theta_1 = \theta_1(m_1, m_2)$ and $\theta_2 = \theta_2(m_1, m_2)$. Now we already know that $\overline{X}_n \xrightarrow{P} m_1$ and $V_n = (1/n)\sum_{k=1}^{n} X_k^2 \xrightarrow{P} m_2$. Finally suppose that the functions $\theta_1(x, y)$ and $\theta_2(x, y)$ are such that $\theta_1(\overline{X}_n, V_n) \xrightarrow{P} \theta_1(m_1, m_2)$ and $\theta_2(\overline{X}_n, V_n) \xrightarrow{P} \theta_2(m_1, m_2)$. Then we see that $\{\theta_1(\overline{X}_n, V_n)\}$ and $\{\theta_2(\overline{X}_n, V_n)\}$ are consistent sequences of estimates of θ_1 and θ_2, respectively. However, the question arises: what properties should the functions $\theta_1(x, y)$ and $\theta_2(x, y)$ have in order that this last assumption above be satisfied. The answer is that they be continuous at all possible points (m_1, m_2) where $m_2 > m_1^2$ (remember the Schwarz inequality!), and we prove this in the following theorem.

1. Theorem. *Let $f(x, y)$ be a function of two variables, and let $\{X_n\}$ and $\{Y_n\}$ be two sequences of random variables such that $X_n \xrightarrow{P} a$ and $Y_n \xrightarrow{P} b$ (where a and b are constants). If f is continuous at (a, b), and if $f(X_n, Y_n)$ is a random variable for every n, then $f(X_n, Y_n) \xrightarrow{P} f(a, b)$.*

Proof. It should be recalled that the definition of f being continuous at (a, b) means that for every $\epsilon > 0$ there exists a $\delta_\epsilon > 0$ such that $|x - a| < \delta_\epsilon$ and $|y - b| < \delta_\epsilon$ imply that $|f(x, y) - f(a, b)| < \epsilon$. Consequently,

$$[|X_n - a| < \delta_\epsilon][|Y_n - b| < \delta_\epsilon] \subset [|f(X_n, Y_n) - f(a, b)| < \epsilon].$$

Using the fact that $A \subset B$ implies $B^c \subset A^c$, we obtain (using the DeMorgan formula) that

$$[|X_n - a| \geqq \delta_\epsilon] \cup [|Y_n - b| \geqq \delta_\epsilon] \supset [|f(X_n, Y_n) - f(a, b)| \geqq \epsilon].$$

Now making use of Boole's inequality and the fact that $A \subset B$ implies $P(A) \leqq P(B)$, we obtain

$$\begin{aligned} P[|X_n - a| \geqq \delta_\epsilon] + P[|Y_n - b| \geqq \delta_\epsilon] & \\ &\geqq P([|X_n - a| \geqq \delta_\epsilon] \cup [|Y_n - b| \geqq \delta_\epsilon]) \\ &\geqq P[|f(X_n, Y_n) - f(a, b)| \geqq \epsilon] \geqq 0. \end{aligned}$$

By hypothesis the first two terms of the above inequality converge to zero, thus establishing the theorem.

Now let us consider an example. Suppose the distribution of X is absolutely continuous with a density

$$f_X(x) = \begin{cases} 1/\theta_2 & \text{if} \quad \theta_1 \leqq x \leqq \theta_1 + \theta_2 \\ 0 & \text{if} \quad x < \theta_1 \quad \text{or} \quad x > \theta_1 + \theta_2, \end{cases}$$

where $-\infty < \theta_1 < \infty$ and $\theta_2 > 0$. The student should be able to show that

$$EX = \theta_1 + \theta_2/2,$$

and

$$E(X^2) = \theta_1^2 + \theta_1\theta_2 + \theta_2^2/3.$$

If one solves the first equation for θ_1, substitutes this into the second equation, and solves the second equation for θ_2, one obtains

$$\theta_2 = \sqrt{12\{EX^2 - (EX)^2\}}.$$

Substituting now in the first equation we get

$$\theta_1 = EX - \sqrt{12\{EX^2 - (EX)^2\}}/2.$$

Now the function f defined by

$$f(x, y) = \sqrt{12(y - x^2)}$$

is continuous at every point (x, y) at which $y > x^2$ (because it is the square root of the difference of two continuous functions), and hence we can conclude by Theorem 1 that the sequence of random variables $\{Z_n\}$ is a consistent sequence of estimates of θ_2, where

$$Z_n = \sqrt{12}\left\{\frac{1}{n}\sum_{k=1}^{n} X_k^2 - \overline{X}_n^2\right\}^{1/2}.$$

In the same manner $\{\overline{X}_n - Z_n/2\}$ is a consistent sequence of estimates of θ_1.

The discussion and theorem presented prior to the above example can be easily worked through by the student for the case of any finite number of constants.

EXERCISES

1. Prove: If X is a random variable such that $X(\omega) \geqq 0$ for every $\omega \in \Omega$, then $X^{1/2n}$ is a random variable (where n is any positive integer).

2. Theorem. If $X_n \xrightarrow{P} a$, $Y_n \xrightarrow{P} b$, and $Z_n \xrightarrow{P} c$, where a, b, c are constants, if $f(x, y, z)$ is a function of three variables which is continuous at the point (a, b, c), and if $f(X_n, Y_n, Z_n)$ is a random variable for each n, then $f(X_n, Y_n, Z_n) \xrightarrow{P} f(a, b, c)$.

3. Suppose X has an absolutely continuous distribution with density

$$f_X(x) = \begin{cases} \dfrac{1}{\Gamma(\alpha + 1)\beta^{\alpha+1}} x^\alpha e^{-x/\beta} & \text{if } x > 0 \\ 0 & \text{if } x \leqq 0, \end{cases}$$

where $\beta > 0$ and $\alpha > -1$. Find consistent estimates of α and β by the method of moments.

4. Suppose X has the Pascal distribution, i.e.,

$$f_X(x) = (1 - p)^x p, \quad x = 0, 1, 2, \cdots,$$

where $0 < p < 1$. Find a consistent sequence of estimates of p by the method of moments.

8.4 Minimum Variance Estimates

Sometimes it is difficult or impossible to find an unbiased or consistent estimate of an unknown constant. This, however, is not the only unhappy situation one might encounter. Sometimes one has too many (i.e., more than one) estimates of an unknown constant which are both unbiased and consistent. Let us consider just such a case.

Let X be a random variable (defined over some population Ω) which has a Poisson distribution, i.e.,

$$P[X = x] = e^{-\lambda}\lambda^x/x! \quad \text{if} \quad x = 0, 1, 2, \cdots,$$

where $\lambda > 0$ is an unknown constant. The problem is to take n independent observations $X_1, X_2, \cdots, X_n$ on X and to construct an estimate of λ from these random variables. First let us compute the mean and the variance of X. Easily,

$$\begin{aligned} EX &= \sum_{k=0}^{\infty} \frac{ke^{-\lambda}\lambda^k}{k!} = e^{-\lambda} \sum_{k=0}^{\infty} \frac{k\lambda^k}{k!} \\ &= e^{-\lambda}\lambda \sum_{j=0}^{\infty} \frac{\lambda^j}{j!} = \lambda. \end{aligned}$$

Also,

$$\begin{aligned} EX^2 &= \sum_{k=0}^{\infty} \frac{k^2e^{-\lambda}\lambda^k}{k!} \\ &= \sum_{k=1}^{\infty} \frac{k(k-1)e^{-\lambda}\lambda^k}{k!} + \sum_{k=1}^{\infty} \frac{ke^{-\lambda}\lambda^k}{k!} \\ &= \lambda^2 + \lambda. \end{aligned}$$

Thus $\text{Var}(X) = E(X^2) - (EX)^2 = \lambda$. We see that both the expectation and variance of X are λ. Consequently, by Theorems 1 and 2 in Section 8.2 we know that both $\overline{X}_n$ and s_n^2 are unbiased and consistent estimates of λ. Here we have a case where we know of two estimates of λ which have the desired properties, and the question arises: which estimate should we want to use, $\overline{X}_n$ or s_n^2? We might select that estimate which has the smaller variance. We next discuss why an estimate of this kind could be preferable.

If U is an unbiased estimate of θ, i.e., $EU = \theta$, and if $EU^2 < \infty$, then we have an upper bound to the probability that U will differ from θ in absolute value by an amount not less than $\epsilon > 0$. This upper bound is $\text{Var}(U)/\epsilon^2$, which we obtain from the Chebishev inequality

$$P[|U - \theta| \geqq \epsilon] \leqq \text{Var}(U)/\epsilon^2.$$

It seems reasonable that one should want the variance to be small. Hence, a criterion for selecting an estimate out of the set of all unbiased estimates of θ might be to select that estimate which has the smallest variance (if such an estimate exists). The problem therefore is how to determine such estimates when they exist. This problem is solved to some extent by the Cramér-Rao inequality, which we now derive.

Let X be an observable random variable defined over some population Ω. Let $X_1, \cdots, X_n$ denote n independent observations on X. We shall consider here the case where X has an absolutely continuous distribution; in the discrete case the development is analogous. In what follows the reader should not be too shocked if he encounters a random variable $f_X(X)$, where $f_X(x)$ is a density of X. We now suppose that a density of X is some function of the unknown constant; we write such a density $f(x|\theta)$. For example, if X is $N(\theta, 1)$, then

$$f(x|\theta) = \frac{1}{\sqrt{2\pi}} \exp -\frac{(x-\theta)^2}{2}, \quad -\infty < x < \infty.$$

Let $\hat{\theta} = \hat{\theta}(X_1, \cdots, X_n)$ be an *unbiased* estimate of θ, which we assume to exist. We make the following assumptions:

(i) the set of possible values, D, of θ constitute an open interval which is either bounded or unbounded,

(ii) $\partial f(x|\theta)/\partial\theta$ exists for all $x \in (-\infty, +\infty)$,

(iii) $\int_{-\infty}^{\infty} \cdots \int_{-\infty}^{\infty} \left(\prod_{i=1}^{n} f(x_i|\theta) \right) dx_1 \cdots dx_n$ can be differentiated under the integral sign with respect to θ,

(iv) $E(\partial \log f(X|\theta)/\partial\theta)^2 < \infty$ for all $\theta \in D$, and

(v) $\int_{-\infty}^{\infty} \cdots \int_{-\infty}^{\infty} \hat{\theta}(x_1, \cdots, x_n) \left(\prod_{i=1}^{n} f(x_i|\theta) \right) dx_1 \cdots dx_n$ can be differentiated under the integral sign with respect to θ.

1. Theorem. (Cramér-Rao Inequality.) *Under the above assumptions,*

$$\operatorname{Var}(\hat{\theta}(X_1, \cdots, X_n)) \geqq 1/nE\{\partial \log f(X|\theta)/\partial\theta\}^2,$$

and equality holds if and only if there exists a constant K (which possibly depends on θ and n) such that, with probability one,

$$\sum_{k=1}^{n} \frac{\partial}{\partial\theta} \log f(X_k|\theta) = K\{\hat{\theta}(X_1, \cdots, X_n) - \theta\}.$$

Proof. Since $\hat{\theta}(X_1, \cdots, X_n)$ is an unbiased estimate of θ, and since

$$f_{X_1,\cdots,X_n}(x_1, \cdots, x_n) = \prod_{k=1}^{n} f(x_k|\theta),$$

we obtain

$$\theta = \int_{-\infty}^{\infty} \cdots \int_{-\infty}^{\infty} \hat{\theta}(x_1, \cdots, x_n) \left\{ \prod_{k=1}^{n} f(x_k|\theta) \right\} dx_1 \cdots dx_n. \tag{1}$$

If we differentiate both sides with respect to θ we get

$$1 = \int_{-\infty}^{\infty} \cdots \int_{-\infty}^{\infty} \hat{\theta}(x_1, \cdots, x_n) \left\{ \sum_{k=1}^{n} \left(\prod_{\substack{j=1 \\ j \neq k}}^{n} f(x_j|\theta) \right) \frac{\partial f(x_k|\theta)}{\partial\theta} \right\} dx_1 \cdots dx_n$$

$$= \int_{-\infty}^{\infty} \cdots \int_{-\infty}^{\infty} \hat{\theta}(x_1, \cdots, x_n) \left\{ \sum_{k=1}^{n} \left(\prod_{j=1}^{n} f(x_j|\theta) \right) \frac{\partial \log f(x_k|\theta)}{\partial\theta} \right\} dx_1 \cdots dx_n,$$

which may be written:

$$(2) \qquad 1 = \sum_{k=1}^{n} E\left\{\hat{\theta}(X_1, \cdots, X_n)\frac{\partial}{\partial\theta}\log f(X_k|\theta)\right\}.$$

Also, beginning with the fact that

$$1 = \int_{-\infty}^{\infty} \cdots \int_{-\infty}^{\infty} \left(\prod_{j=1}^{n} f(x_j|\theta)\right) dx_1 \cdots dx_n,$$

we may differentiate both sides with respect to θ, and obtain

$$0 = \sum_{k=1}^{n} \int_{-\infty}^{\infty} \cdots \int_{-\infty}^{\infty} \left(\frac{\partial}{\partial\theta}\log f(x_k|\theta)\right)\left(\prod_{j=1}^{n} f(x_j|\theta)\right) dx_1 \cdots dx_n,$$

or

$$(3) \qquad 0 = \sum_{k=1}^{n} E\left(\frac{\partial}{\partial\theta}\log f(X_k|\theta)\right).$$

If we multiply both sides of (3) by θ and subtract from (2) we get

$$1 = E\left\{(\hat{\theta}(X_1, \cdots, X_n) - \theta)\sum_{k=1}^{n}\frac{\partial}{\partial\theta}\log f(X_k|\theta)\right\}.$$

Now we apply Schwarz' inequality and get

$$(4) \qquad 1 \leqq E(\hat{\theta}(X_1, \cdots, X_n) - \theta)^2 E\left(\sum_{k=1}^{n}\frac{\partial}{\partial\theta}\log f(X_k|\theta)\right)^2,$$

where the equality holds if and only if there exists a constant K (possibly depending on θ and n) such that, with probability one,

$$\sum_{k=1}^{n}\frac{\partial}{\partial\theta}\log f(X_k|\theta) = K\{\hat{\theta}(X_1, \cdots, X_n) - \theta\}.$$

The first expectation on the right of (4) is obviously Var $(\hat{\theta}(X_1, \cdots, X_n))$; we next evaluate the second expectation. Since

$$1 = \int_{-\infty}^{\infty} f(x_i|\theta)\, dx_i,$$

then, upon differentiating both sides with respect to θ, we obtain

$$0 = \int_{-\infty}^{\infty} \left(\frac{\partial}{\partial\theta}\log f(x_i|\theta)\right) f(x_i|\theta)\, dx_i,$$

or

$$0 = E\left(\frac{\partial}{\partial\theta}\log f(X_i|\theta)\right).$$

Also, from this it follows that, for $i \neq j$,

$$E\left\{\left(\frac{\partial}{\partial\theta}\log f(X_i|\theta)\right)\left(\frac{\partial}{\partial\theta}\log f(X_j|\theta)\right)\right\} =$$

$$= \int_{-\infty}^{\infty}\cdots\int_{-\infty}^{\infty}\left(\frac{\partial}{\partial\theta}\log f(x_i|\theta)\right)\left(\frac{\partial}{\partial\theta}\log f(x_j|\theta)\right)\left(\prod_{k=1}^{n} f(x_k|\theta)\right)dx_1\cdots dx_n$$

$$= E\left(\frac{\partial}{\partial\theta}\log f(X_i|\theta)\right)E\left(\frac{\partial}{\partial\theta}\log f(X_j|\theta)\right) = 0.$$

Hence

$$E\left\{\sum_{k=1}^{n}\frac{\partial}{\partial\theta}\log f(X_k|\theta)\right\}^2 = \sum_{k=1}^{n}E\left(\frac{\partial}{\partial\theta}\log f(X_k|\theta)\right)^2$$

$$= nE\left(\frac{\partial}{\partial\theta}\log f(X|\theta)\right)^2.$$

With this the inequality is established, and the theorem is proved.

Thus we see that among all unbiased estimates of θ, if there exists an estimate whose variance is $1/nE(\partial \log f(X|\theta)/\partial\theta)^2$, then we have an estimate whose variance is a minimum. However, in order to find this minimum variance unbiased estimate we should use the equation given to us in Theorem 1. Let us consider some examples.

Example 1. *The Poisson Distribution.* In this case, $f(x|\lambda) = e^{-\lambda}\lambda^x/x!$, $x = 0, 1, 2, \cdots$. Thus we have

$$\log f(x|\lambda) = -\lambda + x\log\lambda - \log x!,$$

and

$$\frac{\partial}{\partial\lambda}\log f(x|\lambda) = -1 + \frac{x}{\lambda}.$$

Thus

$$nE\left(\frac{\partial}{\partial\lambda}\log f(X|\lambda)\right)^2 = nE\left(-1 + \frac{X}{\lambda}\right)^2$$

$$= n\left\{1 - \frac{2}{\lambda}EX + \left(\frac{1}{\lambda}\right)^2 E(X^2)\right\} = \left(\frac{\lambda}{n}\right)^{-1}.$$

Thus by the Cramér-Rao inequality, the minimum variance possible for an unbiased estimate of λ is λ/n. We now use the theorem to see if this minimum variance is attainable. We see that

$$\sum_{k=1}^{n}\frac{\partial}{\partial\lambda}\log f(X_k|\lambda) = -n + \frac{1}{\lambda}\sum_{k=1}^{n}X_k$$

$$= \frac{n}{\lambda}\left(\frac{1}{n}\sum_{k=1}^{n}X_k - \lambda\right).$$

Now, $(1/n)\sum_{k=1}^{n}X_k$ is an unbiased estimate of λ, and hence by Theorem 1 it is that unbiased estimate of minimum variance.

Example 2. *The Normal Distribution.* In this case

$$f(x|\mu) = \frac{1}{\sqrt{2\pi}} \exp -\frac{(x-\mu)^2}{2}, \quad -\infty < x < \infty.$$

We want to find that unbiased estimate of μ which has the minimum variance. We first compute the minimum variance. Since $\log f(x|\mu) = -\log \sqrt{2\pi} - (x-\mu)^2/2$, and $\partial(\log f(x|\mu))/\partial\mu = x - \mu$, we easily compute

$$nE\left(\frac{\partial}{\partial\mu} \log f(X|\mu)\right)^2 = nE(X-\mu)^2 = n.$$

Thus by the Cramér-Rao inequality the minimum variance possible among all unbiased estimates of μ is $1/n$. In order to find the hoped-for minimum variance unbiased estimate of μ we verify that the equation of Theorem 1 holds for some unbiased estimate. We easily verify that

$$\sum_{k=1}^{n} \frac{\partial}{\partial\mu} \log f(X_k|\mu) = \sum_{k=1}^{n} X_k - n\mu = n(\overline{X}_n - \mu).$$

Hence $\overline{X}_n$ is the minimum variance unbiased estimate of μ.

EXERCISES

1. Write the proof of the Cramér-Rao inequality in the discrete case.

2. Let X be a random variable with an absolutely continuous distribution, where

$$f_X(x|\theta) = \begin{cases} \frac{1}{2} & \text{if } \theta - 1 \leqq x \leqq \theta + 1 \\ 0 & \text{if } x < \theta - 1 \text{ or } x > \theta + 1. \end{cases}$$

Let Y be a discrete random variable where

$$P[Y = x] = \begin{cases} 1 - 2 \times 10^{-6} & \text{if } x = \theta \\ 10^{-6} & \text{if } x = \theta - 10^{12} \\ 10^{-6} & \text{if } x = \theta + 10^{12}. \end{cases}$$

(a) Verify that both X and Y are unbiased estimates of θ.
(b) Compute Var (X) and Var (Y).
(c) Which estimate of θ would you prefer?
(d) Is your answer in (c) the minimum variance estimate?

In problems 3, 4, and 5 the distribution of X is given. Let $X_1, \cdots, X_n$ denote n independent observations on X. Find the minimum variance estimate of θ *if it exists.* Be sure to check that your estimates are unbiased.

3.

$$f_X(x|\theta) = \begin{cases} \theta & \text{if } x = 1 \\ 1 - \theta & \text{if } x = 0, \end{cases}$$

where $0 < \theta < 1$.

4.

$$f_X(x|\theta) = \begin{cases} \theta e^{-\theta x} & \text{if } x > 0 \\ 0 & \text{if } x \leqq 0, \end{cases}$$

where $\theta > 0$.

5.

$$f_X(x|\theta) = \begin{cases}(1/\theta)e^{-x/\theta} & \text{if } x > 0\\ 0 & \text{if } x \leqq 0,\end{cases}$$

where $\theta > 0$.

8.5 The Principle of Maximum Likelihood

Let X be a random variable, defined over some population Ω, which has either an absolutely continuous or a discrete distribution. Suppose that a density in either case being considered is denoted by $f(x|\theta)$, i.e., this density is a certain function of x which depends on an unknown parameter θ. The problem is to estimate θ.

Let $X_1, \cdots, X_n$ denote n observations on X (independent or not, depending on the experiment) with joint density which we denote by $f(x_1, x_2, \cdots, x_n|\theta)$, i.e.,

$$f_{X_1, \cdots, X_n}(x_1, \cdots, x_n) = f(x_1, \cdots, x_n|\theta).$$

The principle of maximum likelihood asserts that the value of θ should be that value for which the probability of "observing what one actually observes" is maximum. More formally, the principle of maximum likelihood states: one should always want an estimate $\theta(X_1, \cdots, X_n)$ of θ for which $f(X_1, \cdots, X_n|\theta)$ is maximized. (*Note:* the random variables are substituted for arguments.)

In a practical way, the problem of finding a maximum likelihood estimate of θ is to find that value of θ as a function of $x_1, \cdots, x_n$, i.e., $\hat{\theta}(x_1, \cdots, x_n)$, for which $f(x_1, \cdots, x_n|\theta)$ is maximized and then substitute the "observations" (i.e., random variables) for the arguments. Let us consider some examples.

Example 1. *The Normal Distribution.* Let X have a distribution which is $N(\mu, \sigma^2)$, where μ and $\sigma^2 > 0$ are unknown. The problem is to find a maximum likelihood estimate of μ, whatever be the value of σ^2. Let $X_1, \cdots, X_n$ denote n independent observations on X. Then

$$f(x_1, \cdots, x_n|\mu, \sigma^2) = (2\pi\sigma^2)^{-n/2} \exp\left(-\frac{1}{2\sigma^2}\sum_{k=1}^{n}(x_k - \mu)^2\right).$$

We want to find the value of μ (if it exists), $\hat{\mu} = \hat{\mu}(x_1, \cdots, x_n)$, which when substituted for μ maximizes $f(x_1, \cdots, x_n|\mu, \sigma^2)$. In order to do this, we solve for μ in the equation

$$\frac{\partial}{\partial\mu} f(x_1, \cdots, x_n|\mu, \sigma^2) = 0,$$

and a small amount of work yields $\hat{\mu}(x_1, \cdots, x_n) = (x_1 + \cdots + x_n)/n$. Hence the maximum likelihood estimate of μ alone is $\hat{\mu}(X_1, \cdots, X_n) = \overline{X}_n$.

Example 2. *The Uniform Distribution.* Suppose

$$f_X(x) = \begin{cases} 1/\beta & \text{if} \quad 0 \leqq x \leqq \beta \\ 0 & \text{if} \quad x < 0 \quad \text{or} \quad x > \beta, \end{cases}$$

where $\beta > 0$. The problem is: Given n independent observations $X_1, \cdots,$ X_n on X, find a maximum likelihood estimate of β. First we write

$$f(x_1, \cdots, x_n|\beta) = \begin{cases} 1/\beta^n & \text{if} \quad 0 < x_i < \beta, \quad i = 1, 2, \cdots, n \\ 0 & \text{otherwise.} \end{cases}$$

From this expression for the joint density of $X_1, \cdots, X_n$, it is clear that if we take $\hat{\beta}$ such that $0 < \hat{\beta} < \max\{x_1, \cdots, x_n\}$, then $f(x_1, \cdots, x_n|\hat{\beta}) = 0$. Such a value of $\hat{\beta}$ does not maximize the joint density at $(x_1, \cdots, x_n)$, and we must search for a value of $\hat{\beta}$ such that $\hat{\beta} \geqq \max\{x_1, \cdots, x_n\}$. Now suppose that $\hat{\beta}_0$ and $\hat{\beta}_1$ are any two possible values of $\hat{\beta}$ such that

$$\max\{x_1, \cdots, x_n\} \leqq \hat{\beta}_0 < \hat{\beta}_1.$$

Then we have $f(x_1, \cdots, x_n|\hat{\beta}_0) = 1/\hat{\beta}_0^n > 1/\hat{\beta}_1^n = f(x_1, \cdots, x_n|\hat{\beta}_1)$. (Note that $\max\{X_1, \cdots, X_n\} > 0$ with probability one.) Consequently, the closer we take $\hat{\beta}$ to $\max\{x_1, \cdots, x_n\}$ the larger becomes the density function. Therefore the maximum likelihood estimate of β is

$$\hat{\beta}(X_1, \cdots, X_n) = \max\{X_1, \cdots, X_n\}.$$

Example 3. *The Hypergeometric Distribution.* In a lake there are N fish, where N is unknown. The problem is to estimate N. One catches r fish (all at the same time), marks each with a red spot, and returns them alive into the lake. After a reasonable period of time, during which these "tagged" fish are assumed to have distributed themselves "at random" in the lake, one catches s fish (again, all at once). (*Note:* r and s are considered as fixed, predetermined constants.) Among these s fish caught there will be X tagged fish, where X is a random variable. The discrete density of X is given by

$$f_X(x|N) = \frac{\binom{r}{x}\binom{N-r}{s-x}}{\binom{N}{s}},$$

where x is an integer and

$$\max(0, s - N + r) \leqq x \leqq \min(s, r),$$

and $f_X(x|N) = 0$ for all other values of x. The problem is to find that value $\hat{N} = \hat{N}(x)$ of N for which $f_X(x|N)$ is maximum. It is not easy to differentiate this density with respect to N, set this derivative equal to zero, and solve for N. What we do instead is consider the ratio

$$R(N) = f_X(x|N)/f_X(x|N-1).$$

For those values of N for which $R(N) > 1$ we know that $f_X(x|N)$ is an increasing function of N, and for those values of N for which $R(N) < 1$ we know that $f_X(x|N)$ is a decreasing function of N. Using the formula for the density of X we note (after a certain amount of algebra) that $R(N) > 1$ if and only if $N < rs/x$, and $R(N) < 1$ if and only if $N > rs/x$. We see that $f_X(x|N)$ reaches its maximum value (as a function of N) when N is approximately equal to rs/x. Hence, as maximum likelihood estimate of N we take

$$\hat{N}(X) = rs/X.$$

In conclusion we show that an unbiased estimate whose variance is the minimum variance in the Cramér-Rao inequality is a maximum likelihood estimate.

1. Theorem. *Assume the conditions of Theorem 1 in Section* 8.4. *If* $\hat{\theta}(X_1, \cdots, X_n)$ *is an unbiased estimate of* θ *whose variance is the minimum in the sense of the Cramér-Rao inequality, then* $\hat{\theta}(X_1, \cdots, X_n)$ *is a maximum likelihood estimate of* θ.

Proof. In order to find that value of θ for which $f(x_1, \cdots, x_n|\theta)$ is maximum, we need only find that θ for which $\log f(x_1, \cdots, x_n|\theta)$ is maximum. Now we set

$$\begin{aligned}\frac{\partial}{\partial\theta}\log f(x_1, \cdots, x_n|\theta) &= \frac{\partial}{\partial\theta}\log\prod_{k=1}^{n} f(x_k|\theta)\\ &= \sum_{k=1}^{n}\frac{\partial}{\partial\theta}\log f(x_k|\theta) = 0.\end{aligned}$$

By Theorem 1 in Section 8.4 and this last equation, we obtain

$$K(\hat{\theta}(x_1, \cdots, x_n) - \theta) = 0,$$

where $\hat{\theta}(x_1, \cdots, x_n)$ is the minimum variance estimate. Thus $\hat{\theta}(x_1, \cdots, x_n)$ is also the maximum likelihood estimate.

EXERCISES

1. Let X be a random variable whose distribution is $N(0, \sigma^2)$, where $\sigma^2 > 0$ is unknown. Let $X_1, \cdots, X_n$ be n independent observations on X. Find the maximum likelihood estimate of σ^2.

2. Let X be a random variable whose distribution is $N(\mu, \sigma^2)$, where both μ and σ^2 are unknown. Let $X_1, \cdots, X_n$ be n independent observations on X. Does there exist a maximum likelihood estimate of σ^2 alone?

3. In problem 2, do there exist *joint* maximum likelihood estimates of μ and σ^2?

4. Let X be a random variable with a discrete distribution whose density is $f_X(x) = p$ if $x = 1$ and $= 1 - p$ if $x = 0$, where $0 < p < 1$. Let $X_1, \cdots, X_n$ be n independent observations on X. Find the maximum likelihood estimate of p.

5. In example 3 (the fish-tagging problem), suppose that r is so much smaller than N that the distribution of X can be approximated by the binomial distribution. In this case, find a maximum likelihood estimate of N.

6. Let $X_1, \cdots, X_n$ denote n independent observations on a random variable whose distribution is Poisson with parameter λ. Find the maximum likelihood estimate of λ.

7. Let $X_1, X_2, \cdots, X_n$ denote n independent observations on a random variable X which has a density

$$f_X(x|\theta) = \begin{cases} \theta(1 - x)^{\theta-1} & \text{if } x \in [0, 1] \\ 0 & \text{if } x < 0 \text{ or } x > 1, \end{cases}$$

where $\theta > 1$. Find a maximum likelihood estimate of θ.

8. Let $X_1, X_2, \cdots, X_n$ be n independent observations on a random variable X with discrete distribution with density

$$f_X(x|N) = \begin{cases} 1/N & \text{if } x = 1, 2, \cdots, N \\ 0 & \text{otherwise.} \end{cases}$$

Find a maximum likelihood estimate of N.

CHAPTER 9

Notes on Matrix Theory

This chapter is actually an appendix to this book. However it is inserted here rather than at the end since it takes less effort for a student to read a chapter whose contents he might already be somewhat familiar with rather than interrupt a course of study by a sojourn to the appendix. This chapter is just a series of notes encompassing the minimum amount of material needed for subsequent chapters. *All unproved or partially proved theorems and lemmas should be considered as exercises for the student.*

1. Definition. *A matrix is a real-valued function defined over*

$$\{(i, j)|i = 1, 2, \cdots, m, j = 1, 2, \cdots, n\}.$$

(Informally speaking, a matrix is a rectangular array of real numbers.)

In these notes, a matrix will be called an $m \times n$ (pronounced "m by n") matrix if it has m rows and n columns, i.e., if it can be written in the form

$$\begin{pmatrix} a_{11} & a_{12} & \cdots & a_{1n} \\ a_{21} & a_{22} & \cdots & a_{2n} \\ \cdot & \cdot & & \cdot \\ \cdot & \cdot & & \cdot \\ \cdot & \cdot & & \cdot \\ a_{m1} & a_{m2} & \cdots & a_{mn} \end{pmatrix}.$$

For every entry a_{ij} in a matrix, the integer i denotes the row and the integer j denotes the column in which a_{ij} is located. A matrix like that just written might be denoted either by $||a_{ij}||$ or (a_{ij}) or A.

2. Definition of Addition. *If two matrices have the same number of rows and the same number of columns, then and only then is their sum defined. In the case of two $m \times n$ matrices $A = (a_{ij})$ and $B = (b_{ij})$, we define their sum, $A + B$ to be the matrix $C = (c_{ij})$, where $c_{ij} = a_{ij} + b_{ij}$ for all i and all j.*

Clearly, if A and B are two $m \times n$ matrices, then $A + B = B + A$.

3. Definition. *If $A = (a_{ij})$ is an $m \times n$ matrix and $B = (b_{ij})$ is an $n \times p$ matrix, then their product $C = AB$ is defined to be that matrix (c_{ij}) where $c_{ij} = \sum_{k=1}^{n} a_{ik}b_{kj}$ for every i and j. In multiplying two matrices, the number of columns in the pre-multiplier must equal the number of rows in the post-multiplier; otherwise, multiplication is not defined.*

It should be noted that matrix multiplication of square matrices is not necessarily commutative.

4. Definition of Kronecker delta.

$$\delta_{ij} = \begin{cases} 1 & \text{if } i = j \\ 0 & \text{if } i \neq j \end{cases}$$

where i and j are integers.

5. Theorem. *If $I = (\delta_{ij})$ is an $n \times n$ matrix, then for every $n \times p$ matrix B, $IB = B$, and for every $m \times n$ matrix A, $AI = A$.*

Proof. Left to the student.

If $I = (\delta_{ij})$ is an $n \times n$ matrix, then it is an identity for the set $\mathfrak{M}_n$ of all $n \times n$ matrices, i.e., for every $A \in \mathfrak{M}_n$, $IA = AI = A$.

6. Theorem. *I is the only identity matrix in $\mathfrak{M}_n$ with respect to matrix multiplication.*

Proof. We shall show that any identity matrix in $\mathfrak{M}_n$ is I. Let I' be any right identity matrix in $\mathfrak{M}_n$, i.e., $AI' = A$ for all $A \in \mathfrak{M}_n$. Then, since I' is a right identity matrix, $II' = I$. But since I is a "two-sided" identity matrix, $II' = I'$. Thus $I = I'$. A similar argument works for left identity matrices.

7. Theorem. *Let A be an $m \times n$ matrix, B an $n \times p$ matrix, C a $p \times r$ matrix, and D an $n \times p$ matrix. Then $(AB)C = A(BC)$* (associativity property), *and* $A(B + D) = AB + AD$ *and* $(B + D)C = BC + DC$ (distributivity property).

Proof. Let $A = (a_{ij})$, $B = (b_{ij})$, and $C = (c_{ij})$. We first find the element in the ith row and jth column of $(AB)C$ and then do the same for $A(BC)$. The element in the ith row and βth column of AB is $\sum_{\alpha=1}^{n} a_{i\alpha}b_{\alpha\beta}$, and the element in the ith row and jth column of $(AB)C$ is

$$\sum_{\beta=1}^{p} \sum_{\alpha=1}^{n} a_{i\alpha}b_{\alpha\beta}c_{\beta j} \quad \text{or} \quad \sum_{\alpha=1}^{n} \sum_{\beta=1}^{p} a_{i\alpha}b_{\alpha\beta}c_{\beta j}.$$

A similar treatment shows that this is the same entry in the ith row and jth column of $A(BC)$. The proof of the two distributivity properties is straightforward and is left to the student.

8. Definition. *A submatrix A of a matrix B is a matrix obtained from B by deleting certain entire rows and/or entire columns.*

It is possible to express a matrix in terms of submatrices or as a partitioned matrix. For example, the $m \times n$ matrix A might be written $A = (B|C)$, where B and C are matrices with m rows each and such that the total number of their columns is n. Another example of this is to write

$$A = \left(\begin{array}{c|c} A_{11} & A_{12} \\ \hline A_{21} & A_{22} \end{array}\right)$$

where A_{11}, A_{12}, A_{21}, A_{22} are submatrices of A such that A_{11} and A_{12} have the same number of rows and A_{11} and A_{21} have the same number of columns.

9. Theorem. *If A is an $m \times n$ matrix which is written as*

$$A = \left(\begin{array}{c|c} A_{11} & A_{12} \\ \hline A_{21} & A_{22} \end{array}\right)$$

where A_{11} is an $r \times s$ submatrix, and if B is an $n \times p$ matrix which is written

$$B = \left(\begin{array}{c|c} B_{11} & B_{12} \\ \hline B_{21} & B_{22} \end{array}\right)$$

where B_{11} is an $s \times t$ submatrix of B, then

$$AB = \left(\begin{array}{c|c} A_{11} & A_{12} \\ \hline A_{21} & A_{22} \end{array}\right)\left(\begin{array}{c|c} B_{11} & B_{12} \\ \hline B_{21} & B_{22} \end{array}\right)$$

$$= \left(\begin{array}{c|c} A_{11}B_{11} + A_{12}B_{21} & A_{11}B_{12} + A_{12}B_{22} \\ \hline A_{21}B_{11} + A_{22}B_{21} & A_{21}B_{12} + A_{22}B_{22} \end{array}\right)$$

Proof. Left to the student.

10. Definition. *By the transpose of an $m \times n$ matrix $A = (a_{ij})$ we mean an $n \times m$ matrix $A' = (a'_{ij})$ where $a'_{ij} = a_{ji}$.*

11. Theorem. $(A')' = A$ *for every matrix A.*

Proof. Left to the student.

12. Theorem. $(AB)' = B'A'$.

Proof. Left to the student.

13. Theorem. *Let $C = (c_{ij})$ be an $n \times n$ matrix obtained from the identity by interchanging the αth and βth rows. If A is an $m \times n$ matrix and B is an $n \times p$ matrix, then AC is the same as A except that the αth and βth* *columns are interchanged, and CB is the same as B except that the αth and βth rows are interchanged.*

Proof. Left to the student.

14. Theorem. *Let $C = I + D$, where I is the $n \times n$ identity matrix, and $D = (d_{ij})$ is defined as follows: $d_{ij} = 0$ if $i \neq \alpha$ or $j \neq \beta$, and $d_{\alpha\beta} = K$ (a constant), where $\alpha \neq \beta$, $1 \leqq \alpha, \beta \leqq n$. If A is an $m \times n$ matrix and B is an $n \times p$ matrix, then AC is the same matrix as A except that K times the αth column has been added to the βth column, and CB is the same matrix as B except that K times the βth row has been added to the αth row.*

Proof. Left to the student.

15. Theorem. *Let $C = (c_{ij})$ be an $n \times n$ matrix defined as follows: $c_{\alpha\alpha} = K \neq 0$, and $c_{ij} = \delta_{ij}$ for $i \neq \alpha$ or $j \neq \alpha$. If A is an $m \times n$ matrix and B is an $n \times p$ matrix, then AC is the same as A except that its αth column is multiplied by K, and CB is the same as B except that the αth row is multiplied by K.*

Proof. Left to the student.

16. Definition. *An elementary transformation on a matrix A is any transformation effected by a matrix C occurring in Theorems* 13, 14, *and* 15. *The matrix C is called an elementary transformation matrix.*

17. Definition. *Let $A = (a_{ij})$ be an $n \times n$ matrix. By the determinant $|A|$ or* Det *A of A we mean*

$$|A| = \sum_{\{i_1, \cdots, i_n\}} (-1)^{\rho(i_1, \cdots, i_n)} a_{1i_1} a_{2i_2} \cdots a_{ni_n},$$

where the sum is taken over all permutations $\{(i_1, \cdots, i_n)\}$ of the integers $1, 2, \cdots, n$ *and where $\rho(i_1, \cdots, i_n)$ denotes a number of pairwise interchanges of the integers $i_1, i_2, \cdots, i_n$ needed to bring them into the order* $1, 2, \cdots, n$.

Note: $\rho(i_1, \cdots, i_n)$ is not uniquely defined. For a particular permutation $i_1, i_2, \cdots, i_n$ it could equal any number of values. However, we now show that the difference between any such pair of values, ρ' and ρ'', is an even integer, and thus $(-1)^{\rho'} = (-1)^{\rho''}$. In order to prove this, let $x_1, \cdots, x_n$ denote n unequal real numbers and let us define

$$P(x_1, \cdots, x_n) = \prod_{i<j} (x_i - x_j).$$

Then, since ρ' is one number of pairwise interchanges needed to put $i_1, \cdots, i_n$ into ascending order, we have

$$P(x_{i_1}, \cdots, x_{i_n}) = (-1)^{\rho'} P(x_1, \cdots, x_n),$$

because if i and j are to be interchanged the factors involved are $(x_i - x_j)$ and $+(x_i - x_k)(x_j - x_k)$. By the same token

$$P(x_{i_1}, x_{i_2}, \cdots, x_{i_n}) = (-1)^{\rho''}P(x_1, \cdots, x_n).$$

Consequently, $(-1)^{\rho'} = (-1)^{\rho''}$, which was to be proved.

18. Theorem. *If A is an $n \times n$ matrix which can be represented as a partitioned matrix,*

$$A = \left(\begin{array}{c|c} B & 0 \\ \hline D & C \end{array}\right),$$

where B and C are square submatrices and 0 is a submatrix of which all elements are zero, then $|A| = |B|\,|C|$.

Proof. Let B be a $k \times k$ matrix and C an $(n-k) \times (n-k)$ matrix. Then

$$|A| = \sum_{\{(i_1, \cdots, i_n)\}} (-1)^{\rho(i_1, \cdots, i_n)} a_{1i_1} \cdots a_{ki_k} a_{k+1,i_{k+1}} \cdots a_{ni_n}.$$

Necessarily $a_{ij_i} = 0$ if $i \leqq k$ and $j_i > k$. Hence

$$|A| = \sum_{\substack{\{(i_1, \cdots, i_k)\} \\ \{(i_{k+1}, \cdots, i_n)\}}} (-1)^{\rho(i_1, \cdots, i_n)} \prod_{j=1}^{n} a_{ji_j},$$

where $\{(i_1, \cdots, i_k)\}$ denotes the set of all permutations of $1, 2, \cdots, k$ and $\{(i_{k+1}, \cdots, i_n)\}$ denotes the set of all permutations of $k+1, k+2, \cdots, n$. In such a case, one easily verifies that $\rho(i_1, \cdots, i_n) = \rho(i_1, \cdots, i_k) + \rho(i_{k+1}, \cdots, i_n)$. Thus

$$|A| = \left(\sum_{\{(i_1, \cdots, i_n)\}} (-1)^{\rho(i_1, \cdots, i_n)} \prod_{j=1}^{k} a_{ji_j}\right)$$
$$\left(\sum_{\{(i_{k+1}, \cdots, i_n)\}} (-1)^{\rho(i_{k+1}, \cdots, i_n)} \prod_{j=k+1}^{n} a_{ji_j}\right)$$
$$= |B|\,|C|,$$

which proves the theorem.

19. Theorem. *If A is an $n \times n$ matrix, then $|A'| = |A|$.*

Proof. If $A = (a_{ij})$ and $A' = (a'_{ij})$, then

$$|A'| = \sum_{\{(i_1, \cdots, i_n)\}} (-1)^{\rho(i_1, \cdots, i_n)} a'_{1i_1} a'_{2i_2} \cdots a'_{ni_n}$$
$$= \sum_{\{(i_1, \cdots, i_n)\}} (-1)^{\rho(i_1, \cdots, i_n)} a_{i_1 1} a_{i_2 2} \cdots a_{i_n n}.$$

But we can write

$$\prod_{j=1}^{n} a_{i_j j} = \prod_{k=1}^{n} a_{k\mu_k},$$

where $\rho(\mu_1, \cdots, \mu_n) = \rho(i_1, \cdots, i_n)$. Hence $|A| = |A'|$.

20. Theorem. *If a square (i.e., $n \times n$) matrix B is obtained from A by interchanging two rows (or two columns) of A, then $|B| = -|A|$.*

Proof. (In the case of rows only.) Assume that the two rows in question are the αth and βth rows, where $\alpha < \beta$. Then

$$\begin{aligned}|A| &= \sum_{\{(i_1, \cdots, i_n)\}} (-1)^{\rho(i_1, \cdots, i_\alpha, \cdots, i_\beta, \cdots, i_n)} a_{1i_1} \cdots a_{\alpha i_\alpha} \cdots a_{\beta i_\beta} \cdots a_{ni_n} \\ &= \sum_{\{(i_1, \cdots, i_\beta, \cdots, i_\alpha, \cdots, i_n)\}} (-1)^{\rho(i_1, \cdots, i_\beta, \cdots, i_\alpha, \cdots, i_n)-1} \\ &\qquad\qquad \cdot a_{1i_1} \cdots a_{\beta i_\beta} \cdots a_{\alpha i_\alpha} \cdots a_{ni_n} \\ &= -|B|.\end{aligned}$$

This completes the proof.

21. Theorem. *If two rows (or columns) of a square matrix A are identical, then $|A| = 0$.*

Proof. If one interchanges these two rows (or columns), one obtains the same matrix A. By Theorem 20, $|A| = -|A|$, which implies that $|A| = 0$.

22. Definition. *If $A = (a_{ij})$ is an $m \times n$ matrix, and if c is a constant, then by cA we mean the $m \times n$ matrix $B = (b_{ij})$, where $b_{ij} = ca_{ij}$ for every i and every j.*

23. Theorem. *If the square matrix B is obtained from square matrix A by adding to one row (column) a constant times another row (column), then $|B| = |A|$.*

Proof. Suppose p times the βth row is added to the αth row (where, say $\beta > \alpha$). Then

$$\begin{aligned}|B| &= \sum_{\{(i_1, \cdots, i_n)\}} (-1)^{\rho(i_1, \cdots, i_n)} a_{1i_1} \cdots (a_{\alpha i_\alpha} + pa_{\beta i_\alpha}) \cdots a_{\beta i_\beta} \cdots a_{ni_n} \\ &= \sum_{\{(i_1, \cdots, i_n)\}} (-1)^{\rho(i_1, \cdots, i_n)} a_{1i_1} \cdots a_{\alpha i_\alpha} \cdots a_{\beta i_\beta} \cdots a_{ni_n} \\ &\quad + p \sum_{\{(i_1, \cdots, i_n)\}} (-1)^{\rho(i_1, \cdots, i_n)} a_{1i_1} \cdots a_{\beta i_\alpha} \cdots a_{\beta i_\beta} \cdots a_{ni_n}.\end{aligned}$$

The first of these two sums is simply $|A|$. The second of the two sums is p times the determinant of a matrix where the αth row is the same as the βth row. Theorem 21 implies that this sum is zero. The same proof holds for $\alpha > \beta$, and the proof is valid for columns by Theorem 19.

24. Theorem. *If the square matrix B is obtained from the matrix A by multiplying one row (column) of A by a constant p, then $|B| = p|A|$.*

Proof. Suppose that the αth row of A is multiplied by p in order to obtain B. Then

$$|B| = \sum_{\{(i_1, \cdots, i_n)\}} (-1)^{\rho(i_1, \cdots, i_n)} a_{1i_1} \cdots p a_{\alpha i_\alpha} \cdots a_{ni_n}$$

$$= p \sum_{\{(i_1, \cdots, i_n)\}} (-1)^{\rho(i_1, \cdots, i_n)} a_{1i_1} \cdots a_{\alpha i_\alpha} \cdots a_{ni_n} = p|A|.$$

25. Definition. *Let $A = (a_{ij})$ be a square matrix. The cofactor A_{ij} of a_{ij} is defined to be $(-1)^{i+j}$ times the determinant of that submatrix of A obtained by deleting the* ith *row and the* jth *column.*

26. Theorem. *If A is an $n \times n$ matrix, then*

$$|A| = \sum_{j=1}^{n} a_{kj} A_{kj}$$

for every k, $1 \leqq k \leqq n$.

Proof. By definition,

$$|A| = \sum_{\{(i_1, \cdots, i_n)\}} (-1)^{\rho(i_1, \cdots, i_n)} a_{1i_1} \cdots a_{ki_k} \cdots a_{ni_n}$$

$$= (-1)^{k-1} \sum_{\{(i_1, \cdots, i_n)\}} (-1)^{\rho(i_1, \cdots, i_n)} a_{ki_1} a_{1i_2} \cdots a_{k-1, i_k} a_{k+1, i_{k+1}} \cdots a_{ni_n}$$

(note that $k - 1$ interchanges of $i_1, \cdots, i_n$ were added)

$$= (-1)^{k-1} \sum_{j=1}^{n} a_{kj} (-1)^{j-1} \sum_{\{(i_2, \cdots, i_n)\}} (-1)^{\rho(i_2, \cdots, i_n)} \cdot a_{1i_2} \cdots a_{k-1, i_k} a_{k+1, i_{k+1}} \cdots a_{ni_n}$$

where, for each j, $(i_2, \cdots, i_n)$ is a permutation of

$$(1, 2, \cdots, j-1, j+1, \cdots, n).$$

The $(-1)^{j-1}$ is due to the fact that once $i_2, \cdots, i_n$ are arranged in increasing order, the integer j can undergo $j - 1$ pairwise (consecutive) interchanges in order that $(j, i_2, \cdots, i_n)$ be in ascending order. Since $(-1)^{k+j-2} = (-1)^{k+j}$, we have

$$|A| = \sum_{j=1}^{n} a_{kj} A_{kj}.$$

27. Corollary. *If $k \neq m$, then $\sum_{j=1}^{n} a_{kj} A_{mj} = 0$.*

Proof. The expansion given is the determinant of a matrix in which two rows, namely, the kth and mth ones, are the same.

28. Theorem. *If A and B are two $n \times n$ matrices, then $|AB| = |A|\,|B|$.*

Proof. Consider the partitioned matrix

$$C = \left(\begin{array}{c|c} A & 0 \\ \hline -I & B \end{array}\right),$$

where I is the identity $n \times n$ matrix. By Theorem 18, $|C| = |A|\,|B|$. If, for $1 \leqq i \leqq n$, the ith column of C is multiplied by b_{ij} and is added to the $(n+j)$th column, then the value of $|C|$ does not change (by Theorem 23). When this is done for all values of i and j, $1 \leqq i \leqq n$, $1 \leqq j \leqq n$, the matrix C is transformed into

$$\left(\begin{array}{c|c} A & AB \\ \hline -I & 0 \end{array}\right).$$

Thus, by Theorem 18,

$$|C| = \left|\left(\begin{array}{c|c} AB & A \\ \hline 0 & -I \end{array}\right)\right| (-1)^n = |AB|\,|-I|(-1)^n.$$

Since $(-1)^n = |-I|$, the theorem is proved.

29. Definition. *A square matrix A is called singular if $|A| = 0$, and it is called nonsingular if $|A| \neq 0$.*

30. Theorem. *If A is a nonsingular $n \times n$ matrix, then there exists one and only one inverse matrix A^{-1}, i.e., an $n \times n$ matrix such that $A^{-1}A = AA^{-1} = I$.*

Proof. We first prove that there does exist one such inverse A^{-1} of $A = (a_{ij})$. Let $A^{-1} = (b_{ij})$, where $b_{ij} = A_{ji}/|A|$ and A_{ji} is the cofactor of a_{ji}. By using Theorem 26 and Corollary 27, the student can easily prove that $AA^{-1} = I$ and $A^{-1}A = I$. Now we prove that there is at most one inverse matrix for A. Let B be any right inverse to A, i.e., $AB = I$. Then, by associativity, $B = IB = (A^{-1}A)B = A^{-1}(AB) = A^{-1}I = A^{-1}$. So $A^{-1} = B$. In the same manner, any left inverse C of A is equal to A^{-1} also.

31. Corollary. *If A and B are two nonsingular $n \times n$ matrices, then $(AB)^{-1} = B^{-1}A^{-1}$.*

Proof. This follows by the uniqueness proved in Theorem 30 and the fact that $(AB)B^{-1}A^{-1} = A(BB^{-1})A^{-1} = (AI)A^{-1} = AA^{-1} = I$.

32. Theorem. (Cramer's Rule.) *Let A be an $n \times n$ matrix, let X be an $n \times 1$ matrix, and let Y be an $n \times 1$ matrix such that $AX = Y$. If A is nonsingular, then X has a unique solution, namely, $X = A^{-1}Y$.*

Proof. Left to the student.

33. Definition. *Let A and B be two $m \times n$ matrices. We write $A \sim B$ and say "A is equivalent to B" if there exist a nonsingular $m \times m$ matrix C and a nonsingular $n \times n$ matrix D such that $A = CBD$.*

34. Theorem. *The relation $\sim$ defined in Definition 33 is an equivalence relation, i.e.,* (*r*) $A \sim A$ *for all* A (*reflexivity*),

(*s*) *if* $A \sim B$, *then* $B \sim A$ (*symmetry*),

and

(*t*) *if* $A \sim B$ *and* $B \sim C$, *then* $A \sim C$ (*transitivity*).

Proof. Left to the student.

35. Definition. *If* A *is an* $n \times n$ *matrix, then* n *is called the order of* A.

36. Definition. *The rank of an* $m \times n$ *matrix* A *is the largest order of the nonsingular (square) submatrices of* A, *and is denoted by* $r(A)$ *or rank* (A).

37. Theorem. *The rank of a matrix remains unchanged after undergoing elementary transformations (see Definition* 16).

Proof. Left to the student.

38. Theorem. *If matrix* B *is obtained from matrix* A *by elementary transformations on* A, *then* $B \sim A$.

Proof. The conclusion of this theorem follows because any of the elementary transformations on A can be accomplished by pre-multiplying or post-multiplying A by nonsingular matrices.

39. Theorem. *If* A *is an* $m \times n$ *matrix of rank* r, *then*

$$A \sim \left(\begin{array}{c|c} B & 0 \\ \hline 0 & 0 \end{array}\right),$$

where B *is an* $r \times r$ *nonsingular submatrix of* A.

Proof. Since the rank of A is r, there exists an $r \times r$ nonsingular submatrix B of A. By interchanging rows and columns we may put B in the upper left-hand corner of A and thus obtain

$$A \sim \left(\begin{array}{c|c} B & C \\ \hline D & E \end{array}\right).$$

Since $|B| \neq 0$, we know by Cramer's rule that there exist constants $x_1, \cdots, x_r$ such that when multiplying the first r columns in the matrix

$$\left(\begin{array}{c|c} B & C \\ \hline D & E \end{array}\right)$$

by them, respectively, and adding their sum to the $(r + 1)$st column, we obtain zeros in the first column of C. The same can be done for every column of C. Repeating the argument on rows, D can be made into zeros. Thus, by Theorem 38,

$$A \sim \left(\begin{array}{c|c} B & 0 \\ \hline 0 & F \end{array}\right).$$

We now assert that F is made up entirely of zeros. If it were not, then it is easy to see that the rank of

$$\left(\begin{array}{c|c} B & 0 \\ \hline 0 & F \end{array}\right)$$

is not less than $r + 1$, which contradicts the hypothesis that the rank of A is r. (Remember Theorem 37.)

40. Corollary. *If A is an $m \times n$ matrix with rank r, then it is equivalent to a diagonal matrix with r 1's and $q - r$ 0's in the main diagonal, where $q = \min(m, n)$. (A diagonal matrix $D = (d_{ij})$ is a matrix such that $d_{ij} = 0$ if $i \neq j$.)*

Proof. Let B be an $r \times r$ nonsingular submatrix of A. The assertion then follows from Theorems 39 and 9 and from the fact that

$$\left(\begin{array}{c|c} I & 0 \\ \hline 0 & 0 \end{array}\right) = \left(\begin{array}{c|c} B^{-1} & 0 \\ \hline 0 & I \end{array}\right)\left(\begin{array}{c|c} B & 0 \\ \hline 0 & 0 \end{array}\right).$$

41. Theorem. *Every elementary transformation matrix C (see Definition 16) is nonsingular, and C^{-1} is an elementary transformation matrix.*

Proof. Left to the student.

42. Theorem. *Every nonsingular $n \times n$ matrix A is a product of elementary transformation matrices.*

Proof. We shall first prove that there are elementary transformation matrices $C_1, \cdots, C_r, D_1, \cdots, D_s$ such that $C_1 \cdots C_rAD_1 \cdots D_s = I$. We first note that at least one of the elements of the first column of A is not zero, since A is nonsingular. If necessary, interchange the first row with another row so that the first element in the first column is not zero. Then multiply every element in the first column by the reciprocal of its first element. Next, multiply the first row by the first element in the ith row, and then subtract from the ith row, $i = 2, \cdots, n$. Thus in the first column, by means of elementary row transformations, the first element is 1 and the rest are 0's. In the same way (i.e., by elementary row transformations) the second element in the second column can be made 1 and all the elements below it can be made 0's. One can continue in this fashion until all the diagonal elements are 1's and all elements below the main diagonal are 0's. Then by elementary column transformations the nonzero elements above the main diagonal can be made into 0's. We thus obtain elementary transformation matrices $C_1, \cdots, C_r, D_1, \cdots, D_s$ such that

$$C_1 \cdots C_rAD_1 \cdots D_s = I.$$

From this we obtain $A = C_r^{-1} \cdots C_1^{-1}D_s^{-1} \cdots D_1^{-1}$, and by Theorem 41 the conclusion is established.

43. Theorem. *Two $m \times n$ matrices are equivalent if and only if they have the same rank.*

Proof. We first prove the "if" part of the theorem. Assume that A and B are two $m \times n$ matrices such that $r = \text{rank}\,(A) = \text{rank}\,(B)$. Then by Theorem 39,

$$A \sim \left(\begin{array}{c|c} C & 0 \\ \hline 0 & 0 \end{array}\right) \quad \text{and} \quad B \sim \left(\begin{array}{c|c} D & 0 \\ \hline 0 & 0 \end{array}\right),$$

where C and D are $r \times r$ nonsingular submatrices of A and B, respectively. Since the two partitioned matrices above are obtained through pre- and post-multiplication by nonsingular matrices, there exist nonsingular $m \times m$ matrices E and G and nonsingular $n \times n$ matrices F and H such that

$$A = E\left(\begin{array}{c|c} C & 0 \\ \hline 0 & 0 \end{array}\right)F \quad \text{and} \quad B = G\left(\begin{array}{c|c} D & 0 \\ \hline 0 & 0 \end{array}\right)H.$$

It is clear that the matrices

$$E\left(\begin{array}{c|c} D^{-1} & 0 \\ \hline 0 & I \end{array}\right)G^{-1} \quad \text{and} \quad H^{-1}\left(\begin{array}{c|c} C & 0 \\ \hline 0 & I \end{array}\right)F$$

are nonsingular of order m and n, respectively. Further,

$$A = E\left(\begin{array}{c|c} D^{-1} & 0 \\ \hline 0 & I \end{array}\right)G^{-1}BH^{-1}\left(\begin{array}{c|c} C & 0 \\ \hline 0 & I \end{array}\right)F.$$

Consequently $A \sim B$. Conversely, if $A \sim B$, then the fact that $r(A) = r(B)$ follows from Theorems 42 and 37.

44. Definition. *A matrix $A = (a_{ij})$ is said to be symmetric if $a_{ij} = a_{ji}$ for all i and j.*

45. Theorem. *The matrix $A = (a_{ij})$ is symmetric if and only if $A' = A$.*

Proof. Left to the student.

46. Definition. *Euclidean n-space, denoted by $E^{(n)}$, is the set of all $n \times 1$ matrices.*

47. Definition. *A subset L of $E^{(n)}$ is called a linear subspace of $E^{(n)}$ if for every $A \in L$, $B \in L$, and for every pair of real numbers x, y, then $xA + yB \in L$.*

We shall refer to the $n \times 1$ matrices in $E^{(n)}$ by boldface lower case Roman letters at the end of the alphabet, e.g., $\mathbf{x}, \mathbf{y}, \mathbf{z}$ are elements in $E^{(n)}$. We shall frequently refer to these matrices as vectors. The vector $\mathbf{0}$ is the $n \times 1$ matrix composed entirely of zeros, and we shall call it the null vector or zero vector.

48. Definition. *If* $\mathbf{x}_1, \cdots, \mathbf{x}_k$ *are* k *vectors in* $E^{(n)}$, *and if* $a_1, \cdots, a_k$ *are numbers, then the vector* $a_1\mathbf{x}_1 + \cdots + a_k\mathbf{x}_k$ *is called a linear combination of the vectors.*

49. Definition. *The* k *vectors* $\mathbf{x}_1, \cdots, \mathbf{x}_k$ *in* $E^{(n)}$ *are said to be* **linearly independent** *if* $a_1\mathbf{x}_1 + \cdots + a_k\mathbf{x}_k = \mathbf{0}$ *implies that* $a_1 = 0, a_2 = 0, \cdots, a_k = 0$. *The* k *vectors are said to be* **linearly dependent** *if they are not linearly independent, i.e., if there exist constants* $a_1, \cdots, a_k$, *not all of them zeros, such that* $a_1\mathbf{x}_1 + \cdots + a_k\mathbf{x}_k = \mathbf{0}$.

50. Definition. *Let* L *be a linear subspace of* $E^{(n)}$. *Suppose that there are* k *vectors in* L *which are linearly independent, but suppose that every* $k + 1$ *vectors are linearly dependent. Then we say that the dimension of* L *is* k, *and we denote the dimension of* L *by* dim L.

51. Lemma. *The vectors* $\mathbf{x}_1, \cdots, \mathbf{x}_k$ *in* $E^{(n)}$ *are linearly independent if and only if, for any constants* $a_1, \cdots, a_{k-1}$, *the vectors* $\mathbf{x}_1 + a_1\mathbf{x}_k$, $\mathbf{x}_2 + a_2\mathbf{x}_k, \cdots, \mathbf{x}_{k-1} + a_{k-1}\mathbf{x}_k, \mathbf{x}_k$ *are linearly independent also.*

Proof. Suppose $\mathbf{x}_1, \cdots, \mathbf{x}_k$ are linearly independent. The equation

$$\beta_1(\mathbf{x}_1 + a_1\mathbf{x}_k) + \cdots + \beta_{k-1}(\mathbf{x}_{k-1} + a_{k-1}\mathbf{x}_k) + \beta_k\mathbf{x}_k = \mathbf{0}$$

may be written in the form

$$\beta_1\mathbf{x}_1 + \beta_2\mathbf{x}_2 + \cdots + \beta_{k-1}\mathbf{x}_{k-1} + (\beta_k + \beta_1 a_1 + \cdots + \beta_{k-1}a_{k-1})\mathbf{x}_k = \mathbf{0}.$$

This implies that $\quad \beta_1 = 0, \beta_2 = 0, \cdots, \beta_{k-1} = 0,$

and $\quad \beta_k + \beta_1 a_1 + \cdots + \beta_{k-1}a_{k-1} = 0.$

From this we also obtain $\beta_k = 0$, which proves that

$$\mathbf{x}_1 + a_1\mathbf{x}_k, \cdots, \mathbf{x}_{k-1} + a_{k-1}\mathbf{x}_k, \mathbf{x}_k$$

are linearly independent. The assertion just proved is easily seen to imply its own converse.

52. Theorem. *In* $E^{(n)}$, *every* $n + 1$ *vectors are linearly dependent.*

Proof. We prove this by induction on n. The theorem is trivial in the case $n = 1$. We next assume it is true for arbitrary n and prove that this implies it is true for $n + 1$. Let $\mathbf{x}_1, \cdots, \mathbf{x}_{n+2}$ be any $n + 2$ vectors in $E^{(n+1)}$, where

$$\mathbf{x}_j = \begin{pmatrix} a_{j,1} \\ \cdot \\ \cdot \\ \cdot \\ a_{j,n+1} \end{pmatrix}.$$

We may assume that these vectors are numbered so that $a_{n+2,n+1} \neq 0$ (since otherwise, if $a_{j,n+1} = 0$ for all j, we have essentially $n + 2$ vectors in $E^{(n)}$ which by induction hypothesis are linearly dependent). We now define vectors $\mathbf{y}_1, \cdots, \mathbf{y}_{n+2}$ as follows: $\mathbf{y}_j = \mathbf{x}_j - (a_{j,n+1}/a_{n+2,n+1})\mathbf{x}_{n+2}$, $1 \leqq j \leqq n + 1$, and $\mathbf{y}_{n+2} = \mathbf{x}_{n+2}$. By induction hypothesis, $\mathbf{y}_1, \cdots, \mathbf{y}_{n+1}$ are linearly dependent, and hence $\mathbf{y}_1, \cdots, \mathbf{y}_{n+2}$ are linearly dependent. By Lemma 51, we conclude that $\mathbf{x}_1, \cdots, \mathbf{x}_{n+2}$ are linearly dependent.

53. Theorem. *The dimension of $E^{(n)}$ is n.*

Proof. We first exhibit n linearly independent vectors in $E^{(n)}$:

$$\begin{pmatrix}1\\0\\0\\\cdot\\\cdot\\\cdot\\0\end{pmatrix}\begin{pmatrix}0\\1\\0\\\cdot\\\cdot\\\cdot\\0\end{pmatrix}, \cdots, \begin{pmatrix}0\\0\\\cdot\\\cdot\\\cdot\\0\\1\end{pmatrix}.$$

By Theorem 52, there are no more than n linearly independent vectors in $E^{(n)}$. The conclusion follows from the definition of dimension.

54. Theorem. *If L and M are two linear subspaces of $E^{(n)}$, if $L \subset M$, and if* $\dim L \geqq \dim M$, *then $L = M$.*

Proof. Left to the student.

55. Theorem. *If $\mathbf{x}_1, \cdots, \mathbf{x}_k$ are k linearly independent vectors in a linear subspace L of $E^{(n)}$, and if every $\mathbf{x} \in L$ can be written in the form $\mathbf{x} = c_1\mathbf{x}_1 + \cdots + c_k\mathbf{x}_k$, where $c_1, \cdots, c_k$ are constants, then* $\dim L = k$.

Proof. Since $\mathbf{x}_i \in L$ for $i = 1, 2, \cdots, k$, we need only show that every $k + 1$ vectors in L are linearly dependent. Let $\mathbf{u}_1, \cdots, \mathbf{u}_{k+1}$ be any $k + 1$ vectors in L. Then

$$\mathbf{u}_i = c_{1i}\mathbf{x}_1 + c_{2i}\mathbf{x}_2 + \cdots + c_{ki}\mathbf{x}_k$$

for $i = 1, 2, \cdots, k + 1$. Now consider the vectors

$$\mathbf{c}_1 = \begin{pmatrix}c_{11}\\c_{21}\\\cdot\\\cdot\\\cdot\\c_{k1}\end{pmatrix}, \mathbf{c}_2 = \begin{pmatrix}c_{12}\\c_{22}\\\cdot\\\cdot\\\cdot\\c_{k2}\end{pmatrix}, \cdots, \mathbf{c}_{k+1} = \begin{pmatrix}c_{1,k+1}\\c_{2,k+1}\\\cdot\\\cdot\\\cdot\\c_{k,k+1}\end{pmatrix}.$$

By Theorem 52, these $k + 1$ vectors are linearly dependent, i.e., there exist constants $K_1, K_2, \cdots, K_{k+1}$, not all zero, such that

$$K_1\mathbf{c}_1 + \cdots + K_{k+1}\mathbf{c}_{k+1} = \mathbf{0}.$$

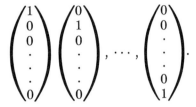

Thus we have $K_1\mathbf{u}_1 + \cdots + K_{k+1}\mathbf{u}_{k+1} = \mathbf{0}$, and $\mathbf{u}_1, \cdots, \mathbf{u}_{k+1}$ are linearly dependent.

56. Lemma. *If*

$$\begin{pmatrix} a_{11} \\ a_{21} \\ \cdot \\ \cdot \\ \cdot \\ a_{n1} \end{pmatrix}, \begin{pmatrix} a_{12} \\ a_{22} \\ \cdot \\ \cdot \\ \cdot \\ a_{n2} \end{pmatrix}, \cdots, \begin{pmatrix} a_{1k} \\ a_{2k} \\ \cdot \\ \cdot \\ \cdot \\ a_{nk} \end{pmatrix}$$

are k vectors in $E^{(n)}$, and if $\lambda a_{j\alpha}$ is added to $a_{i\alpha}$ for $\alpha = 1, \cdots, k$, then the new vectors are linearly independent if and only if the original ones were. Also, if the same two rows are interchanged in all the vectors, the new vectors are linearly independent if and only if the original ones were.

Proof. Left to the student.

57. Theorem. *If C is an $n \times n$ matrix, then the columns of C are linearly dependent if and only if $|C| = 0$.*

Proof. It is obvious that if the columns are linearly dependent, then $|C| = 0$. Conversely, suppose $|C| = 0$. By Lemma 56, any elementary operations on the rows of C leave the columns of C as linearly dependent or independent as they were before. Let $r(C) = r$. Since $|C| = 0$, then $r < n$. We may interchange rows to get the $r \times r$ nonsingular matrix in the first r rows. Since interchange of columns does not affect their linear dependence or independence, we may obtain the $r \times r$ nonsingular matrix in the first r columns as well. By Cramer's rule and Lemma 56, the last $n - r$ rows of these first r columns can be made into zeros without affecting the linear independence of the columns. However, it automatically follows that the last $n - r$ rows of the last $n - r$ columns are zeros, for if not, the rank of C would not be less than $r + 1$, which contradicts the hypothesis and Theorem 37. Thus we effectively have n vectors in r-dimensional space $E^{(r)}$. By Theorem 52, these columns are linearly dependent.

58. Lemma. *If $\mathbf{x}_1, \cdots, \mathbf{x}_k$ are k linearly independent vectors in $E^{(n)}$, if $\mathbf{u} = \alpha_1\mathbf{x}_1 + \cdots + \alpha_k\mathbf{x}_k$ and $\mathbf{u} = \beta_1\mathbf{x}_1 + \cdots + \beta_k\mathbf{x}_k$, where the α's and β's are constants, then $\alpha_1 = \beta_1, \alpha_2 = \beta_2, \cdots, \alpha_k = \beta_k$.*

Proof. Subtracting one equation from the other we obtain

$$\mathbf{0} = (\alpha_1 - \beta_1)\mathbf{x}_1 + \cdots + (\alpha_k - \beta_k)\mathbf{x}_k.$$

The linear independence of $\mathbf{x}_1, \cdots, \mathbf{x}_k$ implies that

$$\alpha_1 - \beta_1 = 0, \cdots, \alpha_k - \beta_k = 0,$$

which proves the lemma.

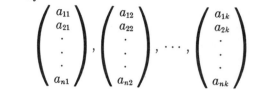

59. Theorem. *If A is an $n \times n$ matrix, and if* rank $(A) = r < n$, *then*

$$\dim \{\mathbf{x} \in E^{(n)} | A\mathbf{x} = \mathbf{0}\} = n - r.$$

Proof. The student can easily check that the set $L = \{\mathbf{x} \in E^{(n)} | A\mathbf{x} = \mathbf{0}\}$ is a linear subspace of $E^{(n)}$. The student can also easily prove that if B is an $n \times n$ nonsingular matrix, then $L = \{\mathbf{x} \in E^{(n)} | BA\mathbf{x} = \mathbf{0}\}$. Let B denote the product of those matrices which interchange the rows of A in such a way as to locate an $r \times r$ nonsingular submatrix of A in the first r rows of BA. By Lemma 56, the dimension of L remains the same if certain pairs of rows are interchanged in all vectors in L. Hence we may assume that the upper left $r \times r$ submatrix of BA is nonsingular. We may include in B products of more matrices which (by Cramer's rule) make all the elements of the last $n - r$ rows of the first r columns of BA zeros. We immediately see that all elements of the last $n - r$ rows of BA are zeros, for otherwise $r(BA) \geqq r + 1$, which contradicts the fact that $r(BA) = r(A)$. Let C be an $n \times n$ nonsingular matrix so that

$$BAC = \left(\begin{array}{c|c} D & 0 \\ \hline 0 & 0 \end{array}\right),$$

where D is an $r \times r$ nonsingular matrix in the upper left-hand corner of BA. If we denote

$$M = \{\mathbf{x} \in E^{(n)} | BAC\mathbf{x} = 0\},$$

then, by Lemma 56, $\dim M = \dim L$. However, the uniqueness property in Cramer's rule implies that M is the set of all vectors in $E^{(n)}$ in which the first r coordinates are zeros. Hence M is essentially $E^{(n-r)}$ (i.e., M is isomorphic to $E^{(n-r)}$), and by Theorem 53, $\dim M = n - r$.

60. Theorem. *The rank of a matrix equals the maximum number of linearly independent rows and equals the maximum number of linearly independent columns.*

Proof. Let $\mathbf{x}_1, \cdots, \mathbf{x}_r$ denote a maximal set of linearly independent columns of the matrix A, and let us consider the partitioned matrix

$$B = (\mathbf{x}_1 | \mathbf{x}_2 | \cdots | \mathbf{x}_r).$$

By Theorem 53, the maximum number of linearly independent rows of B is $\leqq r$. We now prove that there are exactly r linearly independent rows of B. Suppose to the contrary that there are at most r_1 linearly independent rows of B, where $r_1 < r$. By Lemma 56, we may assume that these occupy the top r_1 rows of B. All remaining rows of B are linear combinations of the first r_1 rows, and thus (by Lemma 56), if the rows below the first r_1 rows are all replaced by zeros, the linear independence of the columns is not changed. However, since these columns are essentially r r_1-dimensional vectors, they are linearly dependent (by Theorem 53), thus contradicting the fact that the columns are linearly independent. Hence in B and therefore in A there are at least as many linearly independent rows as there are linearly independent columns. By a symmetrical argument there are as many linearly independent columns as there are linearly independent rows. Thus, the maximum number of linearly independent rows equals the maximum number of linearly independent columns, and this fact coupled with Theorem 57 proves the theorem.

61. Theorem. *If $A_1, A_2, \cdots, A_s$ are $m \times n$ matrices, then $r(\sum_{k=1}^{s} A_k) \leqq \sum_{k=1}^{s} r(A_k)$.*

Proof. By means of Theorem 60, we deduce that

$$\sum_{i=1}^{s} r(A_i) \geqq r\begin{pmatrix} A_1 \\ \hline A_2 \\ \hline \cdot \\ \cdot \\ \cdot \\ \hline A_s \end{pmatrix} = r\begin{pmatrix} A_1 + \cdots + A_s \\ \hline A_2 \\ \hline \cdot \\ \cdot \\ \cdot \\ \hline A_s \end{pmatrix} \geqq r(A_1 + \cdots + A_s).$$

62. Theorem. *If A is an $m \times n$ matrix, and if B is an $n \times p$ matrix, then*

$$r(AB) \leqq \min \{r(A), r(B)\}.$$

Proof. We shall prove that $r(AB) \leqq r(B)$. By Theorem 39, there exists a nonsingular $n \times n$ matrix P and a nonsingular $p \times p$ matrix Q such that

$$PBQ = \left(\begin{array}{c|c} B_0 & 0 \\ \hline 0 & 0 \end{array}\right),$$

where B_0 is an $r \times r$ nonsingular submatrix of B and where $r = r(B)$. Let us denote

$$AP^{-1} = \left(\begin{array}{c|c} A_{11} & A_{12} \\ \hline A_{21} & A_{22} \end{array}\right),$$

where A_{11} is an $r \times r$ matrix. Then

$$AB \sim AP^{-1}(PBQ) = \left(\begin{array}{c|c} A_{11}B_0 & 0 \\ \hline A_{21}B_0 & 0 \end{array}\right),$$

which has at most r nonzero columns. By Theorem 43, rank $(AB) \leqq r = r(B)$. By a similar argument, $r(AB) \leqq r(A)$, and the conclusion of the theorem follows.

63. Theorem. *If A is an $m \times n$ matrix, and if B is a nonsingular $n \times n$ matrix, then $r(AB) = r(A)$.*

Proof. Since $A \sim AB$, the conclusion follows by Theorem 43.

64. Definition. *In $E^{(n)}$, any set of n linearly independent vectors is called a basis of $E^{(n)}$. If $L \subset E^{(n)}$ is a linear subspace of dimension k, any set of k linearly independent vectors in L is called a basis of L.*

65. Theorem. *If $\mathbf{x}$ is a nonzero vector in $E^{(n)}$, then there is a basis of $E^{(n)}$ which includes $\mathbf{x}$.*

Proof. Let i denote a row in $\mathbf{x}$ in which a nonzero number appears. Consider the $n - 1$ vectors

$$\begin{pmatrix} 1 \\ 0 \\ 0 \\ \cdot \\ \cdot \\ \cdot \\ 0 \end{pmatrix} \begin{pmatrix} 0 \\ 1 \\ 0 \\ \cdot \\ \cdot \\ \cdot \\ 0 \end{pmatrix}, \cdots, \begin{pmatrix} 0 \\ 0 \\ 0 \\ \cdot \\ \cdot \\ \cdot \\ 1 \end{pmatrix}$$

from which the one that has 1 in the ith row is excluded. These vectors together with $\mathbf{x}$ are easily seen to constitute a basis of $E^{(n)}$.

66. Definition. *Let $\mathbf{x}$ and $\mathbf{y}$ be two vectors in $E^{(n)}$. We define the inner product $(\mathbf{x}, \mathbf{y})$ by $(\mathbf{x}, \mathbf{y}) = \mathbf{x}'\mathbf{y} = \mathbf{y}'\mathbf{x}$.*

67. Definition. *The length or norm of $\mathbf{x}$, $||\mathbf{x}||$, is defined by $||\mathbf{x}|| = \sqrt{(\mathbf{x}, \mathbf{x})}$.*

68. Definition. *Two vectors $\mathbf{x}$ and $\mathbf{y}$ in $E^{(n)}$ are said to be orthogonal if $(\mathbf{x}, \mathbf{y}) = 0$.*

69. Theorem. *If $\mathbf{x}_1, \cdots, \mathbf{x}_n$ are n nonzero vectors in $E^{(n)}$, and if every pair of them are orthogonal, then $\mathbf{x}_1, \cdots, \mathbf{x}_n$ constitute a basis of $E^{(n)}$.*

Proof. Let $c_1\mathbf{x}_1 + \cdots + c_n\mathbf{x}_n = \mathbf{0}$. If we take the inner product of both sides with $\mathbf{x}_i$, we obtain $c_i||\mathbf{x}_i||^2 = 0$ or $c_i = 0$ for all i.

70. Definition. *Vectors $\mathbf{x}_1, \cdots, \mathbf{x}_n$ in $E^{(n)}$ are said to form an orthonormal basis of $E^{(n)}$ if $||\mathbf{x}_k|| = 1$, $k = 1, \cdots, n$, and if $(\mathbf{x}_i, \mathbf{x}_j) = 0$ for $i \neq j$.*

71. Theorem. (Gram-Schmidt Orthogonalization Process.) *Let $\mathbf{y}_1, \cdots, \mathbf{y}_n$ be a basis of $E^{(n)}$. Then an orthonormal basis $\mathbf{x}_1, \cdots, \mathbf{x}_n$ can be constructed, where each $\mathbf{x}_i$ is a linear combination of $\mathbf{y}_1, \cdots, \mathbf{y}_n$.*

Proof. Let us define

$$\mathbf{x}_1 = \frac{1}{||\mathbf{y}_1||} \mathbf{y}_1,$$

$$\mathbf{x}_2 = \frac{1}{||\mathbf{y}_2 - (\mathbf{x}_1, \mathbf{y}_2)\mathbf{x}_1||} (\mathbf{y}_2 - (\mathbf{x}_1, \mathbf{y}_2)\mathbf{x}_1),$$

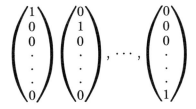

$$\mathbf{x}_3 = \frac{1}{\|\mathbf{y}_3 - \sum_{k=1}^{2} (\mathbf{x}_k, \mathbf{y}_3)\mathbf{x}_k\|} \left(\mathbf{y}_3 - \sum_{k=1}^{2} (\mathbf{x}_k, \mathbf{y}_3)\mathbf{x}_k\right),$$

$$\vdots$$

$$\mathbf{x}_n = \frac{1}{\|\mathbf{y}_n - \sum_{k=1}^{n-1} (\mathbf{x}_k, \mathbf{y}_n)\mathbf{x}_k\|} \left(\mathbf{y}_n - \sum_{k=1}^{n-1} (\mathbf{x}_k, \mathbf{y}_n)\mathbf{x}_k\right).$$

The student can easily verify that $\mathbf{x}_1, \cdots, \mathbf{x}_n$ form an orthonormal basis of $E^{(n)}$.

72. Definition. *Let A be an $n \times n$ matrix. The determinant $|A - \lambda I|$, where λ is any real or complex number, is called the characteristic polynomial (in λ) of the matrix A. The solutions (or roots) of $|A - \lambda I| = 0$ are called the characteristic roots of A.*

73. Theorem. *A matrix of order n has n characteristic roots (which are not necessarily distinct and are real or complex).*

Proof. This is an immediate consequence of the fundamental theorem of algebra.

74. Theorem. *If A is a symmetric $n \times n$ matrix, its characteristic roots are real.*

Proof. Assume to the contrary that $a + ib$ is a characteristic root of A, where $b \neq 0$. Then $a - ib$ is a characteristic root also. Hence $A - (a + ib)I$ and $A - (a - ib)I$ and their product, $B = (A - (a + ib)I)(A - (a - ib)I)$, are singular matrices. One easily computes that $B = (A - aI)^2 + b^2I$. The student can easily show that there exists a nonzero n-dimensional vector $\mathbf{x}$ such that $B\mathbf{x} = \mathbf{0}$, and consequently $\mathbf{x}'B\mathbf{x} = 0$. If we let $\mathbf{y} = (A - aI)\mathbf{x}$, then $0 = \mathbf{x}'B\mathbf{x} = \mathbf{y}'\mathbf{y} + b^2\mathbf{x}'\mathbf{x}$. But $\mathbf{x}'\mathbf{x} > 0$ and $\mathbf{y}'\mathbf{y} \geqq 0$, and hence it follows that $b = 0$ thus giving us the contradiction.

75. Definition. *An $n \times n$ matrix P is said to be an orthogonal matrix if $P'P = I$.*

76. Theorem. *Let P and Q be two orthogonal $n \times n$ matrices. Then*
(i) $P' = P^{-1}$,
(ii) $\|P\mathbf{x}\| = \|\mathbf{x}\|$ *for every* $\mathbf{x} \in E^{(n)}$,
(iii) $(P\mathbf{x}, P\mathbf{y}) = (\mathbf{x}, \mathbf{y})$ *for every* $\mathbf{x} \in E^{(n)}$, $\mathbf{y} \in E^{(n)}$,
(iv) *PQ is an orthogonal matrix,*
(v) *the columns of P form an orthonormal basis of $E^{(n)}$ (and so do the rows),*

(vi) *P' is an orthogonal matrix, and*

(vii) $|P| = \pm 1$.

Proof. Left to the student.

77. Lemma. *Let I be the $k \times k$ identity matrix, and let P be an $m \times m$ orthogonal matrix. Then the partitioned matrix*

$$\left(\begin{array}{c|c} I & 0 \\ \hline 0 & P \end{array}\right)$$

is an orthogonal matrix.

Proof. Left to the student.

78. Lemma. *Let A be an $n \times n$ matrix, and let P be an $n \times n$ orthogonal matrix. Then A and $P'AP$ have the same characteristic roots.*

Proof. This is a consequence of the following easily verified equation:

$$\begin{aligned} |P'AP - \lambda I| &= |P'(A - \lambda I)P| = |P'|\,|A - \lambda I|\,|P| \\ &= |A - \lambda I|. \end{aligned}$$

79. Theorem. *If A is a symmetric matrix, there exists an orthogonal matrix P such that $P'AP$ is a diagonal matrix (i.e., $P'AP = (c_{ij})$, where $c_{ij} = 0$ for $i \neq j$). All the elements in the main diagonal of $P'AP$ are characteristic roots of A.*

Proof. Let $\lambda_1, \lambda_2, \cdots, \lambda_n$ denote the n characteristic roots of A. Since $A - \lambda_1 I$ is singular there exists a vector $\mathbf{x}_1 \neq \mathbf{0}$ such that $(A - \lambda_1 I)\mathbf{x}_1 = \mathbf{0}$. We may assume that $||\mathbf{x}_1|| = 1$. Let S_1 denote an $n \times n$ orthogonal matrix whose first column is $\mathbf{x}_1$; such a matrix exists because of Theorems 65, 71, and 76(v). If we write S_1 as the partitioned matrix $S_1 = (\mathbf{x}_1|B)$, then $AS_1 = (A\mathbf{x}_1|AB) = (\lambda_1\mathbf{x}_1|AB)$. Theorem 76(v) and the fact that $S_1'AS_1$ is symmetric allows us to write $S_1'AS_1$ as the partitioned matrix

$$S_1'AS_1 = \left(\begin{array}{c} \mathbf{x}_1' \\ \hline B' \end{array}\right)(\lambda_1\mathbf{x}_1|AB) = \left(\begin{array}{c|c} \lambda_1 & 0 \\ \hline 0 & A_1 \end{array}\right)$$

where A_1 is a symmetric $(n - 1) \times (n - 1)$ matrix. By Lemma 78, $S_1'AS_1$ has the same characteristic roots that A has. From this it follows that the characteristic roots of A_1 are $\lambda_2, \cdots, \lambda_n$. In the same manner as above there exists an $(n - 1) \times (n - 1)$ orthogonal matrix P_2 such that

$$P_2'A_1P_2 = \left(\begin{array}{c|c} \lambda_2 & 0 \\ \hline 0 & A_2 \end{array}\right)$$

where A_2 is a symmetric $(n - 2) \times (n - 2)$ matrix. Let

$$S_2 = \left(\begin{array}{c|c} 1 & 0 \\ \hline 0 & P_2 \end{array}\right).$$

By Lemma 77, S_2 is an orthogonal matrix, and one easily obtains

$$S_2'S_1'AS_1S_2 = \left(\begin{array}{c|c|c} \lambda_1 & 0 & 0 \\ \hline 0 & \lambda_2 & 0 \\ \hline 0 & 0 & A_2 \end{array}\right).$$

Orthogonal matrices $S_3, S_4, \cdots, S_{n-1}$ are similarly defined. If we denote $P = S_1S_2 \cdots S_{n-1}$, then by Theorem 76(iv) we finally obtain the conclusion of the theorem.

80. Definition. *Let A be an $n \times n$ symmetric matrix. The function Q defined over $E^{(n)}$ by $Q(\mathbf{x}') = \mathbf{x}'A\mathbf{x}$ is called a quadratic form.*

81. Definition. *A symmetric $n \times n$ matrix A is called positive definite if the quadratic form $Q(\mathbf{x}') = \mathbf{x}'A\mathbf{x} > 0$ for every nonnull vector $\mathbf{x} \in E^{(n)}$.*

82. Definition. *A symmetric $n \times n$ matrix A is called positive semidefinite if the quadratic form $Q(\mathbf{x}') = \mathbf{x}'A\mathbf{x} \geqq 0$ for every $\mathbf{x} \in E^{(n)}$, and if A is not positive definite.*

83. Theorem. *A symmetric matrix A is positive definite if and only if all its characteristic roots are positive.*

Proof. We first assume that A is positive definite and prove that all its characteristic roots are positive. By Theorem 79 there is an orthogonal matrix P such that $P'AP$ is a diagonal matrix whose characteristic roots are in the main diagonal. If at least one characteristic root, say λ_i, is not positive, then there is a nonnull vector $\mathbf{x}$ which has these properties: all of its coordinates except the ith are zeros, the ith coordinate is 1, and $\mathbf{x}'P'AP\mathbf{x} = \lambda_i \leqq 0$. Let $\mathbf{z} = P\mathbf{x}$. By Theorem 76(ii), $\mathbf{z}$ is a nonnull vector, and $\mathbf{z}'A\mathbf{z} = \mathbf{x}'P'AP\mathbf{x} = \lambda_i \leqq 0$, thus violating the hypothesis that A is positive definite. Hence all characteristic roots are positive. Conversely, suppose that all characteristic roots of A are positive. Let P be as above. If $\mathbf{x}$ is any nonnull vector, and if y_i is the ith component of the nonnull vector $P'\mathbf{x}$, then we have

$$\mathbf{x}'A\mathbf{x} = \mathbf{x}'P(P'AP)P'\mathbf{x} = \sum_{i=1}^{n} \lambda_i y_i^2 > 0,$$

which proves that A is positive definite.

84. Theorem. *A symmetric matrix A is positive semidefinite if and only if at least one characteristic root is zero and all nonzero characteristic roots are positive.*

Proof. Left to the student.

85. Theorem. *The determinant of a symmetric matrix A equals the product of its characteristic roots.*

Proof. Left to the student.

86. Theorem. *Let A be an $n \times n$ symmetric matrix. If A is positive definite, then rank $(A) = n$. If A is positive semidefinite, then rank $(A) < n$.*

Proof. Left to the student.

87. Theorem. *If A is an $n \times n$ symmetric matrix which is positive definite, then there exists a nonsingular $n \times n$ symmetric matrix $A^{1/2}$ such that $A^{1/2} A^{1/2} = A$.*

Proof. By Theorem 79 there is an orthogonal matrix P such that $P'AP = (d_{ij})$, where $d_{ij} = \lambda_i \delta_{ij}$ and $\lambda_1, \cdots, \lambda_n$ are the characteristic roots of A. By Theorem 83, every $\lambda_i > 0$. Let $C = (c_{ij})$, where $c_{ij} = \sqrt{\lambda_i}\delta_{ij}$, i.e., $C^2 = P'AP$, and let $A^{1/2} = PCP'$. It is easy to see that $A^{1/2}$ is symmetric, and $A^{1/2}A^{1/2} = A$.

CHAPTER **10**

The Multivariate Normal Distribution

10.1 The Multivariate Normal Density

Thus far, whenever we have considered several random variables where each has a normal distribution, we have always considered them to be independent. In this case their joint density is simply the product of individual densities. However, it sometimes occurs that one is confronted with a situation in which there are n normally distributed random variables which are not independent. Since their joint density in this case is not the product of individual (or marginal) densities, the problem arises of obtaining a suitable definition of what one might call a multivariate normal distribution. The purpose of this section is to give a definition of the multivariate normal distribution and to derive a density for it.

Definition. *The n random variables $X_1, \cdots, X_n$ are said to be jointly normal or are said to have a multivariate normal distribution if there exist n independent random variables $Z_1, \cdots, Z_n$, each having a $N(0, 1)$ distribution, and if there exist n constants $\mu_1, \cdots, \mu_n$ and a nonsingular $n \times n$ matrix $A = (a_{ij})$ such that*

$$\begin{pmatrix} X_1 \\ \cdot \\ \cdot \\ \cdot \\ X_n \end{pmatrix} = \begin{pmatrix} a_{11} & \cdots & a_{1n} \\ \cdot & & \cdot \\ \cdot & & \cdot \\ \cdot & & \cdot \\ a_{n1} & \cdots & a_{nn} \end{pmatrix} \begin{pmatrix} Z_1 \\ \cdot \\ \cdot \\ \cdot \\ Z_n \end{pmatrix} + \begin{pmatrix} \mu_1 \\ \cdot \\ \cdot \\ \cdot \\ \mu_n \end{pmatrix}.$$

The above matrix equation involving random variables and real numbers will usually be written as

$$\mathbf{X} = A\mathbf{Z} + \boldsymbol{\mu}.$$

In general, an $n \times 1$ matrix of random variables $X_1, \cdots, X_n$ will be written $\mathbf{X}$, and, as in the previous chapter, a boldface lower case letter will denote a vector in $E^{(n)}$.

We now derive a joint probability density,

$$f_{\mathbf{X}'}(\mathbf{x}') = f_{X_1, \cdots, X_n}(x_1, \cdots, x_n),$$

of the random variables $\mathbf{X}' = (X_1, \cdots, X_n)$, which have a joint normal distribution in accordance with the above definition. From the above definition,

$$f_{\mathbf{Z}'}(\mathbf{z}') = (2\pi)^{-n/2} e^{-\frac{1}{2}\mathbf{z}'\mathbf{z}}.$$

We consider the transformation

$$\mathbf{z} = A^{-1}(\mathbf{x} - \boldsymbol{\mu}).$$

If one denotes $A^{-1} = (b_{ij})$, then it is easy to verify that $\partial z_i/\partial x_j = b_{ij}$. Thus the Jacobian of the transformation is the absolute value of the determinant $|A^{-1}|$, and

$$\begin{aligned} f_{\mathbf{X}'}(\mathbf{x}') &= f_{\mathbf{Z}'}(\mathbf{z}') \left|\frac{\partial \mathbf{z}'}{\partial \mathbf{x}'}\right| \\ &= (2\pi)^{-n/2} \exp\left(-\tfrac{1}{2}(\mathbf{x} - \boldsymbol{\mu})'(A^{-1})'A^{-1}(\mathbf{x} - \boldsymbol{\mu})\right) \big| |A^{-1}| \big|. \end{aligned}$$

Let us define the matrix C by $C = AA'$. Since $(A')^{-1} = (A^{-1})'$, we have

$$C^{-1} = (AA')^{-1} = (A')^{-1}A^{-1} = (A^{-1})'A^{-1},$$

and $|C^{-1}| = |(A^{-1})'|\,|A^{-1}| = |A^{-1}|^2$. Thus,

$$\big| |A^{-1}| \big| = \sqrt{|C^{-1}|}.$$

We now have

$$f_{\mathbf{X}'}(\mathbf{x}') = \frac{\sqrt{|C^{-1}|}}{(2\pi)^{n/2}} \exp\left(-\tfrac{1}{2}(\mathbf{x} - \boldsymbol{\mu})'C^{-1}(\mathbf{x} - \boldsymbol{\mu})\right).$$

The problem of determining the vector $\boldsymbol{\mu}$ and the matrix C remains. First we need an easy lemma.

1. Lemma. *The matrix C^{-1} is symmetric and positive definite.*

Proof. The matrix C^{-1} is symmetric since

$$(C^{-1})' = ((AA')^{-1})' = ((AA')')^{-1} = (AA')^{-1} = C^{-1}.$$

It is a positive definite matrix since

$$\mathbf{x}'C^{-1}\mathbf{x} = \mathbf{x}'(A^{-1})'A^{-1}\mathbf{x} = (A^{-1}\mathbf{x})'(A^{-1}\mathbf{x}) > 0$$

if $\mathbf{x} \neq \mathbf{0}$.

Definition. *If $U = (U_{ij})$ is a matrix of random variables, then EU will denote the matrix of expectations (EU_{ij}). Also, if $G(x) = (g_{ij}(x))$ is a matrix of functions defined over some interval $[a, b]$, then the integral $\int_a^b G(x)\,dx$ will denote the matrix of integrals $\left(\int_a^b g_{ij}(x)\,dx\right)$. In addition, we shall write $d\mathbf{x}'$ instead of $dx_1\,dx_2 \cdots dx_n$ in our integrals.*

From the two definitions already given in this section, it is easy to verify that $E\mathbf{X} = \boldsymbol{\mu}$, i.e., $EX_i = \mu_i$ for $1 \leqq i \leqq n$.

Let C_0 denote the covariance matrix of $\mathbf{X}$, i.e., $C_0 = (\text{Cov}(X_i, X_j))$. Then one may write

$$\begin{aligned} C_0 &= E((\mathbf{X} - \boldsymbol{\mu})(\mathbf{X} - \boldsymbol{\mu})') \\ &= \int_{-\infty}^{\infty} \cdots \int_{-\infty}^{\infty} (\mathbf{x} - \boldsymbol{\mu})(\mathbf{x} - \boldsymbol{\mu})' f_{\mathbf{X}'}(\mathbf{x}')\, d\mathbf{x}' \\ &= \frac{\sqrt{|C^{-1}|}}{(2\pi)^{n/2}} \int_{-\infty}^{\infty} \cdots \int_{-\infty}^{\infty} (\mathbf{x} - \boldsymbol{\mu})(\mathbf{x} - \boldsymbol{\mu})' \exp\left(-\tfrac{1}{2}(\mathbf{x} - \boldsymbol{\mu})' C^{-1}(\mathbf{x} - \boldsymbol{\mu})\right) d\mathbf{x}'. \end{aligned}$$

Let A be as above, and consider the transformation $\mathbf{x} = A\mathbf{z} + \boldsymbol{\mu}$. The absolute value of the Jacobian of the transformation is

$$\left|\frac{\partial \mathbf{x}'}{\partial \mathbf{z}'}\right| = \big||A|\big| = \sqrt{|C|}.$$

Thus in making a change of variable in the above multiple integral we obtain

$$\begin{aligned} C_0 &= \frac{\sqrt{|C^{-1}|}}{(2\pi)^{n/2}} \int_{-\infty}^{\infty} \cdots \int_{-\infty}^{\infty} A\mathbf{z}\,\mathbf{z}' A' e^{-\frac{1}{2}\mathbf{z}'\mathbf{z}} \sqrt{|C|}\, d\mathbf{z}' \\ &= A(2\pi)^{-n/2} \int_{-\infty}^{\infty} \cdots \int_{-\infty}^{\infty} \mathbf{z}\,\mathbf{z}' e^{-\frac{1}{2}\mathbf{z}'\mathbf{z}}\, d\mathbf{z}' A'. \end{aligned}$$

It is not at all difficult to verify that

$$(2\pi)^{-n/2} \int_{-\infty}^{\infty} \cdots \int_{-\infty}^{\infty} \mathbf{z}\,\mathbf{z}' e^{-\frac{1}{2}\mathbf{z}'\mathbf{z}}\, d\mathbf{z}' = I,$$

the $n \times n$ identity matrix. Consequently,

$$C_0 = AIA' = AA' = C.$$

With this we have concluded the proof of the following theorem.

2. Theorem. *If $X_1, X_2, \cdots, X_n$ have a joint normal distribution, then*

$$f_{\mathbf{X}'}(\mathbf{x}') = \frac{\sqrt{|C^{-1}|}}{(2\pi)^{n/2}} \exp -\tfrac{1}{2}(\mathbf{x} - \boldsymbol{\mu})' C^{-1}(\mathbf{x} - \boldsymbol{\mu}),$$

where $\boldsymbol{\mu} = E\mathbf{X}$ and C is the covariance matrix.

EXERCISES

1. In the transformation $\mathbf{z} = B\mathbf{x}$, where B is an $n \times n$ matrix, prove that

$$\left|\frac{\partial(z_1, \cdots, z_n)}{\partial(x_1, \cdots, x_n)}\right| = \big||B|\big|.$$

2. Prove: If A is an $n \times n$ nonsingular matrix, then $(A')^{-1} = (A^{-1})'$.

3. In the first definition in this section, prove that $EX_i = \mu_i$, $1 \leqq i \leqq n$.

4. Prove that

$$(2\pi)^{-n/2} \int_{-\infty}^{\infty} \cdots \int_{-\infty}^{\infty} \mathbf{z}\,\mathbf{z}' e^{-\frac{1}{2}\mathbf{z}'\mathbf{z}}\, d\mathbf{z}' = I,$$

the $n \times n$ identity matrix.

5. Give at least two proofs of the following: If A is a positive definite symmetric matrix, then so is A^{-1}.

6. Prove: If A is a nonsingular $n \times n$ matrix, and if $\mathbf{x} \in E^{(n)}$, then $A\mathbf{x} \neq \mathbf{0}$ if and only if $\mathbf{x} \neq \mathbf{0}$.

7. Prove that the covariance matrix C of a multivariate normal distribution is symmetric and positive definite.

8. Prove: If $X_1, \cdots, X_n$ have a joint normal distribution, and if D is a nonsingular $n \times n$ matrix, then $\mathbf{U} = D\mathbf{X}$ has a joint normal distribution.

9. Let $\{k_1, k_2, \cdots, k_n\}$ be a permutation of the integers $\{1, 2, \cdots, n\}$. Let $\mathbf{x} \in E^{(n)}$ and $\mathbf{y} \in E^{(n)}$ be such that

$$\mathbf{x} = \begin{pmatrix} a_1 \\ a_2 \\ \cdot \\ \cdot \\ \cdot \\ a_n \end{pmatrix} \quad \text{and} \quad \mathbf{y} = \begin{pmatrix} a_{k_1} \\ a_{k_2} \\ \cdot \\ \cdot \\ \cdot \\ a_{k_n} \end{pmatrix}.$$

Determine the $n \times n$ matrix A for which $\mathbf{y} = A\mathbf{x}$ and evaluate its determinant.

10. Prove: If $X_1, \cdots, X_n$ are multivariate normal, and if $\{k_1, \cdots, k_n\}$ is a permutation of the integers $\{1, 2, \cdots, n\}$, then $X_{k_1}, X_{k_2}, \cdots, X_{k_n}$ are also multivariate normal.

10.2 Properties of the Multivariate Normal Distribution

We begin this section by proving the converse to Theorem 2 in Section 10.1. Before doing so, it must be remarked that the statement of this particular theorem is usually given in most textbooks as the definition of the multivariate normal distribution, except that C^{-1} is only assumed to be some positive definite symmetric matrix and $\sqrt{|C^{-1}|}/(2\pi)^{n/2}$ is assumed to be some positive constant.

1. Theorem. *If* $\mathbf{X}' = (X_1, \cdots, X_n)$ *are* n *random variables with a joint absolutely continuous distribution with density*

$$f_{\mathbf{X}'}(\mathbf{x}') = Ke^{-\frac{1}{2}(\mathbf{x}'-\boldsymbol{\mu}')A(\mathbf{x}-\boldsymbol{\mu})},$$

where $-\infty < x_i < \infty$ *for all* i, *where* $\boldsymbol{\mu}$ *is a vector of constants,* $K > 0$ *is some constant, and* A *is a positive definite matrix, then the distribution of* $\mathbf{X}'$ *is multivariate normal.*

Proof. By Theorem 87 in Chapter 9, there exists a nonsingular symmetric $n \times n$ matrix $A^{1/2}$ such that $A^{1/2}A^{1/2} = A$. Let $\mathbf{Y}$ be a vector of n random variables defined by $\mathbf{Y} = A^{1/2}(\mathbf{X} - \boldsymbol{\mu})$. We note that $\mathbf{X} = (A^{1/2})^{-1}\mathbf{Y} + \boldsymbol{\mu}$, and the proof will be accomplished by showing that $Y_1, \cdots, Y_n$ are independent, each having a $N(0, 1)$ distribution. The Jacobian of the transformation $\mathbf{x} = (A^{1/2})^{-1}\mathbf{y} + \boldsymbol{\mu}$ is seen to be $1/\sqrt{|A|}$. Hence

$$f_{\mathbf{Y}'}(\mathbf{y}') = (K/\sqrt{|A|})e^{-\frac{1}{2}\mathbf{y}'\mathbf{y}}.$$

Since this last expression is a density, its integral is

$$(K/\sqrt{|A|}) \int_{-\infty}^{\infty} \cdots \int_{-\infty}^{\infty} e^{-\frac{1}{2}\mathbf{y}'\mathbf{y}}\, d\mathbf{y} = 1.$$

One can easily prove that $K = \sqrt{|A|}(2\pi)^{-n/2}$. Hence $Y_1, \cdots, Y_n$ are independent $N(0, 1)$ random variables, and the theorem is proved.

The next question that arises is whether every subset of a set of jointly normal random variables is also jointly normal. This question is answered with the following lemma and theorem.

2. Lemma. *Let C be the covariance matrix of n jointly normal random variables, and let C be partitioned as follows:*

$$C = \left(\begin{array}{c|c} C_{11} & C_{12} \\ \hline C_{21} & C_{22} \end{array}\right),$$

where C_{11} is a $k \times k$ submatrix, $1 \leqq k < n$. Then C_{11} is nonsingular, symmetric, and positive definite.

Proof. We first prove that C_{11} is nonsingular. Suppose to the contrary that $|C_{11}| = 0$. Then there exist constants $c_1, \cdots, c_k$, not all zero, such that the corresponding linear combination of the columns is zero. Let us define the $n \times 1$ matrix $\mathbf{z}$ by

$$\mathbf{z} = \begin{pmatrix} c_1 \\ c_2 \\ \cdot \\ \cdot \\ \cdot \\ c_k \\ 0 \\ \cdot \\ \cdot \\ \cdot \\ 0 \end{pmatrix}.$$

Then clearly the first k rows of $C\mathbf{z}$ are zeros, and $\mathbf{z}'C\mathbf{z} = 0$, thus contradicting the fact that C is positive definite (which we know because of

Lemma 1 in Section 10.1 and problem 5 in Section 10.1). Hence C_{11} is nonsingular. It is not difficult to see that C_{11} is symmetric. We now prove that C_{11} is positive definite. By Lemma 1 in Section 10.1 and exercise 5 of Section 10.1, C is positive definite. Let $\mathbf{x} \in E^{(k)}$, $\mathbf{x} \neq \mathbf{0}$, and let $\mathbf{y} \in E^{(n)}$ be defined by the partitioned matrix

$$\mathbf{y} = \left(\frac{\mathbf{x}}{\mathbf{0}}\right).$$

Then $\mathbf{y} \neq \mathbf{0}$, and

$$\begin{aligned} 0 < \mathbf{y}'C\mathbf{y} &= (\mathbf{x}'|\mathbf{0}) \left(\begin{array}{c|c} C_{11} & C_{12} \\ \hline C_{21} & C_{22} \end{array}\right) \left(\frac{\mathbf{x}}{\mathbf{0}}\right) \\ &= (\mathbf{x}'C_{11}|\mathbf{x}'C_{12}) \left(\frac{\mathbf{x}}{\mathbf{0}}\right) = \mathbf{x}'C_{11}\mathbf{x}, \end{aligned}$$

which establishes that C_{11} is positive definite and thus concludes the proof of the lemma.

We are now able to prove the theorem which asserts that every marginal distribution of a multivariate normal distribution is also multivariate normal.

3. Theorem. *If the random variables $X_1, X_2, \cdots, X_n$ have a multivariate normal distribution, then any subset of them also has a multivariate normal distribution.*

Proof. Let k be any fixed integer such that $1 \leqq k < n$. Because of problem 10 in Section 10.1, it is sufficient to prove that $X_1, \cdots, X_k$ are multivariate normal.

By Lemma 1 in Section 10.1 and exercise 5 in Section 10.1, the covariance matrix C is positive definite. Let us partition C as was done in Lemma 2:

$$C = \left(\begin{array}{c|c} C_{11} & C_{12} \\ \hline C_{21} & C_{22} \end{array}\right),$$

where C_{11} is a $k \times k$ submatrix. By Lemma 1, C_{11} is nonsingular. Let B denote the $k \times n$ partitioned matrix

$$B = (I|0),$$

let A_1 denote the $(n - k) \times k$ matrix

$$A_1 = (C_{11}^{-1}(-C_{12}))',$$

and let A_2 denote the $(n - k) \times n$ partitioned matrix

$$A_2 = (A_1|I).$$

Then

$$\left(\frac{B}{A_2}\right) C(B'|A_2') = \left(\frac{I}{(C_{11}^{-1}(-C_{12}))'}\middle|\frac{0}{I}\right)\left(\frac{C_{11}}{C_{21}}\middle|\frac{C_{12}}{C_{22}}\right)\left(\frac{I}{0}\middle|\frac{C_{11}^{-1}(-C_{12})}{I}\right)$$

$$= \left(\frac{C_{11}}{0}\middle|\frac{C_{12}}{-C_{21}C_{11}^{-1}C_{12}+C_{22}}\right)\left(\frac{I}{0}\middle|\frac{C_{11}^{-1}(-C_{12})}{I}\right)$$

$$= \left(\frac{C_{11}}{0}\middle|\frac{0}{C_{22}-C_{21}C_{11}^{-1}C_{12}}\right) = \left(\frac{C_{11}}{0}\middle|\frac{0}{D}\right),$$

where $D = C_{22} - C_{21}C_{11}^{-1}C_{12}$ is an $(n-k) \times (n-k)$ symmetric nonsingular positive definite matrix. We now consider the vectors

$$\mathbf{u} = \begin{pmatrix} u_1 \\ \cdot \\ \cdot \\ \cdot \\ u_k \end{pmatrix}, \quad \mathbf{v} = \begin{pmatrix} v_1 \\ \cdot \\ \cdot \\ \cdot \\ v_{n-k} \end{pmatrix},$$

and the transformation

$$\left(\frac{\mathbf{u}}{\mathbf{v}}\right) = \left(\frac{B}{A_2}\right)(\mathbf{x} - \boldsymbol{\mu})$$

or

$$\mathbf{x} = \left(\frac{B}{A_2}\right)^{-1}\left(\frac{\mathbf{u}}{\mathbf{v}}\right) + \boldsymbol{\mu}.$$

The Jacobian of the transformation is

$$\frac{\partial(\mathbf{x}')}{\partial(\mathbf{u}'|\mathbf{v}')} = 1 \quad \text{since} \quad \left|\left(\frac{B}{A_2}\right)\right| = 1.$$

But

$$(\mathbf{x}' - \boldsymbol{\mu}')C^{-1}(\mathbf{x} - \boldsymbol{\mu}) = (\mathbf{u}'|\mathbf{v}')(B'|A_2')^{-1}C^{-1}\left(\frac{B}{A_2}\right)^{-1}\left(\frac{\mathbf{u}}{\mathbf{v}}\right)$$

$$= (\mathbf{u}'|\mathbf{v}')\left(\left(\frac{B}{A_2}\right)C(B'|A_2')\right)^{-1}\left(\frac{\mathbf{u}}{\mathbf{v}}\right)$$

$$= (\mathbf{u}'|\mathbf{v}')\left(\frac{C_{11}^{-1}}{0}\middle|\frac{0}{D^{-1}}\right)\left(\frac{\mathbf{u}}{\mathbf{v}}\right)$$

$$= \mathbf{u}'C_{11}^{-1}\mathbf{u} + \mathbf{v}'D^{-1}\mathbf{v}.$$

Since the determinant

$$\left|\left(\frac{B}{A_2}\right)\right| = 1,$$

it follows that $|C^{-1}| = |C_{11}^{-1}|\,|D^{-1}|$. Consequently, if we denote

$$\mathbf{U} = \begin{pmatrix} X_1 - \mu_1 \\ \cdot \\ \cdot \\ \cdot \\ X_k - \mu_k \end{pmatrix} \quad \text{and} \quad \mathbf{V} = A_2(\mathbf{X} - \boldsymbol{\mu}),$$

we obtain

$$f_{\mathbf{U}',\mathbf{V}'}(\mathbf{u}',\mathbf{v}') = \frac{\sqrt{|C_{11}^{-1}|}}{(2\pi)^{k/2}} \exp\left(-\tfrac{1}{2}\mathbf{u}'C_{11}^{-1}\mathbf{u}\right) \frac{\sqrt{|D^{-1}|}}{(2\pi)^{(n-k)/2}} \exp -\tfrac{1}{2}\mathbf{v}'D^{-1}\mathbf{v}.$$

The marginal distribution of $U' = (U_1, \cdots, U_k)$ is obtained by integrating out the v's above, and we obtain

$$f_{\mathbf{U}'}(\mathbf{u}') = \frac{\sqrt{|C_{11}^{-1}|}}{(2\pi)^{k/2}} \exp -\tfrac{1}{2}\mathbf{u}'C_{11}\mathbf{u}.$$

Thus, the joint distribution of $X_1, \cdots, X_k$ has a density

$$f_{X_1, \cdots, X_k}(\mathbf{w}') = \frac{\sqrt{C_{11}^{-1}}}{(2\pi)^{k/2}} \exp -\tfrac{1}{2}(\mathbf{w}' - \boldsymbol{\nu}')C_{11}(\mathbf{w} - \boldsymbol{\nu})$$

where

$$\mathbf{w} = \begin{pmatrix} w_1 \\ \cdot \\ \cdot \\ \cdot \\ w_k \end{pmatrix} \quad \text{and} \quad \boldsymbol{\nu} = \begin{pmatrix} \mu_1 \\ \cdot \\ \cdot \\ \cdot \\ \mu_k \end{pmatrix}.$$

This completes the proof.

It should be pointed out that it is possible that each of n random variables $X_1, \cdots, X_n$ has a normal distribution and yet, together, they do not have a joint normal distribution. As an example, for $n = 2$ consider the random variables X and Y which have a joint absolutely continuous distribution with a density

$$f_{X,Y}(x, y) = \begin{cases} (1/\pi) \exp -\tfrac{1}{2}(x^2 + y^2) & \text{if } \; x < 0, \quad y \geqq 0 \\ & \text{or } \; x \geqq 0, \quad y < 0 \\ 0 & \text{otherwise.} \end{cases}$$

It is easy to verify these facts about X and Y: each of X and Y has a $N(0, 1)$ distribution, X and Y are not independent, and (X, Y) are not multivariate normal.

EXERCISES

1. Prove: If A is a positive definite symmetric matrix, then

$$|(A^{1/2})^{-1}| = |(A^{-1})^{1/2}| = 1/\sqrt{|A|}.$$

2. Prove: If $\mathbf{y} \in E^{(n)}$, then

$$\int_{-\infty}^{\infty} \cdots \int_{-\infty}^{\infty} e^{-\frac{1}{2}\mathbf{y}'\mathbf{y}}\, d\mathbf{y} = (2\pi)^{n/2}.$$

3. Prove: If $X_1, \cdots, X_n$ are multivariate normal, and if not all the constants $c_1, \cdots, c_n$ are zeros, then the random variable $c_1X_1 + \cdots + c_nX_n$ has a normal distribution.

4. Solve problem 1 in Section 6.2 using the methods you have learned so far in this chapter.

5. Prove the assertion made in the second sentence of the proof of Theorem 3.

6. In the proof of Theorem 3, prove that $D = C_{22} - C_{21}C_{11}^{-1}C_{12}$ is a symmetric positive definite $(n - k) \times (n - k)$ matrix.

7. Let X and Y be two random variables with a joint absolutely continuous distribution with a density

$$f_{X,Y}(x, y) = \begin{cases} (1/\pi) \exp -\frac{1}{2}(x^2 + y^2) & \text{if } \quad x > 0 \quad \text{and} \quad y \leqq 0 \\ & \text{or } \quad x \leqq 0 \quad \text{and} \quad y > 0, \\ 0 & \text{otherwise.} \end{cases}$$

(a) Prove that $\int_{-\infty}^{\infty} \int_{-\infty}^{\infty} f_{X,Y}(x, y)\, dxdy = 1$.
(b) Find the marginal density $f_X(x)$.
(c) Find the marginal density $f_Y(y)$.
(d) Compute $P([X \leqq 0][Y \leqq 0])$ using $f_{X,Y}(x, y)$.
(e) Compute $P[X \leqq 0]$ using $f_X(x)$.
(f) Compute $P[Y \leqq 0]$ using $f_Y(y)$.
(g) Are X and Y independent?
(h) Are X and Y multivariate normal?
(i) Are X and Y each normal?
(j) What do the answers to questions 7(a)–7(i) imply?

8. Prove: If $X_1, \cdots, X_n$ are multivariate normal, then each X_i has a normal distribution.

9. Prove that if D is a nonsingular diagonal matrix, then D^{-1} is a diagonal matrix.

10. Prove: If $X_1, \cdots, X_n$ are multivariate normal with expectation vector $\boldsymbol{\mu}$ and covariance matrix C, then they are independent if and only if C is a diagonal matrix. (*Hint:* use Theorem 2 in Section 5.1.)

10.3 Cochran's Theorem

This section is devoted to a proof of Cochran's theorem. This theorem is of extreme importance in that part of statistical inference known as analysis of variance. An application of this sort will be given in Chapter 12. We begin this section with an important and very interesting theorem in matrix theory.

1. Theorem. *If $B_0, B_1, \cdots, B_k$ are $k + 1$ $n \times n$ symmetric matrices, if $n = r_0 + r_1 + \cdots + r_k$, where $r_i = \text{rank}\, B_i$, and if $B_0 + B_1 + \cdots + B_k = I$, the $n \times n$ identity matrix, then there exists an orthogonal matrix P such that, for every i, $P'B_iP$ is a diagonal matrix whose nonzero diagonal elements are 1's.*

Proof. Part of the proof given here is due to Herman Rubin. By Theorem 79 in Chapter 9 there exists an orthogonal matrix P_0 such that $P_0'B_0P_0$ is diagonal. Let $A_i = P_0'B_iP_0$ for $i = 0, 1, \cdots, k$. Then $I - A_0 =$

$A_1 + \cdots + A_k$. We prove first that the nonzero diagonal elements of A_0 are 1's. Let p denote that number of the r_0 nonzero elements of A_0 which are not 1. Then by Theorem 61 of Chapter 9,

$$\begin{aligned}\text{rank}\,(I - A_0) &= n - r_0 + p = \text{rank}\,(A_1 + \cdots + A_k)\\ &\leqq r_1 + r_2 + \cdots + r_k = n - r_0.\end{aligned}$$

This implies that $p = 0$ and in addition

$$\text{rank}\,(I - A_0) = \text{rank}\,(A_1 + \cdots + A_k) = r_1 + \cdots + r_k.$$

Without loss of generality we may assume that these r_0 1's of A_0 occupy the first r_0 places along the main diagonal (starting from the upper left-hand corner). We now prove that for every i, $1 \leqq i \leqq k$, all first r_0 columns of A_i consist entirely of zeros, and consequently by symmetry, all first r_0 rows do also. We first note that

$$\sum_{i=1}^{k} A_i = \left(\begin{array}{c|c} 0 & 0 \\ \hline 0 & I_0 \end{array}\right),$$

where I_0 is the $(n - r_0) \times (n - r_0)$ identity matrix. We next define the linear subspace S of $E^{(n)}$ by

$$S = \{\mathbf{x} \in E^{(n)} | A_i\mathbf{x} = \mathbf{0},\ 1 \leqq i \leqq k\} = \{\mathbf{x} \in E^{(n)} | C\mathbf{x} = \mathbf{0}\},$$

where C is a $kn \times n$ partitioned matrix written as

$$C = \begin{pmatrix} A_1 \\ \hline A_2 \\ \hline \cdot \\ \cdot \\ \cdot \\ \hline A_k \end{pmatrix}.$$

Since rank $C \leqq r_1 + \cdots + r_k = n - r_0$, then by Theorem 59 in Chapter 9,

$$\text{dimension of } S = n - \text{rank}\, C \geqq r_0.$$

We also define the linear subspace T of $E^{(n)}$ by

$$T = \{\mathbf{x} | (A_1 + \cdots + A_k)\mathbf{x} = \mathbf{0}\}.$$

Clearly $T \supset S$. However, by Theorem 59 in Chapter 9,

$$\text{dimension of } T = n - \text{rank}\,(A_1 + \cdots + A_k) = r_0 \leqq \text{dimension of } S.$$

Using Theorem 54 of Chapter 9 we obtain $S = T$. From this we see that a basis of T is a basis of S. But a basis of T is easily seen to be $\mathbf{x}_1, \cdots, \mathbf{x}_{r_0}$, where $\mathbf{x}_i$ is composed entirely of zeros except for a 1 in the ith place. Hence $A_i\mathbf{x}_j = 0$ for all i and j for which $1 \leqq i \leqq k$ and $1 \leqq j \leqq r_0$, from which it follows that the first r_0 columns of each A_i are composed entirely of zeros. Thus we may write

$$A_i = \left(\begin{array}{c|c} 0 & 0 \\ \hline 0 & A_{1i} \end{array}\right), \quad 1 \leq i \leq k,$$

where A_{1i} is an $(n - r_0) \times (n - r_0)$ symmetric matrix, and $I_0 = A_{11} + \cdots + A_{1k}$. Again, by Theorem 79 in Chapter 9 there exists an $(n - r_0) \times (n - r_0)$ orthogonal matrix P_{11} such that $P'_{11}A_{11}P_{11}$ is a diagonal matrix. Let P_1 be the $n \times n$ orthogonal matrix defined by

$$P_1 = \left(\begin{array}{c|c} I_1 & 0 \\ \hline 0 & P_{11} \end{array}\right),$$

where I_1 is the $r_0 \times r_0$ identity matrix. Then easily $P'_1A_1P_1$ is a diagonal matrix with nonzero diagonal elements occurring after the r_0th place. Since $P'_1(I - A_0)P_1 = I - A_0$, we have

$$I - A_0 - P'_1A_1P_1 = P'_1A_2P_1 + \cdots + P'_1A_kP_1.$$

By using the same method as before we can prove that the nonzero diagonal elements of $P'_1A_1P_1$ are 1's, and, assuming that these 1's are in a block immediately below those of A_0, one can prove in exactly the same manner as before that the first $r_0 + r_1$ columns (and hence rows) of $P'_1A_iP_1$ for $i = 2, \cdots, k$ are composed entirely of zeros. Continuing in this manner, orthogonal matrices $P_0, P_1, \cdots, P_{k-1}$ are defined. The desired orthogonal matrix P is easily seen to be $P = P_0P_1 \cdots P_{k-1}$, and the theorem is proved.

We shall need the following theorem in order to prove Cochran's theorem.

2. Theorem. *If $\mathbf{X}' = (X_1, \cdots, X_n)$ are n independent random variables, each having a $N(0, 1)$ distribution, if P is an orthogonal matrix, and if $\mathbf{Y}' = (Y_1, \cdots, Y_n)$ is such that $\mathbf{Y} = P\mathbf{X}$, then $Y_1, \cdots, Y_n$ are also independent random variables, each having a $N(0, 1)$ distribution.*

Proof. A joint density of $\mathbf{X}'$ is given by

$$f_{\mathbf{X}'}(\mathbf{x}') = (2\pi)^{-n/2}e^{-\frac{1}{2}\mathbf{x}'\mathbf{x}}.$$

We consider the transformation $\mathbf{y} = P\mathbf{x}$. By Theorem 76 of Chapter 9 and exercise 1 in Section 10.1, the absolute value of the Jacobian is 1. Hence

$$\begin{aligned} f_{\mathbf{Y}'}(\mathbf{y}') &= (2\pi)^{-n/2}e^{-\frac{1}{2}\mathbf{y}'PP'\mathbf{y}} \\ &= (2\pi)^{-n/2}e^{-\frac{1}{2}\mathbf{y}'\mathbf{y}} \end{aligned}$$

which proves the assertion.

In what follows we shall always consider (as was stated in the definition) the matrix of a quadratic form to be symmetric. A quadratic form will be called positive definite or positive semidefinite if its matrix has this property. By the rank of a quadratic form we shall mean the rank of its matrix.

3. Theorem. (Cochran's Theorem.) *If $\mathbf{X}' = (X_1, \cdots, X_n)$ are n independent random variables, each having an $N(0, 1)$ distribution, if $Q_1(\mathbf{x}'), \cdots, Q_k(\mathbf{x}')$ are k quadratic forms defined over $E^{(n)}$ such that*

$$\mathbf{x}'\mathbf{x} = \sum_{j=1}^{k} Q_j(\mathbf{x}') \quad \text{for all} \quad \mathbf{x} \in E^{(n)},$$

and if $r_1 + r_2 + \cdots + r_k = n$, *where* $r_j = \text{rank } Q_j(\mathbf{x}')$, *then*

$$Q_1(\mathbf{X}'), \cdots, Q_k(\mathbf{X}')$$

are k independent random variables, and $Q_j(\mathbf{X}')$ *has a chi-square distribution with* r_j *degrees of freedom.*

Proof. Let A_j denote the $n \times n$ matrix associated with the quadratic form $Q_j(\mathbf{X}')$. Then we may write

$$\mathbf{X}'\mathbf{X} = \sum_{i=1}^{k} \mathbf{X}'A_i\mathbf{X} = \mathbf{X}'\left(\sum_{i=1}^{k} A_i\right)\mathbf{X}.$$

Hence $I = A_1 + \cdots + A_k$, and by Theorem 1 there exists an orthogonal matrix P such that, for every i, $P'A_iP$ is diagonal with 1's for nonzero diagonal elements. Since P' is also orthogonal, we know by Theorem 2 that $\mathbf{Y} = P'\mathbf{X}$ are n independent $N(0, 1)$ random variables. We thus obtain that $Q_j(\mathbf{X}') = \mathbf{Y}'(P'A_jP)\mathbf{Y}$ is a sum of r_j squares of independent $N(0, 1)$ random variables and consequently has the chi-square distribution with r_j degrees of freedom. Also, by Theorem 1, each quadratic form is a sum of squares of different Y_j's. By Lemma 6 in Section 7.5, $Y_1^2, Y_2^2, \cdots, Y_n^2$ are independent, and by Theorem 2 of Section 5.2 the random variables $Q_1(\mathbf{X}'), \cdots, Q_k(\mathbf{X}')$ are independent. This completes the proof.

EXERCISES

1. In the proof of Theorem 1, prove the assertion made there that "without loss of generality we may assume that these r_0 1's of A_0 occupy the first r_0 places along the main diagonal (starting from the upper left-hand corner)."

2. In the proof of Theorem 1, prove that

(i) $\bigcap_{i=1}^{k} \{\mathbf{x} \in E^{(n)} | A_i\mathbf{x} = \mathbf{0}\} = \{\mathbf{x} \in E^{(n)} | C\mathbf{x} = \mathbf{0}\}$,

and

(ii) S is a linear subspace of $E^{(n)}$.

3. In the proof of Theorem 1 prove that

(i) T is a linear subspace of $E^{(n)}$,

and

(ii) $T \supset S$.

4. In the proof of Theorem 1, prove that the vectors $\mathbf{x}_1, \cdots, \mathbf{x}_{r_0}$ form a basis of T.

5. Prove: Two random variables which are jointly normally distributed are independent if and only if their correlation coefficient is zero.

10.4 Proof of the Independence of the Sample Mean and Sample Variance for a Normal Population

Let $X_1, X_2, \cdots, X_n$ be n independent, identically distributed random variables whose common distribution is $N(\mu, \sigma^2)$. The purpose of this section is to prove that s_n^2 and $\overline{X}_n$ are independent and that $(n-1)s_n^2/\sigma^2$ has a chi-square distribution with $n-1$ degrees of freedom. We first need two rather straightforward lemmas.

1. Lemma. *If X and Y are independent random variables, and if $a, b, c,$ and d are constants, then $aX + b$ and $cY + d$ are also independent.*

Proof. We prove the lemma only in the case where $a > 0$ and $c > 0$. For $\alpha_1 < \beta_1$ and $\alpha_2 < \beta_2$, and because of the independence of X and Y,

$$\begin{aligned} P([\alpha_1 < aX + b \leqq \beta_1][\alpha_2 < cY + d \leqq \beta_2]) & \\ &= P\left(\left[\frac{\alpha_1 - b}{a} < X \leqq \frac{\beta_1 - b}{a}\right]\left[\frac{\alpha_2 - d}{c} < Y \leqq \frac{\beta_2 - d}{c}\right]\right) \\ &= P\left[\frac{\alpha_1 - b}{a} < X \leqq \frac{\beta_1 - b}{a}\right]P\left[\frac{\alpha_2 - d}{c} < Y \leqq \frac{\beta_2 - d}{c}\right] \\ &= P[\alpha_1 < aX + b \leqq \beta_1]P[\alpha_2 < cY + d \leqq \beta_2]. \end{aligned}$$

For other cases the proof is similar and is left to the student.

2. Lemma. *If $X_1, \cdots, X_n$ are independent random variables, then $X_1, X_2^2, X_3^2, \cdots, X_n^2$ are independent random variables.*

Proof. For any real β_1 and $0 \leqq \beta_2, \cdots, 0 \leqq \beta_n$ we have

$$\begin{aligned} P\left([X_1 \leqq \beta_1] \bigcap_{i=2}^{n} [X_i^2 \leqq \beta_i]\right) & \\ &= P\left([X_1 \leqq \beta_1] \bigcap_{i=2}^{n} [-\sqrt{\beta_i} \leqq X_i \leqq \sqrt{\beta_i}]\right) \\ &= P[X_1 \leqq \beta_1] \prod_{i=2}^{n} P[-\sqrt{\beta_i} \leqq X_i \leqq \sqrt{\beta_i}] \\ &= P[X_1 \leqq \beta_1] \prod_{i=2}^{n} P[X_i^2 \leqq \beta_i], \end{aligned}$$

which proves the lemma.

We are now ready to prove the main theorem of this section.

3. Theorem. *Let $X_1, X_2, \cdots, X_n$ be n independent observations on a random variable X whose distribution is $N(\mu, \sigma^2)$. Let $\overline{X}_n$ and s_n^2 be defined by*

$$\overline{X}_n = \frac{X_1 + \cdots + X_n}{n} \quad \text{and} \quad s_n^2 = \frac{1}{n-1} \sum_{k=1}^{n} (X_k - \overline{X}_n)^2.$$

Then $\overline{X}_n$ and s_n^2 are independent random variables, and the distribution of $(n-1)s_n^2/\sigma^2$ is chi-square with $n-1$ degrees of freedom.

Proof. By Lemma 1, if we can prove that $(\overline{X}_n - \mu)/\sigma$ and $(n-1)s_n^2/\sigma^2$ are independent, then we have obtained the independence of $\overline{X}_n$ and s_n^2. Let $Z_i = (X_i - \mu)/\sigma$. If we denote $\overline{Z}_n = (Z_1 + \cdots + Z_n)/n$, then one can easily verify that $(\overline{X}_n - \mu)/\sigma = \overline{Z}_n$, and

$$(n-1)s_n^2/\sigma^2 = \sum_{i=1}^n (Z_i - \overline{Z}_n)^2,$$

and each Z_i has an $N(0, 1)$ distribution. For any n-tuple of real numbers $\mathbf{z}' = (z_1, \cdots, z_n)$, (i.e., for any $\mathbf{z} \in E^{(n)}$), we have

$$\begin{aligned}\sum_{i=1}^n z_i^2 &= \sum_{i=1}^n ((z_i - \bar{z}_n) + \bar{z}_n)^2 \\ &= \sum_{i=1}^n (z_i - \bar{z}_n)^2 + n\bar{z}_n^2,\end{aligned}$$

a sum of two quadratic forms in $\mathbf{z}$, where $\bar{z}_n = (z_1 + \cdots + z_n)/n$. We may therefore write

$$\sum_{i=1}^n z_i^2 = \mathbf{z}'A\mathbf{z} + \mathbf{z}'B\mathbf{z}$$

where A and B are two $n \times n$ symmetric matrices for which

$$\mathbf{z}'A\mathbf{z} = \sum_{i=1}^n (z_i - \bar{z}_n)^2 \quad \text{and} \quad \mathbf{z}'B\mathbf{z} = n\bar{z}_n^2.$$

By Theorems 65, 71, and 76(v) in Chapter 9, there exists an $n \times n$ orthogonal matrix P whose first row is $(1/\sqrt{n}, 1/\sqrt{n}, \cdots, 1/\sqrt{n})$. Let $\mathbf{w} = P\mathbf{z}$, where, say, $\mathbf{w}' = (w_1, \cdots, w_n)$. Then

$$\begin{aligned}\sum_{i=1}^n w_i^2 &= \mathbf{w}'\mathbf{w} = \mathbf{z}'A\mathbf{z} + \mathbf{z}'B\mathbf{z} \\ &= \mathbf{z}'A\mathbf{z} + w_1^2.\end{aligned}$$

Hence $\mathbf{z}'A\mathbf{z} = w_2^2 + \cdots + w_n^2$. If we let $\mathbf{W}$ be defined by $\mathbf{W} = P\mathbf{Z}$, then since $Z_1, \cdots, Z_n$ are independent $N(0, 1)$ random variables, it follows from Theorem 2 in Section 10.3, Lemmas 1 and 2 of this section, and Theorem 2 of Section 5.2 that $(1/\sqrt{n})W_1$ and $W_2^2 + \cdots + W_n^2$ are independent. By the above identities, this implies that $\overline{Z}_n$ and $\sum_{k=1}^n (Z_i - \overline{Z}_n)^2$ are independent. Since $\sum_{i=1}^n (Z_i - \overline{Z}_n)^2 = W_2^2 + \cdots + W_n^2$, then, by the very definition of the chi-square distribution, this random variable has a chi-square distribution with $n-1$ degrees of freedom. This completes the proof.

A very useful corollary to the theorem just proved follows.

4. Theorem. *If $X_1, \cdots, X_n$ are n independent observations on a random variable X whose distribution is $N(\mu, \sigma^2)$, then the random variable T, defined by*

$$T = \sqrt{n}(\overline{X}_n - \mu)/s_n,$$

(where $s_n = \sqrt{s_n^2}$) has the t-distribution with $n - 1$ degrees of freedom.

Proof. If we divide both numerator and denominator of T by σ, and if we recall the definition of the t-distribution, we obtain the conclusion of the theorem as a direct consequence of Theorem 3.

EXERCISES

1. Write the proof of Lemma 1 when $a < 0$, $c > 0$ and when $a < 0$, $c < 0$.

2. In the proof of Lemma 2, if any of the constants $\beta_2, \cdots, \beta_n$ is negative, the equality obtained in the proof is trivially true. Why?

3. Let $X_1, \cdots, X_n$ be n independent observations on a random variable X whose distribution is $N(\mu, \sigma^2)$. Let $Z_i = (X_i - \mu)/\sigma$, $1 \leqq i \leqq n$. Then prove that $Z_1, \cdots, Z_n$ are independent, identically distributed, each with an $N(0, 1)$ distribution.

4. Carry out the details of the proof of Theorem 4.

5. Let $X_1, \cdots, X_n$ be n independent observations on a random variable X whose distribution is $N(0, 1)$. Prove independence of $\overline{X}_n^2$ and s_n^2 by using Cochran's theorem.

6. Let $X_1, X_2, \cdots, X_m, Y_1, Y_2, \cdots, Y_n$ be $m + n$ independent $N(0, 1)$ random variables. Let $\overline{X}_m = (X_1 + \cdots + X_m)/m$, $\overline{Y}_n = (Y_1 + \cdots + Y_n)/n$,

$$s_X^2 = \frac{1}{m-1}\sum_{i=1}^{m}(X_i - \overline{X}_m)^2, \quad \text{and} \quad s_Y^2 = \frac{1}{n-1}\sum_{i=1}^{n}(Y_i - \overline{Y}_n)^2.$$

(a) Prove that

$$\sum_{i=1}^{m} X_i^2 + \sum_{j=1}^{n} Y_i^2 = m\overline{X}_m^2 + n\overline{Y}_n^2 + (m-1)s_X^2 + (n-1)s_Y^2.$$

(b) Use Cochran's theorem to prove that s_X^2 and s_Y^2 are independent.

CHAPTER 11

Testing Statistical Hypotheses: Simple Hypothesis vs. Simple Alternative

11.1 Fundamental Notions of Hypothesis Testing

Hypothesis testing is one of the principal branches of mathematical statistics. It is intimately connected with the application of statistics, and, yet, in content it is quite theoretical and abstract. The purpose of this chapter is to present a brief introduction to a few of the basic principles of testing statistical hypotheses. The aim of this first section of this chapter is to provide the reader with an idea of the basic problem and its relation to practice. We shall consider only a very special case in an attempt to keep the explanation clear.

There are many times when an individual in some field of activity is confronted with a question of which of two possible "states of nature" occurs or is true. The problem is that he does not know which state is actually true, and it is up to him to decide which is the actual state of nature. For example, a medical man reading a chest X-ray must decide whether the individual has tuberculosis or not. A food technologist working on margarine must determine whether or not there is a difference in taste between his product and the expensive spreads. Medical researchers still wish to come to a decision on whether or not smoking causes lung cancer. The cosmologist is interested in whether the expanding universe hypothesis is true or false. Recently there has been considerable interest in determining whether or not cloud seeding causes more precipitation. Thus, time after time one is confronted with a problem of deciding which of two (or even more) possible "states of nature" is actually true. If the scientist, engineer, or other professional person involved can reach an absolutely sure decision by means of methods and tools peculiar to his field or discipline and within his field or discipline, then the problem of making the decision ends and is of no concern to anyone else.

However, it might occur that he cannot solve his problem with tools and methods from within his discipline. In such a case, a statistician can possibly be of help. He attacks the problem by purposely introducing an element of chance (if it is not there already). Let us suppose there are two states of nature which for brevity we denote by $\mathcal{S}_1$ and $\mathcal{S}_2$, one and only one being true and the other being false. The statistician must decide which is true and which is not true. He purposely designs a game or experiment in which the outcome is random. He might select some event E which might or might not occur when the experiment is performed. This event E could (hopefully) be such that when $\mathcal{S}_1$ is true, E occurs with a large probability (close to one), and when $\mathcal{S}_2$ is true, then E does not occur (or the negation E^c of E occurs) with high probability (close to one). Then one actually performs the experiment. If E occurs, he decides that $\mathcal{S}_1$ is true. If E does not occur, he then decides that $\mathcal{S}_2$ is true. Thus, when all sure methods within a certain discipline fail, the statistician tries to provide a method in which a chance mechanism indicates the correct answer a high proportion of the times it is applied.

The problem of determining the experiment and the event E referred to above is left to the statistician. This problem cannot always be solved, and many times it is only partially solved. A distinguishing feature of hypothesis testing in the field of mathematical statistics (in our particular two states of nature scheme) is that there is always one particular state of nature which one does not wish to eliminate unless there is overwhelming evidence or reason for doing so. For example, in the problem of deciding whether or not a new manufacturing process is more efficient than an old one, we should not want to eliminate the state of nature which stipulates that the old process is just as efficient as the new one unless there is overwhelming evidence for doing so (because of retooling costs, new investment required, etc.). If $\mathcal{S}_1$ denotes that a person has a certain communicable disease and if $\mathcal{S}_2$ denotes that he does not, then we do not wish to rule out $\mathcal{S}_1$ as being true unless we have overwhelming evidence for doing so. In the case of a certain drug about to go out on the market, if it is suspected that it contains too much of a toxic ingredient, and if $\mathcal{S}_1$ and $\mathcal{S}_2$ denote the two states of nature that it does or does not, we should not wish to rule out $\mathcal{S}_1$ unless there is conclusive evidence for doing so.

One more thing should be noted in this section. In the experiment the statistician designs, the outcomes are usually values of one or more random variables. The two states of nature will imply that there are two distinct probability distributions of these random variables. The problem of selecting the true state of nature then becomes the problem of determining which is the correct probability distribution function of these observable random variables.

The exercises which follow are very artificial and are used only to illustrate the ideas.

EXERCISES

1. Let $\mathcal{S}_1$ and $\mathcal{S}_2$ be two states of nature. Let X be a random variable which takes values $1, 2, \cdots, 20$. Suppose it is known that when $\mathcal{S}_1$ is true, $P[X = n] = .05$, $1 \leqq n \leqq 20$, and when $\mathcal{S}_2$ is true, $P[X = 7] = .95$ and $P[X = n] = .05/19$, $n = 1, 2, \cdots, 6, 8, \cdots, 20$. Let E denote the event $[X \neq 7]$.

(a) Evaluate PE and PE^c when $\mathcal{S}_1$ is true.

(b) Evaluate PE and PE^c when $\mathcal{S}_2$ is true.

(c) If you wish to make correct statements 95% of the time (or give yourself odds of 19 to 1), and if the event E^c occurs when you perform the experiment which results in X, which state of nature would you assert is true?

2. Let $\mathcal{S}_1$ and $\mathcal{S}_2$ be two states of nature. An experiment is designed whose outcome is a random variable which takes values $1, 2, \cdots, 10$. When $\mathcal{S}_1$ is true suppose it is known that $P[X = 1] = P[X = 2] = .45$, and $P[X = n] = .0125$ for $3 \leqq n \leqq 10$. When $\mathcal{S}_2$ is true, suppose it is known that $P[X = 1] = P[X = 2] = .05$ and $P[X = n] = .1125$ for $3 \leqq n \leqq 10$. Define an event E in terms of the outcome of X such that if $\mathcal{S}_1$ is true, then $PE = .90$, and such that if $\mathcal{S}_2$ is true, $P(E^c) = .90$. In this case, if E does occur, which state of nature would you assert as being correct?

3. Let $\mathcal{S}_1$ and $\mathcal{S}_2$ be two states of nature. An experiment is designed whose outcome is a random variable X. Suppose it is known that when $\mathcal{S}_1$ is true the distribution of X is $N(0, 1)$, and when $\mathcal{S}_2$ is true the distribution of X is $N(4, 1)$. Let E be the event $[X \leqq 2]$. Use the table of the normal distribution to find

(a) PE and PE^c when $\mathcal{S}_1$ is true, and

(b) PE and PE^c when $\mathcal{S}_2$ is true.

(c) Suppose the experiment is performed, and the value of X observed is 1.99. What state of nature would you say is true?

4. Let $\mathcal{S}_1$ and $\mathcal{S}_2$ be two states of nature. An experiment is designed for which the outcome is a random variable X. Suppose that when $\mathcal{S}_1$ is true it is known that $P[X = k] = .05$ when $1 \leqq k \leqq 5$ and $P[X = 6] = .75$. Suppose that when $\mathcal{S}_2$ is true it is known that $P[X = 2] = P[X = 3] = .45$, and $P[X = k] = .025$ for $k = 1, 4, 5, 6$.

(a) List all possible events (in terms of the outcome of X) with probability .90 when $\mathcal{S}_1$ is true.

(b) Find the probabilities of all the events you listed in part (a) when $\mathcal{S}_2$ is true.

(c) Which of the events listed in (a) would be best in distinguishing between $\mathcal{S}_1$ and $\mathcal{S}_2$.

(d) Suppose that when $\mathcal{S}_2$ is true you want to say it is true with probability .975. What event (in terms of the outcome of X) would you use to distinguish between $\mathcal{S}_1$ and $\mathcal{S}_2$ so that if $\mathcal{S}_1$ is true you assert it is true with largest probability?

5. Let $\mathcal{S}_1$ and $\mathcal{S}_2$ be two states of nature. An experiment is designed whose outcome is a random variable X. Suppose it is known that when $\mathcal{S}_1$ is true the distribution of X is $N(0, 1)$ and when $\mathcal{S}_2$ is true, its distribution is $N(3, 1)$.

(a) Evaluate x_1, x_2, x_3, x_4 and x_5 such that when $\mathcal{S}_1$ is true the probability of each of the events $[X < x_1]$, $[-3.0 < X < x_2]$, $[-2.51 < X < x_3]$, $[-2.0 < X < x_4]$, and $[-1.75 < X < x_5]$ is .95.

(b) Evaluate the probability of each of the events in part (a) when $\mathcal{S}_2$ is true.

(c) Find $P[X < 1.5]$ when $\mathcal{S}_1$ is true, and find $P[X \geqq 1.5]$ when $\mathcal{S}_2$ is true.

(d) Suppose it would be just as bad to say $\mathcal{S}_1$ is true when actually $\mathcal{S}_2$ is true as it would be to say $\mathcal{S}_2$ is true when actually $\mathcal{S}_1$ is true. What is the best event E (in terms of X) that can be used to distinguish between $\mathcal{S}_1$ and $\mathcal{S}_2$.

(e) Suppose one wants to say that $\mathcal{S}_1$ is true, when it actually is true, with probability .95. What is the best event E to use, and what is $P(E^c)$ when $\mathcal{S}_2$ is true?

11.2 Simple Hypothesis vs. Simple Alternative

As we remarked in the last section, when distinguishing between two states of nature, the statistician identifies with each state of nature a probability distribution function of some (observable) random variables, say $\mathbf{X}' = (X_1, \cdots, X_n)$. He then sets for himself the problem of determining which distribution is the correct one by observing an outcome (an n-tuple of numbers) of these random variables. In this section we develop the formalism of hypothesis testing in the case of a simple hypothesis versus a simple alternative.

We assume that there are n random variables, independent or not, which have either a joint absolutely continuous distribution or a joint discrete distribution. In either case, let it be assumed that there are two densities, $f_0(\mathbf{x}')$ and $f_1(\mathbf{x}')$, of which one is the true density of $\mathbf{X}'$. The problem is to decide which is the true density of $\mathbf{X}'$.

The first step in formulating this problem consists in recognizing that there are two possible errors that can be made. One error is that one decides that $f_1(\mathbf{x}')$ is the correct density of $\mathbf{X}'$ when actually $f_0(\mathbf{x}')$ is. The second error is that one will decide that $f_0(\mathbf{x}')$ is the correct density of $\mathbf{X}'$ when actually $f_1(\mathbf{x}')$ is. The problem is to make the probabilities of these two errors as small as possible. Of course, one can design an experiment in which the first error is made with probability zero. It is simply this: no matter what the outcome of $\mathbf{X}'$ might be, decide that $f_0(\mathbf{x}')$ is the correct density. However, in this case the probability of making the second error is one.

Also, one can consider a similar trivial experiment in which the second error is committed with probability zero and the first with probability one. It usually happens that the smaller one tries to make the probability of the first error, the larger will be the probability of making the second error, and the smaller one tries to make the probability of the second error the larger will be the probability of making the first error. The problem then becomes one of setting a maximum probability with which one is willing to make the worse of these two errors (worse here is a nonmathematical judgment), and, subject to this condition, one then tries to minimize the probability of the remaining error. The reader should recall the examples in Section 11.1 where one error was considered worse than the other.

Let us suppose that the worse error is to say that $f_1(\mathbf{x})$ is the true density of $\mathbf{X}'$ when actually $f_0(\mathbf{x}')$ is. This worse error is called the *error of the first kind.* The remaining error, asserting that $f_0(\mathbf{x}')$ is the true density of $\mathbf{X}'$ when $f_1(\mathbf{x}')$ is, is called the *error of the second kind.* After one knows which is the worse error he can make, he then fixes a maximum probability $\alpha > 0$ with which he can afford, or is willing to make, such an error. Of course, α is usually quite small, perhaps .10, .05, .01, or .001. This maximum probability with which one is willing to commit the worse of the two errors is called the *level of significance.* It is usual practice at this point to refer to the density $f_0(\mathbf{x}')$ as the *hypothesis* or the *hypothesis tested* or the *null hypothesis,* and one simply writes $\mathrm{H}{:}f_0(\mathbf{x}')$. The density $f_1(\mathbf{x}')$ is called the *alternative* or *alternative hypothesis,* and one simply writes either $\mathrm{Alt}{:}f_1(\mathbf{x}')$ or $\mathrm{H}'{:}f_1(\mathbf{x}')$. In order to decide whether $f_0(\mathbf{x}')$ or $f_1(\mathbf{x}')$ is the true density of $\mathbf{X}'$ it is clearly sufficient to decide whether or not we should reject the hypothesis H. The expression "to reject the hypothesis H" means to decide that $f_0(\mathbf{x}')$ is not the true density of $\mathbf{X}'$. Consequently, a statistical test of the hypothesis H is defined to be an event R. If R occurs, then we reject the hypothesis H, and if R does not occur, then we *fail to reject* H. The event R must be such that $P(R) \leqq \alpha$ when H is true. This is frequently written $P(R|\mathrm{H}) \leqq \alpha$ as if it were a conditional probability (and statisticians usually say in words "the probability of R *given* the hypothesis H").

The event $R =$ [reject H] must be defined in terms of the random variables $\mathbf{X}' = (X_1, \cdots, X_n)$. This is done by deciding that if $\mathbf{X}'$ takes certain values in $E^{(n)}$ we shall reject H, and if $\mathbf{X}'$ takes any other values in $E^{(n)}$ we shall fail to reject H. This amounts to determining a subset W of $E^{(n)}$ such that if $[\mathbf{X} \in W]$ occurs we shall reject the hypothesis, and if $[X \notin W]$ occurs we shall fail to reject H. Thus an event $R =$ [reject H] is determined by a subset W of $E^{(n)}$ for which $P[X \in W] \leqq \alpha$ when H is true. Hence the event R can really be defined by $R = [\mathbf{X} \in W]$. The set W is called a *critical region.* We must add a reservation here in the absolutely continuous case. The set W cannot be any subset of $E^{(n)}$ for which $[\mathbf{X} \in W]$ is an event, i.e., is an element of $\mathcal{A}$. We must restrict our critical regions $\{W\}$ to be those for which, in addition, the two integrals

$$\int \underset{W}{\cdots} \int f_0(\mathbf{x}')\, d\mathbf{x}', \quad \int \underset{W}{\cdots} \int f_1(\mathbf{x}')\, d\mathbf{x}'$$

exist. (See the first unproved theorem of Section 5.2.)

A critical region W is usually not too difficult to find. However, one usually finds many critical regions, and the next problem becomes the following: which one of the many critical regions that can be found should be used? The reader should notice that up to now we really have not made use of the fact that we should like to make the error of the second kind as small as possible. In other words, among all W's for which

$$P([\mathbf{X} \in W]|\mathrm{H}) \leqq \alpha$$

we should want that W for which $P[\mathbf{X} \notin W]$ is "smallest" when $f_1(\mathbf{x}')$ is the true density (or when H$'$ is true). This latter requirement is usually written:

$$P([\mathbf{X} \notin W]|\mathrm{H}') \quad \text{is minimum,}$$

or, equivalently,

$$P([\mathbf{X} \in W]|\mathrm{H}') \quad \text{is maximum.}$$

If such a critical region exists, it is called a *best critical region.* We call it *a best critical region* rather than *the best critical region,* since there could be many critical regions with this property. We define now a critical region and a best critical region in a formal manner.

Definition. *In testing an hypothesis* $\mathrm{H}{:}f_0(\mathbf{x}')$ *against an alternative* $\mathrm{H}'{:}f_1(\mathbf{x}')$ *with level of significance* α, *a critical region* W *is a subset of* $E^{(n)}$ *for which*

$$P\{\mathbf{X} \in W|\mathrm{H}\} = \int \underset{W}{\cdots} \int f_0(\mathbf{x}')\, d\mathbf{x}' \leqq \alpha.$$

If $\mathcal{W}$ *denotes the set of all such critical regions, and if among them there is a critical region* W^* *such that*

$$P\{\mathbf{X} \in W^*|\mathrm{H}'\} \geqq P\{\mathbf{X} \in W|\mathrm{H}'\}$$

or, equivalently (by the first unproved theorem in Section 5.2)

$$\int \underset{W^*}{\cdots} \int f_1(\mathbf{x}')\, d\mathbf{x}' \geqq \int \underset{W}{\cdots} \int f_1(\mathbf{x}')\, d\mathbf{x}'$$

for all $W \in \mathcal{W}$, *then* W^* *is called a best critical region.*

Thus, in a testing problem of a simple hypothesis against a simple alternative (the word "simple" used like this means "single"), we should always look for a best critical region. The method of finding this is discussed in the next section.

Before we conclude this section we emphasize the following remarks. In testing a simple hypothesis against a simple alternative, the primary objects under consideration are a set of random variables and two possible joint densities for them, one of which is true. The hypothesis tested is always *one of these densities* (and *not* a state of nature or a constant or "parameter"), and the alternative hypothesis is the other density. The level of significance is the maximum probability with which one is willing to reject the hypothesis when it is true. The problems of selecting which density is to be H and the value of α is a nonmathematical problem connected with other demands or requirements.

EXERCISES

1. Let X be a single (observable) random variable. We want to test the hypothesis

$$\text{H}: f_X(x) = .05, \quad x = 1, 2, \cdots, 20,$$

against the alternative

$$\text{H}': f_X(x) = \begin{cases} .60 & \text{if} \quad x = 1 \\ .15 & \text{if} \quad x = 2, 3 \\ .10/17 & \text{if} \quad x = 4, 5, \cdots, 19, 20, \end{cases}$$

with level of significance $\alpha = .10$. Let

$$W_1 = \{1, 2\}, \quad W_2 = \{1, 3\}, \quad \text{and} \quad W_3 = \{1, 4\}.$$

(a) Show that W_1, W_2, and W_3 are critical regions.
(b) Prove that W_1 and W_2 are both best critical regions.

2. Let X be a random variable. We want to test the hypothesis, with level of significance $\alpha = .10$,

$$\text{H}: f_X(x) = f_0(x) = \begin{cases} .10 & \text{if} \quad x \in [0, 10] \\ 0 & \text{if} \quad x < 0 \quad \text{or} \quad x > 10 \end{cases}$$

against the alternative

$$\text{H}': f_X(x) = f_1(x) = \begin{cases} 1.2 & \text{if} \quad x \in [0, \frac{1}{2}) \\ 0.3 & \text{if} \quad x \in [\frac{1}{2}, 1.5] \\ 1/85 & \text{if} \quad x \in [1.5, 10] \\ 0 & \text{if} \quad x < 0 \quad \text{or} \quad x > 10. \end{cases}$$

Let $W_1 = [0, 1)$, $W_2 = [0, \frac{1}{2}) \cup [1, 1.5)$, $W_3 = [0, \frac{1}{2}) \cup [.75, 1.25)$, $W_4 = [0, .5) \cup [1.5, 2)$, and $W_5 = [5.2, 6.2)$.

(a) Show that W_1, W_2, W_3, W_4, and W_5 are critical regions.
(b) Can you give reasons to show why W_1, W_2, and W_3 are best critical regions?

3. Let $X_1, X_2, \cdots, X_n$ be n random variables. We want to test the hypothesis

$$\text{H}: f_{\mathbf{X}'}(\mathbf{x}') = f_0(x_1, \cdots, x_n) = (2\pi)^{-n/2} \exp -\tfrac{1}{2} \sum_{i=1}^{n} x_i^2$$

against the alternative

$$\text{H}': f_{\mathbf{X}'}(\mathbf{x}') = f_1(x_1, \cdots, x_n) = (2\pi)^{-n/2} \exp -\tfrac{1}{2} \sum_{i=1}^{n} (x_i - 1)^2,$$

using level of significance $\alpha = .05$.

(a) Use the table of the normal distribution to find a constant K_1 such that

$$W_1 = \{\mathbf{x} \in E^{(n)} | x_i \geqq K_1, \quad 1 \leqq i \leqq n\}$$

is a critical region (where x_i is the ith coordinate of $\mathbf{x}$).

(b) Find a constant K_2 such that

$$W_2 = \{\mathbf{x} \in E^{(n)} | x_1 + x_2 + \cdots + x_n \geqq K_2\}$$

is a critical region.

(c) Compute $P\{\mathbf{X} \in W_1 | \mathrm{H}'\}$ and $P\{\mathbf{X} \in W_2 | \mathrm{H}'\}$ when $n = 10$.

(d) Which of the critical regions W_1, W_2 is the "better" one?

11.3 The Neyman-Pearson Fundamental Lemma

Let $X_1, X_2, \cdots, X_n$ be n observable random variables, i.e., random variables whose values can be observed in a physical sense. As was shown in the last section, there might exist more than one critical region W for testing the hypothesis $\mathrm{H}{:}f_0(\mathbf{x}')$ against the alternative $\mathrm{H}'{:}f_1(\mathbf{x}')$ with level of significance α. For each critical region W, the probability of the error of the second kind is (in the absolutely continuous case)

$$P([\mathbf{X} \notin W] | \mathrm{H}') = 1 - \int \underset{W}{\cdots} \int f_1(\mathbf{x}')\, d\mathbf{x}'.$$

We of course desire that $P([\mathbf{X} \notin W] | \mathrm{H}')$ be small or (equivalently)

$$P([\mathbf{X} \in W] | \mathrm{H}') = \int \underset{W}{\cdots} \int f_1(\mathbf{x}')\, d\mathbf{x}'$$

be large. This last statement merely says that we want the probability of rejecting the hypothesis when the hypothesis is not true to be large. This probability, $P([\mathbf{X} \in W] | \mathrm{H}')$, is called the *power of the test* when W is used as a critical region. Consequently, a best critical region will also be called a *most powerful test* or a *most powerful critical region*. In this section we show how a best critical region may be obtained by means of a very important theorem due to J. Neyman and E. S. Pearson, a theorem which is basic to problems of statistical inference.

1. Theorem. (The Neyman-Pearson Fundamental Lemma.) *Let*

$$f_0(x_1, \cdots, x_n) \quad \textit{and} \quad f_1(x_1, \cdots, x_n)$$

be two joint probability densities, both of them being densities of joint discrete or joint absolutely continuous distributions. Let $\mathcal{W}$ *denote the collection of all subsets* W *of* $E^{(n)}$ *for which*

$$\sum_{\mathbf{x} \in W} f_0(\mathbf{x}') = \alpha \quad \text{(in the discrete case)}$$

or

$$\int \underset{W}{\cdots} \int f_0(\mathbf{x}')\, d\mathbf{x}' = \alpha \quad \text{(in the absolutely continuous case),}$$

where $0 < \alpha < 1$. *Suppose there exists a* $W^* \in \mathcal{W}$ *such that, for some* $K \geqq 0$,

$$f_1(\mathbf{x}') \geqq K f_0(\mathbf{x}')$$

for all points $\mathbf{x} \in W^*$ *and*

$$f_1(\mathbf{x}') \leqq K f_0(\mathbf{x}')$$

for all points $\mathbf{x} \notin W^*$. *Then*

$$\sum_{\mathbf{x} \in W^*} f_1(\mathbf{x}') \geqq \sum_{\mathbf{x} \in W} f_1(\mathbf{x}') \quad \text{(in the discrete case)}$$

or

$$\int \underset{W^*}{\cdots} \int f_1(\mathbf{x}')\, d\mathbf{x}' \geqq \int \underset{W}{\cdots} \int f_1(\mathbf{x}')\, d\mathbf{x}' \quad \text{(in the absolutely continuous case)}$$

for all $W \in \mathcal{W}$, *i.e.,* W^* *is a best critical region.*

Proof. We shall prove this theorem only in the discrete case; the proof in the absolutely continuous case is left to the student. Let $W \in \mathcal{W}$ be arbitrary, and let

$$\Delta = \sum_{\mathbf{x} \in W^*} f_1(\mathbf{x}') - \sum_{\mathbf{x} \in W} f_1(\mathbf{x}').$$

We want to prove that $\Delta \geqq 0$. Since

$$\sum_{\mathbf{x} \in W^*} f_1(\mathbf{x}') = \sum_{\mathbf{x} \in W^* W^c} f_1(\mathbf{x}') + \sum_{\mathbf{x} \in W^* W} f_1(\mathbf{x}')$$

and

$$\sum_{\mathbf{x} \in W} f_1(\mathbf{x}') = \sum_{\mathbf{x} \in W (W^*)^c} f_1(\mathbf{x}') + \sum_{\mathbf{x} \in W W^*} f_1(\mathbf{x}'),$$

we obtain

$$\Delta = \sum_{\mathbf{x} \in W^* W^c} f_1(\mathbf{x}') - \sum_{\mathbf{x} \in W (W^*)^c} f_1(\mathbf{x}').$$

Since, by hypothesis, $f_1(\mathbf{x}') \geqq K f_0(\mathbf{x}')$ for all $\mathbf{x}' \in W^*$, it follows that

$$\sum_{\mathbf{x} \in W^* W^c} f_1(\mathbf{x}') \geqq K \sum_{\mathbf{x} \in W^* W^c} f_0(\mathbf{x}').$$

Also, by hypothesis, $f_1(\mathbf{x}') \leqq K f_0(\mathbf{x}')$ for all $\mathbf{x} \notin W^*$, and so we have

$$-\sum_{\mathbf{x} \in W (W^*)^c} f_1(\mathbf{x}') \geqq -K \sum_{\mathbf{x} \in W (W^*)^c} f_0(\mathbf{x}').$$

Thus

$$\Delta \geqq K \left\{ \sum_{\mathbf{x} \in W^* (W)^c} f_0(\mathbf{x}') - \sum_{\mathbf{x} \in W (W^*)^c} f_0(\mathbf{x}') \right\}$$

$$= K \left\{ \sum_{\mathbf{x} \in W^* W^c} f_0(\mathbf{x}') + \sum_{\mathbf{x} \in W^* W} f_0(\mathbf{x}') - \sum_{\mathbf{x} \in W^* W} f_0(\mathbf{x}') - \sum_{\mathbf{x} \in W (W^*)^c} f_0(\mathbf{x}') \right\}$$

$$= K \left\{ \sum_{\mathbf{x} \in W^*} f_0(\mathbf{x}') - \sum_{\mathbf{x} \in W} f_0(\mathbf{x}') \right\} = K(\alpha - \alpha) = 0,$$

which proves the theorem.

As we mentioned above, the Neyman-Pearson fundamental lemma is indeed fundamental to a great deal of statistical inference. Not only is it constantly useful in hypothesis testing, but, because of the relation which is brought out in Chapter 13, it is frequently most useful in deriving confidence intervals. Before commenting on this theorem we consider an example.

A certain manufacturing company is about to send out a large shipment of some mass produced item. Some of these items are defective. If the proportion of defective items in this shipment is large, the company does not want to send it out. If the proportion of defectives is small, the company definitely wants to make the shipment. No one is certain where the dividing line between "large" and "small" is, but if the percentage of defectives in the shipment is larger than 10%, they definitely do not want to send it. On the other hand, if the percentage of defectives is less than 4%, they definitely do want to make the shipment. A sample of size n is taken, where n is a reasonably large integer but very small compared to the number of items in the shipment. In other words, n items are selected at random from the shipment. They are inspected (or tested), and X of these n items are observed to be defective. Using this value of X, one wants to decide whether the proportion of defectives in the shipment is excessive or not excessive. In order that this company be able to protect its reputation for quality, management considers that the worse error is to decide that the proportion of defective items is not excessive when this is actually the case. Moreover, the company does not want to make this worse error more than 2% of the time.

The mathematical statistician now makes some simplifying assumptions in order to make the problem tractable. He first assumes that this shipment contains either 4 or 10% defectives. Secondly, he assumes (and hopes) that the sampling was done in a random manner and with replacement. (If n is quite small compared to the total number of items in the shipment, the assumption that sampling was done with replacement when it was not is reasonable.) No matter what percentage $100p\%$ of defectives there are ($p = .04$ or $.10$), the sampling that was done thus constituted a sequence of n Bernoulli trials with probability p of success, where success in this case means the selection of a defective item. Now X is a random variable with binomial distribution $B(n, p)$, i.e.,

$$f_X(x) = \binom{n}{x} p^x(1-p)^{n-x}, \qquad x = 0, 1, 2, \cdots, n,$$

where $p = .04$ or $.10$. In line with the company's policy, the hypothesis tested *must be*

$$\text{H}: f_0(x) = \binom{n}{x} (.10)^x(.90)^{n-x}, \qquad x = 0, 1, \cdots, n,$$

the alternative *must be*

$$H': f_1(x) = \binom{n}{x} (.04)^x (.96)^{n-x}, \qquad x = 0, 1, \cdots, n,$$

and the level of significance must be

$$\alpha = .02.$$

We now want to find a best critical region in $E^{(1)}$ for testing H against H′. According to the Neyman-Pearson fundamental lemma, if we can find a critical region W^* such that for some constant K, $f_1(x) \geqq K f_0(x)$ for all $x \in W^*$ and $f_1(x) \leqq K f_0(x)$ for all $x \notin W^*$, then W^* is a best critical region. We therefore consider the inequality

$$\binom{n}{x} (.04)^x (.96)^{n-x} \geqq K \binom{n}{x} (.10)^x (.90)^{n-x},$$

where K is some positive constant. By a little algebraic manipulation we obtain

$$(2/5)^x (96/90)^{n-x} \geqq K$$

or

$$(180/480)^x \geqq K_1,$$

where $K_1 = K(90/96)^n$. This last inequality is equivalent to the inequality $x \leqq K_2$, where $K_2 = (\log K_1)/\log(180/480)$. Thus W^* is a subset of $E^{(1)}$ of the form $(-\infty, K_2]$, where K_2 is yet to be evaluated. The event $[X \in (-\infty, K_2]]$ is simply the event $[X \leqq K_2]$. Now we must find K_2 such that when the hypothesis is true, i.e., when the distribution of X is $B(.10, n)$, then $P[X \leqq K_2] = .02$. If one has access to tables of the binomial distribution (and tables of it do exist; ask your librarian), this integer K_2 can be found. (*Note:* there undoubtedly will not be an integer N such that $P[X \leqq N] = .02$. Instead, one selects the largest value of N for which $P[X \leqq N] \leqq .02$.)

If one does not have extensive tables of the binomial distribution, one can approximate K_2 using the table of the normal distribution. By the Laplace-DeMoivre theorem (Theorem 10 in Section 7.5) we know that

$$\lim_{n\to\infty} P\left[\frac{X - .10n}{\sqrt{(.10)(.90)n}} \leqq x\right] = \frac{1}{\sqrt{2\pi}} \int_{-\infty}^{x} \exp -\frac{t^2}{2}\, dt.$$

The nice thing about limit theorems such as this is that you can use them for approximation purposes. In this case, when n is fairly large we can assume that the value of $P[(X - .10n)/\sqrt{(.10)(.90)n} \leqq x]$ is approximately equal to

$$\frac{1}{\sqrt{2\pi}} \int_{-\infty}^{x} \exp -\frac{t^2}{2}\, dt.$$

Now

$$P[X \leqq K_2] = P\left[\frac{X - .10n}{\sqrt{(.10)(.90)n}} \leqq \frac{K_2 - .10n}{\sqrt{(.10)(.90)n}}\right].$$

Let $x = (K_2 - .10n)/\sqrt{(.10)(.90)n}$. Since we want to find K_2 such that $P[X \leqq K_2] \doteq .02$, we need only find x so that

$$\frac{1}{\sqrt{2\pi}} \int_{-\infty}^{x} \exp -\frac{t^2}{2}\, dt = .02.$$

From the table of the normal distribution we find that $x = -2.05$. We then solve for K_2 to obtain

$$K_2 = .10n - 2.05\sqrt{(.10)(.90)n}.$$

Thus, when the number of defectives in a sample of size n is equal to or less than the value of K_2 just computed, we shall reject the hypothesis H (and shall tell the company that there are not too many defectives in the entire shipment). If the number of defectives in the sample of size n is greater than the value of K_2, we shall fail to reject the hypothesis (and shall tell the company that there are too many defectives in the entire shipment).

Before we leave this example let us discuss the power of the test just obtained. Recall that the power of a test is the probability of rejecting the hypothesis when we want to, i.e., when the alternative is true. When the alternative H′ is true and n is large, the Laplace-DeMoivre theorem tells us that the distribution of $(X - .04n)/\sqrt{(.04)(.96)n}$ is approximately $N(0, 1)$. Hence when H′ is true,

$$P[X \leqq K_2] \approx \frac{1}{\sqrt{2\pi}} \int_{-\infty}^{x_0} \exp -\frac{t^2}{2}\, dt,$$

where

$$x_0 = \frac{K_2 - .04n}{\sqrt{(.04)(.96)n}} = \frac{.06n - 2.05\sqrt{(.10)(.90)n}}{\sqrt{(.04)(.96)n}}.$$

We tabulate in Table 2 the power of the test for different values of n.

TABLE 2

Sample size, n	$P\{X \leq K_2 \mid H'\}$
25	.054
36	.097
49	.160
64	.244
81	.351
100	.469
225	.927

Thus we see that the larger the value of n, the greater will be the probability of rejecting the hypothesis when it is false.

There are several things which should be pointed out concerning the Neyman-Pearson fundamental lemma. First we should note that this lemma tells us how to recognize a best critical region among those of size α, i.e., those W's for which $P([\mathbf{X} \in W]|\mathrm{H}) = \alpha$. Second, it should be observed that the value of K in the theorem will depend on α. The smaller α is, the larger K will be. However, we shall really never care to compute K. We shall only be interested in W^* which will depend on some function of K. We shall want to adjust this function of K in order that

$$P([\mathbf{X} \in W^*]|\mathrm{H}) = \alpha.$$

In order to use the fundamental lemma to obtain a best critical region in the case of an absolutely continuous joint distribution, we consider the following rather artificial problem. Let $X_1, \cdots, X_n$ be n random variables. We want to test the hypothesis

$$\mathrm{H}: f_0(\mathbf{x}') = (2\pi)^{-n/2} \exp -\tfrac{1}{2} \sum_{i=1}^{n} x_i^2$$

against the alternative

$$\mathrm{H}': f_1(\mathbf{x}') = (2\pi)^{-n/2} \exp -\tfrac{1}{2} \sum_{i=1}^{n} (x_i - 1)^2,$$

where the level of significance $\alpha = .001$. In order to obtain a best critical region by the fundamental lemma we consider a subset of $E^{(n)}$ of the form

$$\{\mathbf{x} \in E^{(n)} | f_1(\mathbf{x}') \geqq K f_0(\mathbf{x}')\}.$$

The inequality above is equivalent to

$$(2\pi)^{-n/2} \exp -\tfrac{1}{2} \sum_{i=1}^{n} (x_i - 1)^2 \geqq K(2\pi)^{-n/2} \exp -\tfrac{1}{2} \sum_{i=1}^{n} x_i^2$$

or

$$-\tfrac{1}{2} \sum_{i=1}^{n} (x_i - 1)^2 \geqq \log K - \tfrac{1}{2} \sum_{i=1}^{n} x_i^2,$$

or

$$\sum_{i=1}^{n} x_i \geqq K_1,$$

where $K_1 = \log K + n/2$.

The following equality is obviously true:

$$\left[\mathbf{X} \in \left\{\mathbf{x} \middle| \sum_{i=1}^{n} x_i \geqq K_1\right\}\right] = \left[\sum_{i=1}^{n} X_i \geqq K_1\right].$$

The problem now is to determine K_1 so that $P([\sum_{i=1}^{n} X_i \geqq K_1]|\mathrm{H}) = .001$. When the hypothesis is true, the distribution of each X_i is $N(0, 1)$, and therefore the distribution of $\sum_{i=1}^{n} X_i$ is $N(0, n)$. By Theorems 8 and 9 in

Section 7.3 and the fact that the sum of independent normally distributed random variables is also normal, it follows that the distribution of $(1/\sqrt{n}) \sum_{i=1}^{n} X_i$ is $N(0, 1)$. Using the table of the normal distribution, the value of $K_1/\sqrt{n}$ such that

$$P\left(\left[\sum_{i=1}^{n} X_i/\sqrt{n} \geqq K_1/\sqrt{n}\right] \middle| \mathrm{H}\right) = .001$$

is seen to be 3.09. Hence $K_1 = 3.09\sqrt{n}$, and we reject the hypothesis if and only if the event $[\sum_{i=1}^{n} X_i > 3.09\sqrt{n}]$ occurs. Here again it might be instructive to tabulate the power of the test, i.e., the probability of rejecting H when the alternative is true, for different values of n. In order to compute these probabilities one should notice that when the alternative H′ is true, $X_i - 1$ has an $N(0, 1)$ distribution. One easily verifies that

$$\left[\sum_{i=1}^{n} X_i > 3.09\sqrt{n}\right] = \left[\frac{1}{\sqrt{n}} \sum_{i=1}^{n} (X_i - 1) > 3.09 - \sqrt{n}\right].$$

When H′ is true, $(1/\sqrt{n}) \sum_{i=1}^{n} (X_i - 1)$ has an $N(0, 1)$ distribution, and the probabilities of the above event (to reject H) are easily obtained from the table of the normal distribution. They are recorded in Table 3. Here

TABLE 3

Value of n	$P([\sum_{i=1}^{n} X_i > 3.09\sqrt{n}] \mid \mathrm{H}')$
9	.464
25	.972
36	.998
49	.99995

again one sees that the larger the size of the sample (i.e., the larger n is), the higher the probability of rejecting the hypothesis when it is false.

EXERCISES

1. Show that the best critical regions in problems 1 and 2 in Section 11.2 satisfy the hypothesis of the fundamental lemma.

2. In problem 3 in Section 11.2, show that $\{\mathbf{x} \in E^{(n)} | \sum_{i=1}^{n} x_i > K_2\}$ is a best critical region by using the fundamental lemma.

3. In the binomial example treated in this section, find the (approximate) smallest size of the sample needed in order that the power be equal to or greater than .95.

4. In Theorem 1, assume that a best critical region of the type indicated exists for each $\alpha \in (0, 1)$. Let $K(\alpha)$ denote the value of K corresponding to α. Prove that if $\alpha_1 < \alpha_2$, then $K(\alpha_1) \geqq K(\alpha_2)$.

5. Let X be one observable random variable. Find a best critical region for testing the hypothesis

$$\mathrm{H}: f_X(x) = \binom{n}{x} (\tfrac{1}{2})^n, \quad x = 0, 1, \cdots, n.$$

against the alternative

$$\mathrm{H}': f_X(x) = \binom{n}{x} (.90)^x (.10)^{n-x}, \quad x = 0, 1, \cdots, n,$$

with level of significance $\alpha = .07$.

6. In problem 5, find the power of the test when $n = 10, 20, 30$.

7. Prove the Neyman–Pearson fundamental lemma in the case where the joint distributions are absolutely continuous.

8. Prove that if $K = 0$ in the statement of the Neyman-Pearson fundamental lemma, then the power of the test is one.

11.4 Randomized Tests

The Neyman-Pearson fundamental lemma contains two "if's" which are not always satisfied. The sentence "Let $\mathcal{W}$ denote the collection of all subsets W of $E^{(n)}$ for which $\int \cdots_W \int f_0(\mathbf{x}')\, d\mathbf{x}' = \alpha$" contains a big "if," namely, that $\mathcal{W}$ is nonempty. Then there follows another crucial "if," namely, "Suppose there exists a $W^* \in \mathcal{W}$ such that. . . ." It might occur that one or both of these "if's" might fail to be satisfied. In case the second "if" above is not satisfied, and if we insist that a test of hypothesis is a critical region, then we have no alternative but to select a smaller level of significance, possibly even $\alpha = 0$ (which is of no help at all!). However, if we take α small, then, as we have already pointed out, the power of the test is small. The purpose of this section is to show in the discrete case that if we define a test as a conditional probability, then there *always* exists a most powerful test with level of significance α.

Let us begin with an example to illustrate the problem. Suppose there is a blood test with which one can tell whether a person has a certain communicable disease. However, the outcome of the test is not certain. If a person is positive (i.e., has the disease), then the blood test will indicate this fact with probability .95. However, if the person is negative, the blood test will show this with probability .90. One is allowed to take four blood samples from a person, and each blood sample is tested independently of the others. Because the disease is communicable, in order to prevent an epidemic the public health authorities want no more than 3 out of every 10,000 people who do have the disease out in public. However, because of the shortage of funds, hospital space, etc., they do not want to make the mistake of hospitalizing a well person very often. Let X denote the number of blood samples out of the four in which the test turns out to be positive. If the person tested is actually positive, then the density of X is

$$f_X(x|.95) = \binom{4}{x}(.95)^x(.05)^{4-x}, \quad x = 0, 1, 2, 3, 4.$$

If the person is negative, the density of X is

$$f_X(x|.10) = \binom{4}{x}(.10)^x(.90)^{4-x}, \quad x = 0, 1, 2, 3, 4.$$

From the above considerations it is clear that we want to test the hypothesis $\mathrm{H}:f_X(x|.95)$ against the alternative $\mathrm{H}':f_X(x|.10)$ with level of significance $\alpha = .0003$. These two densities are tabulated in Table 4.

TABLE 4

x	$f_X(x\|.95)$	$f_X(x\|.10)$
0	.0001	.6561
1	.0004	.2916
2	.0135	.0486
3	.1715	.0036
4	.8145	.0001

Now a dilemma arises when we try to use the Neyman-Pearson fundamental lemma. If we select $K > 6561$, then W^* is empty, the level of significance is zero, and the power is zero. If we select $K = 6561$, then W^* can be taken as either the empty set or $\{0\}$. If we select K such that $6561 > K > 2916/4$, then $W^* = \{0\}$. If we select $K = 2916/4$, then W^* can be selected as either $\{0\}$ or $\{0, 1\}$, and if K is such that $2916/4 > K > 486/135$, then $W^* = \{0, 1\}$. We observe that

$$P([X \in \{0\}]|\mathrm{H}) = P([X = 0]|\mathrm{H}) = .0001,$$

and

$$\begin{aligned} P([X \in \{0, 1\}]|\mathrm{H}) &= P([X = 0] + [X = 1]|\mathrm{H}) \\ &= P([X = 0]|\mathrm{H}) + P([X = 1]|\mathrm{H}) = .0001 + .0004 = .0005. \end{aligned}$$

If we select $W^* = \{0, 1\}$ as our critical region, the probability of rejecting the hypothesis when it is true is larger than the level of significance. If we select $W^* = \{0\}$ as our critical region, we reject the hypothesis when it is true with probability .0001, which is less than the level of significance. Moreover, the power of this test is only .6561.

We can, however, devise a procedure by which we reject the hypothesis when it is true with probability .0003 and such that the probability of rejecting it when it is not true is much larger than .6561. We define the event [Reject H] through its conditional probabilities given the different values of X. We define

$$P([\text{Reject H}]|[X = 0]) = 1$$
$$P([\text{Reject H}]|[X = 1]) = \tfrac{1}{2},$$

and

$$P([\text{Reject H}]|[X = x]) = 0 \quad \text{if} \quad x = 2, 3, 4.$$

(Such an event [Reject H] does exist as a collection of elementary events if we reconstruct the fundamental probability set in a natural way. See problem 5 in the exercises.) What this means is this: if the event $[X = 0]$ occurs, we reject the hypothesis H. If the event $[X = 1]$ occurs, we reject H with probability $\frac{1}{2}$, i.e., we toss an unbiased coin and let its outcome determine our decision on whether the person is positive or negative. If one of the events $[X = 2]$, $[X = 3]$, or $[X = 4]$ occurs, we reject the hypothesis with probability zero, i.e., we most certainly fail to reject the hypothesis. We now compute $P([\text{Reject H}]|\text{H})$. By the theorem of total probabilities (Theorem 3 in Section 2.1),

$$\begin{aligned} P([\text{Reject H}]|\text{H}) &= \sum_{x=0}^{4} P([\text{Reject H}]|[X = x])f_X(x|.95) \\ &= .0001 + \tfrac{1}{2}(.0004) + 0 + 0 + 0 = .0003, \end{aligned}$$

which is the maximum probability with which we can reject the hypothesis when it is true. In order to compute the power of the test, we again use the theorem of total probabilities to obtain

$$\begin{aligned} P([\text{Reject H}]|\text{H}') &= \sum_{x=0}^{4} P([\text{Reject H}]|[X = x])f_X(x|.10) \\ &= .6516 + \tfrac{1}{2}(.2916) + 0 + 0 + 0 = .8019, \end{aligned}$$

which is a considerably larger power than the previous .6561. In other words, using this procedure we now decide that (on the average) 8019 out of every 10,000 negative people are negative, whereas before we only released 6561 out of every 10,000 negative people as being negative. A test of this sort in which the hypothesis is rejected with probabilities according to the occurrences of certain events is called a randomized test.

In the example just given, the test (i.e., the rule for rejecting the hypothesis) is a random variable $\Delta(X)$, where Δ is a function of X. For each $\omega \in \Omega$, $\Delta(X)(\omega) = \Delta(X(\omega))$ is the probability with which we reject the hypothesis. In the example above,

$$\Delta(X) = I_{[X=0]} + \tfrac{1}{2}I_{[X=1]}.$$

When we reject an hypothesis with probability $\frac{1}{2}$, the chance mechanism for producing an event with this probability is an unbiased coin (if such exists). If we are to reject an hypothesis with probability $p = .a_1a_2 \cdots a_n$ (expressed in decimal notation) then a chance mechanism that one can construct in order to produce an event E of probability p is as follows. Place ten tags in an urn, the tags being numbered $0, 1, 2, \cdots, 8, 9$. Select a tag at random, denote the digit on it by U_1, and replace it. Select a second tag at random, denote the digit on it by U_2, replace it, $\cdots$, and finally select an nth tag at random, denote the digit on it by U_n, and replace it. Now we define the event E by

$$\begin{aligned} E = [U_1 < a_1] + [U_1 = a_1][U_2 < a_2] & \\ + [U_1 = a_1][U_2 = a_2][U_3 < a_3] & \\ + \cdots & \\ + [U_1 = a_1] \cdots [U_{n-2} = a_{n-2}][U_{n-1} < a_{n-1}] & \\ + [U_1 = a_1] \cdots [U_{n-1} = a_{n-1}][U_n \leqq a_n]. & \end{aligned}$$

It is easy to verify that

$$P(E) = .a_1a_2 \cdots a_n.$$

We now formalize in a more general case what was done in the above example. For the remainder of this section we shall consider n random variables $\mathbf{X}' = (X_1, \cdots, X_n)$, not necessarily independent, which have a joint discrete density $f_{\mathbf{X}'}(\mathbf{x}')$ which is either equal to $f_0(\mathbf{x}')$ or $f_1(\mathbf{x}')$. We shall denote the (countable) range of $\mathbf{X}$ by $\{\mathbf{z}_1, \mathbf{z}_2, \cdots, \mathbf{z}_n, \cdots\}$. (By the range of $\mathbf{X}$ here we mean the union of the range of $\mathbf{X}$ when $f_0(\mathbf{x}')$ is the true density and the range of $\mathbf{X}$ when $f_1(\mathbf{x}')$ is the true density.)

Definition. *A random variable $\Delta(\mathbf{X})$, where Δ is a function of $\mathbf{X}$, is called a randomized test of the hypothesis* H:$f_0(\mathbf{x}')$ *against the alternative* H':$f_1(\mathbf{x}')$ *with level of significance α if*

(i) $0 \leqq \Delta(\mathbf{z}_n) \leqq 1$ *for all $\mathbf{z}_n$, and*

(ii) *the expectation of $\Delta(\mathbf{X})$ when the hypothesis is true is α, i.e.,* (and here we introduce new notation)

$$E(\Delta(\mathbf{X})|\mathrm{H}) = \sum_n \Delta(\mathbf{z}_n)f_0(\mathbf{z}_n) = \alpha.$$

For each $\mathbf{z}_n$, $\Delta(\mathbf{z}_n)$ is the probability of rejecting the hypothesis when, or given that, the event $[\mathbf{X} = \mathbf{z}_n]$ occurs, i.e.,

$$P([\text{Reject H}] | [\mathbf{X} = \mathbf{z}_n]) = \Delta(\mathbf{z}_n).$$

Now, by the theorem of total probabilities,

$$\begin{aligned} E(\Delta(\mathbf{X})|\text{H}) &= \sum_n \Delta(\mathbf{z}_n) f_0(\mathbf{z}_n) \\ &= \sum_n P([\text{Reject H}] | [X = \mathbf{z}_n]) f_0(\mathbf{z}_n) = P([\text{Reject H}]|\text{H}). \end{aligned}$$

Similarly, the expectation of $\Delta(\mathbf{X})$ when H′ is true is the power of the test, i.e.,

$$E(\Delta(\mathbf{X})|\text{H}') = P([\text{Reject H}]|\text{H}').$$

Definition. *A randomized test $\Delta(\mathbf{X})$ of the hypothesis $\text{H}: f_0(\mathbf{x}')$ against the alternative $\text{H}': f_1(\mathbf{x}')$ with level of significance α is called a best randomized test if for any other randomized test $\Psi(\mathbf{X})$,*

$$E(\Delta(\mathbf{X})|\text{H}') \geqq E(\Psi(\mathbf{X})|\text{H}').$$

Clearly, in cases where a best critical region W^* exists, it is equivalent to the randomized test

$$\Delta(\mathbf{X}) = I_{[\mathbf{X} \in W^*]}.$$

As we noticed in the above example, a best critical region does not always exist which "uses up" all of the level of significance. However, we shall show that there always exists a best randomized test. We lead up to this result with three lemmas. The following notation will be used: for every real number K, let

$$W(K) = \{\mathbf{z}_n | f_1(\mathbf{z}_n) > K f_0(\mathbf{z}_n)\},$$

and

$$G(K) = \sum_{\mathbf{z}_n \in W(K)} f_0(\mathbf{z}_n) = P([\mathbf{X} \in W(K)]|\text{H}).$$

1. Lemma. *If $K_1 < K_2$, then $W(K_2) \subset W(K_1)$ and $G(K_1) \geqq G(K_2)$.*

Proof. If $\mathbf{z}_n \in W(K_2)$, then

$$f_1(\mathbf{z}_n) > K_2 f_0(\mathbf{z}_n) \geqq K_1 f_0(\mathbf{z}_n),$$

which implies that $\mathbf{z}_n \in W(K_1)$. From this it easily follows that G is a nonincreasing function.

2. Lemma. $G(K) = 1$ *for all* $K < 0$.

Proof. For $K < 0$, $W(K)$ coincides with the range of $\mathbf{X}$, which in turn implies that $G(K) = 1$.

3. Lemma.

$$\lim_{K \to \infty} G(K) = 0.$$

Proof. Let us assume that the lemma is not true. By Lemma 1, $G(K)$ is nonincreasing in K. Hence there exists an $\epsilon > 0$ such that

$$\sum_{\mathbf{z}_n \in W(K)} f_0(\mathbf{z}_n) > \epsilon \quad \text{for all} \quad K \geqq 0.$$

Let $W_1 = W(1/\epsilon)$. Then

$$P([\mathbf{X} \in W_1]|\mathrm{H}') = \sum_{\mathbf{z}_n \in W_1} f_1(\mathbf{z}_n) \geqq \frac{1}{\epsilon} \sum_{\mathbf{z}_n \in W_1} f_0(\mathbf{z}_n)$$

$$= \frac{1}{\epsilon} P([\mathbf{X} \in W_1]|\mathrm{H}) > 1,$$

which contradicts the fact that a probability never exceeds 1.

We are now able to establish the existence of a best randomized test.

4. Theorem. *There exists a best randomized test for testing the hypothesis* $\mathrm{H}: f_0(\mathbf{x}')$ *against the alternative* $\mathrm{H}': f_1(\mathbf{x}')$ *with level of significance* α.

Proof. Suppose there exists a value of K, say K_0, such that $G(K_0) = \alpha$; call this case (i). By the Neyman-Pearson fundamental lemma, $W(K_0)$ is a best critical region, and we construct the random variable

$$\Delta(X) = I_{[X \in W(K_0)]},$$

which satisfies the definition of a randomized test. However, there might not exist a K which satisfies $G(K) = \alpha$; let us call this case (ii). Then by Lemmas 1, 2, and 3 there exists a value of K, which we again denote by K_0, and numbers α_0, α_1, where $\alpha_0 < \alpha \leqq \alpha_1$, such that

$$G(K) \leqq \alpha_0 \quad \text{for all} \quad K > K_0, \quad \text{where} \quad \underset{K > K_0}{\text{l.u.b.}}\, G(K) = \alpha_0,$$

and

$$G(K) \geqq \alpha_1 \quad \text{for all} \quad K < K_0, \quad \text{where} \quad \underset{K < K_0}{\text{g.l.b.}}\, G(K) = \alpha_1.$$

It is easy to see that $P([X \in W(K_0)]|\mathrm{H}) = \alpha_0$. Let us denote

$$B = \{\mathbf{z}_n | f_1(\mathbf{z}_n) = K_0 f_0(\mathbf{z}_n)\}.$$

We then obtain $P([\mathbf{X} \in B]|\mathrm{H}) = \alpha_1 - \alpha_0$. If we denote

$$C = \{\mathbf{z}_n | f_1(\mathbf{z}_n) < K_0 f_0(\mathbf{z}_n)\},$$

then $P([\mathbf{X} \in C]|\mathrm{H}) = 1 - \alpha_1$. Now we construct the randomized test

$$\Delta(\mathbf{X}) = I_{[\mathbf{X} \in W(K_0)]} + \frac{\alpha - \alpha_0}{\alpha_1 - \alpha_0} I_{[\mathbf{X} \in B]}.$$

It is easy to verify that

$$E(\Delta(\mathbf{X})|\mathrm{H}) = \alpha.$$

Note that in both case (i) and case (ii), if $\mathbf{z}_n \in C$, then $\Delta(\mathbf{z}_n) = 0$. We finally want to show that in either case (i) or case (ii), if $\Psi(\mathbf{X})$ is any other randomized test with level of significance α, then

$$E(\Delta(\mathbf{X})|\mathrm{H}') \geqq E(\Psi(X)|\mathrm{H}').$$

In order to prove this it suffices to prove that

$$E(\Delta(\mathbf{X}) - \Psi(\mathbf{X})|\mathrm{H}') \geqq 0.$$

We first write

$$E(\Delta(\mathbf{X}) - \Psi(\mathbf{X})|\mathrm{H}') = \sum_n (\Delta(\mathbf{z}_n) - \Psi(\mathbf{z}_n))f_1(\mathbf{z}_n') = a + b + c,$$

where

$$a = \sum_{\mathbf{z}_n \in W(K_0)} (\Delta(\mathbf{z}_n) - \Psi(\mathbf{z}_n))f_1(\mathbf{z}_n'),$$

$$b = \sum_{\mathbf{z}_n \in B} (\Delta(\mathbf{z}_n) - \Psi(\mathbf{z}_n))f_1(\mathbf{z}_n'),$$

and

$$c = \sum_{\mathbf{z}_n \in C} (\Delta(\mathbf{z}_n) - \Psi(\mathbf{z}_n))f_1(\mathbf{z}_n').$$

For every $\mathbf{z}_n \in W(K_0)$, $\Delta(\mathbf{z}_n) = 1 \geqq \Psi(\mathbf{z}_n)$, and hence, using the definition of $W(K_0)$, we obtain

$$a \geqq K_0 \sum_{\mathbf{z}_n \in W(K_0)} (\Delta(\mathbf{z}_n) - \Psi(\mathbf{z}_n))f_0(\mathbf{z}_n').$$

By the definition of B,

$$b = K_0 \sum_{\mathbf{z}_n \in B} (\Delta(\mathbf{z}_n) - \Psi(\mathbf{z}_n))f_0(\mathbf{z}_n').$$

Since $\Delta(\mathbf{z}_n) = 0$ when $\mathbf{z}_n \in C$ (in both cases (i) and (ii)), we have

$$\Delta(\mathbf{z}_n) - \Psi(\mathbf{z}_n) \leqq 0 \quad \text{for all} \quad \mathbf{z}_n \in C.$$

Also $f_1(\mathbf{z}_n') < K_0 f_0(\mathbf{z}_n')$ for all $\mathbf{z}_n \in C$. Since $K_0 \geqq 0$, it follows that

$$c \geqq K_0 \sum_{\mathbf{z}_n \in C} (\Delta(\mathbf{z}_n) - \Psi(\mathbf{z}_n))f_0(\mathbf{z}_n').$$

Thus

$$E(\Delta(\mathbf{X}) - \Psi(\mathbf{X})|\mathrm{H}) \geqq K_0(E(\Delta(\mathbf{X})|\mathrm{H}) - E(\Psi(\mathbf{X})|\mathrm{H})) = K_0(\alpha - \alpha) = 0,$$

which concludes the proof of the theorem.

In summary, if we cannot find a best critical region for the particular level of significance, α, being used, we construct the randomized test

$$\Delta(X) = I_{[\mathbf{X} \in W(K_0)]} + \frac{\alpha - \alpha_0}{\alpha_1 - \alpha_0} I_{[\mathbf{X} \in B]},$$

where K_0, $W(K_0)$, B, α_0, and α_1 are as defined for Theorem 4. If the event $[\mathbf{X} \in W(K_0)]$ occurs, we reject the hypothesis. If the event $[\mathbf{X} \in B]$ occurs, we reject the hypothesis with probability $(\alpha - \alpha_0)/(\alpha_1 - \alpha_0)$. Otherwise we fail to reject the hypothesis.

EXERCISES

1. Prove that the probability of the event E in the random digits chance mechanism considered in this section is equal to $.\,a_1a_2 \cdots a_n$, and prove that

$$E = [.\,U_1U_2 \cdots U_n \leqq .\,a_1a_2 \cdots a_n].$$

2. If you had to construct a chance mechanism in which a certain event occurs with probability $\frac{2}{3}$, could you design an alternate method to the one considered in this section?

3. Prove: If p is a rational number, $0 < p < 1$, then a chance mechanism and an event E can always be constructed such that $P(E) = p$. If p is irrational, then, for any $\epsilon > 0$, a chance mechanism and an event E can be constructed such that $|p - P(E)| < \epsilon$.

4. In the medical example given at the beginning of this section, find a best randomized test when the level of significance is .05.

5. (First re-read the medical example given at the beginning of this section.) Let $\Omega = \{\omega_1, \omega_2, \omega_3, \omega_4, \omega_5, \omega_6\}$. Define a random variable X over Ω by

$$X(\omega_i) = \begin{cases} i - 1 & \text{if } i = 1, 2 \\ i - 2 & \text{if } i = 3, 4, 5, 6. \end{cases}$$

We next define two probabilities P_0 and P_1 over Ω as follows:

$$\begin{aligned} &P_0(\omega_1) = .0001, \quad P_0(\omega_2) = .0002, \quad P_0(\omega_3) = .0002, \\ &P_0(\omega_4) = .0135, \quad P_0(\omega_5) = .1715, \quad P_0(\omega_6) = .8145, \\ &P_1(\omega_1) = .6561, \quad P_1(\omega_2) = .1458, \quad P_1(\omega_3) = .1458, \\ &P_1(\omega_4) = .0486, \quad P_1(\omega_5) = .0036, \quad P_1(\omega_6) = .0001. \end{aligned}$$

Next we define the event

$$[\text{Reject H}] = \{\omega_1, \omega_2\}.$$

(a) Compute $P_0[\text{Reject H}]$ and $P_1[\text{Reject H}]$.
(b) Show that

$$P_0([\text{Reject H}] \mid [X = x]) = P_1([\text{Reject H}] \mid [X = x])$$

for $x = 0, 1, 2, 3, 4$, and compute these probabilities.

6. Construct a fundamental probability set for problem 4 in which [Reject H] can be represented as a collection of elementary events.

CHAPTER **12**

Testing Simple and Composite Hypotheses

12.1 Uniformly Most Powerful Critical Regions

A hypothesis, or a statistical hypothesis, is a nonempty set of joint density functions of some observable random variables $\mathbf{X}' = (X_1, \cdots, X_n)$. In the last chapter each hypothesis we considered consisted of one joint density function. If a hypothesis does consist of just one density function it is called a *simple hypothesis;* if it consists of more than one density function then it is called a *composite hypothesis.* Many occasions occur where we want to distinguish between two composite hypotheses or between a simple and a composite hypothesis. For example, in acceptance sampling one would select a random sample of size n and would then want to decide whether the entire lot has less than 4% defectives or not less than 4% defectives. Then each of the two hypotheses will be a set of binomial densities where $0 < p < 0.04$ in one of them and $0.04 \leqq p < 1$ in the other. In this chapter we shall consider problems involving a simple hypothesis and a composite hypothesis or involving both composite hypotheses. In this section we shall consider the case only where the hypothesis tested is simple and where the alternative is composite.

Let us suppose that the observable random variables are $\mathbf{X}' = (X_1, \cdots, X_n)$ and that the joint density $f_{\mathbf{X}'}(\mathbf{x}')$ depends on a real number θ (which statisticians call a parameter). We denote this fact by writing the joint density of $\mathbf{X}'$ as $f_{\mathbf{X}'}(\mathbf{x}'|\theta)$. If Θ denotes the set of all possible values of θ for which there is such a joint density, and if θ_0 is a fixed element of Θ, then by

$$f_{\mathbf{X}'}(\mathbf{x}'|\theta), \quad \theta \neq \theta_0$$

we mean the set of densities

$$\{f_{\mathbf{X}'}(\mathbf{x}'|\theta)|\theta \in \Theta, \theta \neq \theta_0\}.$$

We are now concerned with testing the hypothesis

$$\text{H}: f_{\mathbf{X}'}(\mathbf{x}'|\theta_0)$$

against the alternative

$$\text{H}': f_{\mathbf{X}'}(\mathbf{x}'|\theta), \quad \theta \neq \theta_0$$

with the level of significance α. We shall abbreviate this frequently by writing that we are testing the hypothesis

$$\text{H}: \theta = \theta_0$$

against the alternative

$$\text{H}': \theta \neq \theta_0$$

with level of significance α. The problem is to determine a critical region $W \subset E^{(n)}$ such that if the event $[\mathbf{X} \in W]$ occurs, the hypothesis H is rejected, and if $[\mathbf{X} \notin W]$ occurs, then H is accepted. Let us denote

$$\pi_W(\theta) = P([\mathbf{X} \in W]|\theta) = \int \underset{W}{\cdots} \int f_{\mathbf{X}'}(\mathbf{x}'|\theta)\, d\mathbf{x}'.$$

The probability $\pi_W(\theta)$ is the power of the test when the critical region W is used and when $f_{\mathbf{X}'}(\mathbf{x}'|\theta)$ is the true density of $\mathbf{X}'$. As a function of θ, $\pi_W(\theta)$ is called the power of the test W or of the test based on W. We of course desire that $\pi_W(\theta_0) \leqq \alpha$ for all critical regions W. However, if among these there is a critical region W^* such that for every other critical region W,

$$\pi_{W^*}(\theta) \geqq \pi_W(\theta) \quad \text{for all} \quad \theta \in \Theta,$$

then W^* is said to be "uniformly best" or a "uniformly most powerful critical region" (which we shall abbreviate U.M.P.C.R.). If and when such uniformly best critical regions exist, we shall want to use them.

However, how does one go about obtaining a uniformly most powerful critical region when it does exist? What one first does is to select an arbitrary $\theta_1 \in \Theta$, where $\theta_1 \neq \theta_0$. Then one tries to find a best critical region W^* for testing the simple hypothesis $\text{H}: f_{\mathbf{X}'}(\mathbf{x}'|\theta_0)$ against the simple alternative $\text{H}': f_{\mathbf{X}'}(\mathbf{x}'|\theta_1)$ with level of significance α. If this best critical region W^* does not depend on the θ_1 selected, then it is easy to see that W^* satisfies the "uniformly best" property defined above. Thus the problem of finding a U.M.P.C.R. in testing a simple hypothesis against a composite alternative is reduced to finding a best critical region for testing the simple hypothesis against any one of the alternatives and by showing that it does not depend on the alternative.

Let us consider an example. Let X be a random variable with absolutely continuous distribution, whose density is

$$f_X(x|\theta) = \begin{cases} (1/\theta)e^{-x/\theta} & \text{if} \quad x \geqq 0 \\ 0 & \text{if} \quad x < 0, \end{cases}$$

where $\theta > 0$ is a constant (the negative exponential distribution). Let $X_1, \cdots, X_n$ be n independent observations on X. The observable random variables are $\mathbf{X}' = (X_1, \cdots, X_n)$, and their joint density is

$$f_{\mathbf{X}'}(\mathbf{x}'|\theta) = \begin{cases} \left(\frac{1}{\theta}\right)^n \exp -\frac{1}{\theta}\sum_{i=1}^n x_i & \text{if} \quad \min_{1 \leqq i \leqq n} \{x_i\} \geqq 0 \\ 0 & \text{otherwise.} \end{cases}$$

We assume that $\Theta = [1, \infty)$. We want to test the simple hypothesis $\mathrm{H}:\theta = 1$ against the composite alternative $\mathrm{H}':\theta > 1$ with level of significance $\alpha = .03$. We therefore select an arbitrary $\theta_1 > 1$ and try to find a best critical region for testing $\mathrm{H}:\theta = 1$ against the alternative $\mathrm{H}':\theta = \theta_1$, using level of significance α, which does not depend on our choice of θ_1. By the Neyman-Pearson fundamental lemma, we must find a set $W^* \subset E^{(n)}$ such that for some positive constant K,

$$f_{\mathbf{X}'}(\mathbf{x}'|\theta_1) \geqq K f_{\mathbf{X}'}(\mathbf{x}'|1) \quad \text{for all} \quad \mathbf{x} \in W^*,$$

and such that the reverse inequality holds for all $\mathbf{x} \notin W^*$. Clearly the inequality holds for all $\mathbf{x}$ for which $\min \{x_i | 1 \leqq i \leqq n\} < 0$, whatever be $K > 0$. For all other $\mathbf{x}$ we want a set of $\mathbf{x}$'s which satisfy an inequality of the form

$$\left(\frac{1}{\theta_1}\right)^n \exp -\frac{1}{\theta_1}\sum_{i=1}^n x_i \Big/ \exp - \sum_{i=1}^n x_i \geqq K$$

which is equivalent to

$$\left(1 - \frac{1}{\theta_1}\right) \sum_{i=1}^n x_i \geqq \text{(some) } K_1.$$

Since $\theta_1 > 1$, then $1 - 1/\theta_1 > 0$ and the inequality becomes equivalent to

$$\sum_{i=1}^n x_i \geqq \text{(some) } K_2.$$

At this point the reader should notice that all we have to do is prove that K_2 does not depend on the value of θ_1, and thus we shall have a U.M.P.C.R. However, if Θ were taken to be $\Theta = (0, \infty)$, then the best critical region obtained would depend on the value of θ_1. If $\theta_1 > 1$, then $1 - 1/\theta_1 > 0$ and a set of the form $\{\mathbf{x} | \sum_{i=1}^n x_i \geqq K_2\}$ would be a best critical region. If $0 < \theta_1 < 1$, then $1 - 1/\theta_1 < 0$, and a set of the form $\{\mathbf{x} | \sum_{i=1}^n x_i \leqq K_2\}$ would be a best critical region. Hence in this latter case we could not obtain a critical region which is a best critical region for all $\theta_1 \neq 1$.

We proceed with the test. We easily notice that whether the hypothesis is true or not, the following is true:

$$P[\mathbf{X} \in \{\mathbf{x} | \min_{1 \leqq i \leqq n} x_i < 0\}] = 1 - P[\mathbf{X} \in \{\mathbf{x} | \min_{1 \leqq i \leqq n} x_i \geqq 0\}]$$

$$= 1 - P \bigcap_{i=1}^{n} [X_i \geqq 0] = 1 - \prod_{i=1}^{n} P[X_i \geqq 0] = 1 - 1 = 0.$$

Therefore, we need only consider as the event [Reject H] an event of the form

$$\left[\mathbf{X} \in \left\{\mathbf{x} | \sum_{i=1}^{n} x_i \geqq K_2\right\}\right] = \left[\sum_{i=1}^{n} X_i \geqq K_2\right].$$

Our problem is to evaluate K_2 so that

$$P\left(\left[\sum_{i=1}^{n} X_i \geqq K_2\right] | \mathrm{H}\right) = .03,$$

.03 being the level of significance. In Section 6.3 the distribution of $U_1 = \sum_{i=1}^{n} X_i$ was found to have a density

$$f_{U_1}(u_1|\theta) = \begin{cases} u_1^{n-1} e^{-u_1/\theta}/(n-1)!\theta^n & \text{if} \quad u_1 > 0 \\ 0 & \text{if} \quad u_1 \leqq 0. \end{cases}$$

The value of K_2 should thus satisfy

$$\frac{1}{(n-1)!} \int_{K_2}^{\infty} t^{n-1} e^{-t}\, dt = .03.$$

This value of K_2 can be obtained accurately by referring to tables of the incomplete gamma function (see: Karl Pearson, "Tables of the Incomplete Gamma Function," Cambridge Univ. Press, New York and London, 1922). For fixed n, the power function as a function of θ is

$$\pi(\theta) = P\left(\left[\sum_{i=1}^{n} X_i \geqq K_2\right] | \theta\right)$$

$$= \int_{K_2}^{\infty} \frac{u_1^{n-1} e^{-u_1/\theta}}{(n-1)!\theta^n}\, du_1$$

$$= \int_{K_2/\theta}^{\infty} \frac{t^{n-1} e^{-t}}{(n-1)!}\, dt.$$

Since K_2 is now known, $\pi(\theta)$ can be computed for different values of θ by referring to the tables just mentioned.

The value of K_2 and the power function $\pi(\theta)$ may be approximated by use of the central limit theorem. In this case $X_1, \cdots, X_n$ are independent and identically distributed, with common expectation θ and variance θ^2. By the central limit theorem (see Section 7.5), for large n the following equation is approximately true:

$$P\left[\frac{\sum_{i=1}^{n} X_i - n\theta}{\sqrt{n\theta^2}} \leqq x\right] = \frac{1}{\sqrt{2\pi}} \int_{-\infty}^{x} \exp -\frac{t^2}{2}\, dt.$$

Hence (approximately),

$$P\left(\left[\sum_{i=1}^{n} X_i \geqq K_2\right] \| \theta\right) = P\left(\left[\frac{\sum_{i=1}^{n} X_i - n\theta}{\sqrt{n\theta^2}} \geqq \frac{K_2 - n\theta}{\sqrt{n\theta^2}}\right] \| \theta\right)$$

$$= \frac{1}{\sqrt{2\pi}} \int_{(K_2 - n\theta)/\sqrt{n\theta^2}}^{\infty} \exp -\frac{t^2}{2}\, dt.$$

When $\theta = 1$, we want this above probability to equal .03. Thus we have (by referring to the table of the normal distribution) that $(K_2 - n)/\sqrt{n} = 1.881$ or $K_2 = 1.881\sqrt{n} + n$. Therefore, we reject the hypothesis $\text{H}:\theta = 1$ when the event $[\sum_{i=1}^{n} X_i \geqq 1.881\sqrt{n} + n]$ occurs. We may easily compute (approximately) the power $\pi(\theta)$ of the test as a function of θ, $\theta > 1$. One first obtains $EX = \theta$ and $\text{Var}(X) = \theta^2$, whatever be the true value of θ. Then, because of the central limit theorem, the distribution of

$$\left(\sum_{i=1}^{n} X_i - n\theta\right) \Big/ \sqrt{n\theta^2}$$

is seen to be approximately $N(0, 1)$. Hence we obtain (approximately)

$$\pi(\theta) = P\left(\left[\sum_{i=1}^{n} X_i \geqq 1.881\sqrt{n} + n\right] \| \theta\right)$$

$$= P\left(\left[\frac{\sum_{i=1}^{n} X_i - n\theta}{\sqrt{n\theta^2}} \geqq \frac{1.881\sqrt{n} - n(\theta - 1)}{\sqrt{n\theta^2}}\right] \| \theta\right) = \frac{1}{\sqrt{2\pi}} \int_{L(\theta)}^{\infty} \exp -\frac{t^2}{2}\, dt,$$

where

$$L(\theta) = (1.881\sqrt{n} - n(\theta - 1))/\sqrt{n\theta^2}.$$

For a given value of n, the student should find no difficulty in computing points for a graph of $\pi(\theta)$.

As a second example of a U.M.P.C.R. we consider a discrete distribution. Let X be a random variable with discrete density

$$f_X(x|N) = 1/N, \qquad x = 1, 2, \cdots, N.$$

Let $X_1, \cdots, X_n$ denote n independent observations on X. We want to find a U.M.P.C.R. for testing the simple hypothesis $\text{H}:N = N_0$ against the composite alternative $\text{H}':N \geqq 1$, $N \neq N_0$, with level of significance α. Here N_0 is some fixed positive integer, and α is some small fixed probability. We first observe that

$$f_{X_1, \cdots, X_n}(x_1, \cdots, x_n|N) = (1/N)^n$$

if $1 \leqq x_i \leqq N$, $i = 1, 2, \cdots, n$. In order to find a U.M.P.C.R. we select a value N_1 of N, $N_1 \neq N_0$, then find a best critical region W^* for testing the simple hypothesis $\text{H}:N = N_0$ against the simple alternative $\text{H}':N = N_1$, and finally show that this best critical region does not depend on N_1. (In what follows we shall ignore all negative coordinates.)

We first examine the inequality

$$f_{\mathbf{X}}'(\mathbf{x}'|N_1) \geqq K f_{\mathbf{X}}'(\mathbf{x}'|N_0),$$

for some $K > 0$. This inequality holds for all $\mathbf{x}$ in the set

$$A = \{\mathbf{x}| \max_{1 \leqq i \leqq n} x_i > N_0\},$$

no matter what the value of N_1 is, and $P([\mathbf{X} \in A]|N_0) = 0$. If now $N_1 > N_0$, then the ratio $f_{\mathbf{X}}'(\mathbf{x}'|N_1)/f_{\mathbf{X}}'(\mathbf{x}'|N_0)$ is positive and constant over

$$B = \{\mathbf{x}|1 \leqq x_i \leqq N_0, 1 \leqq i \leqq n\}.$$

If we select any subset $S \subset B$ such that $P([\mathbf{X} \in S]|N_0) = \alpha$, then $A \cup S$ is a best critical region. However, as soon as we consider $0 < N_1 < N_0$, then we see that S must be of a more definite form. Since the ratio $f_{\mathbf{X}}'(\mathbf{x}'|N_1)/f_{\mathbf{X}}'(\mathbf{x}'|N_0)$ is positive and constant over

$$C(N_1) = \{\mathbf{x}|1 \leqq x_i \leqq N_1, 1 \leqq i \leqq n\},$$

then we should want to adjoin to A a subset S of $C(N_0)$ such that $P([\mathbf{X} \in S]|N_0) = \alpha$. If N_1 is so small that $P([\mathbf{X} \in C(N_1)]|N_0) < \alpha$, then S would have to include points in B which are not in $C(N_1)$. However if N_1 is such that $P([\mathbf{X} \in C(N_1)]|N_0) = \alpha$, then we must take $S = C(N_1)$. Thus S must take the form

$$S = \{\mathbf{x}| \max_{1 \leqq i \leqq n} x_i \leqq K_0\}.$$

The constant K_0 is yet to be determined. Since we want $P([\mathbf{X} \in S]|N_0) = \alpha$, and since

$$\bigcap_{i=1}^{n} [X_i \leqq K_0] = [\max_{1 \leqq i \leqq n} X_i \leqq K_0]$$
$$= [\mathbf{X} \in S],$$

we shall want to find K_0 such that

$$P\left(\bigcap_{i=1}^{n} [X_i \leqq K_0]|N_0\right) = \alpha.$$

We are given that $X_1, \cdots, X_n$ are independent, and thus

$$P\left(\bigcap_{i=1}^{n} [X_i \leqq K_0]|N_0\right) = \prod_{i=1}^{n} P([X_i \leqq K_0]|N_0).$$

But, for each i,

$$P([X_i \leqq K_0]|N_0) = K_0/N_0,$$

and thus

$$(K_0/N_0)^n = \alpha.$$

From this we obtain

$$K_0 = N_0\alpha^{1/n},$$

and

$$S = \{\mathbf{x}|\ \max_{1 \leqq i \leqq n} x_i \leqq N_0\alpha^{1/n}\}.$$

The test then is to reject the hypothesis when the event $[X \in A \cup S]$ occurs, and $A \cup S$ is a U.M.P.C.R.

We conclude this second example by computing the power of the test as a function of N. If $N \leqq N_0\alpha^{1/n}$, then it is easy to see that $P([\mathbf{X} \in A \cup S]|N) = 1$. If $N_0\alpha^{1/n} < N \leqq N_0$, then $P([\mathbf{X} \in A \cup S]|N) = (N_0/N)^n\alpha$, and if $N > N_0$, one easily computes

$$P([\mathbf{X} \in A \cup S]|N) = 1 - (1 - \alpha)(N_0/N)^n.$$

A graph of the power function

$$\pi(N) = P([\mathbf{X} \in A \cup S]|N)$$

appears as in Fig. 4.

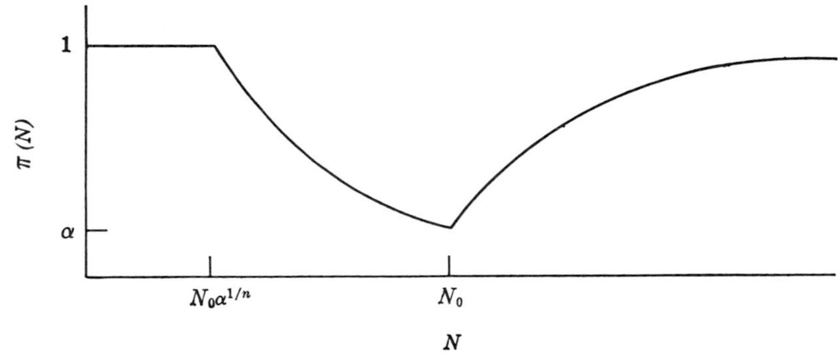

Fig. 4

Unfortunately, a U.M.P.C.R. does not always exist for testing a simple hypothesis against a composite alternative, and other methods of deriving tests are needed. One such method is presented in the next section.

EXERCISES

(In the following problems, X is a random variable, and $X_1, \cdots, X_n$ are n independent observations on X. Thus $X_1, \cdots, X_n$ are the observable random variables.)

1. Assume that the distribution of X is $N(\theta, 1)$. Prove that there exists a U.M.P.C.R. for testing the hypothesis $H:\theta = 0$ against the alternative $H':\theta > 0$ with level of significance $\alpha = .05$. Draw the power curve for your test when $n = 9$.

2. Assume that $P[X = 1] = p$ and $P[X = 0] = 1 - p$, where $0 < p < 1$. Prove that there exists a U.M.P.C.R. for testing the simple hypothesis $H{:}p = .04$ against the composite alternative $H'{:}.04 < p < 1$ with level of significance $\alpha = .02$. Draw the power curve for $n = 64$.

3. In problem 1 find the smallest value θ_1 of θ such that the probability of rejecting the hypothesis when θ_1 is true is not less than .96.

4. In problem 2, find the smallest value p_1 of p such that the probability of rejecting the hypothesis when p_1 is the true value of p is not less than .92.

5. Assume that

$$f_X(x|\theta) = \begin{cases} 1/\theta & \text{if } 0 < x < \theta \\ 0 & \text{if } x \leqq 0 \text{ or } x \geqq 0, \end{cases}$$

where $\theta > 0$. Show that there exists a U.M.P.C.R. for testing the simple hypothesis: $H{:}\theta = 1$ against the composite alternative $H'{:}\theta \neq 1$. If $n = 10$, draw a power curve for the test. Use level of significance $\alpha = .03$.

6. Assume $f_X(x|\theta) = e^{-\theta}\theta^x/x!$, $x = 0, 1, 2, \cdots$, where $\theta > 0$ (the Poisson distribution). Show that there exists a U.M.P.C.R. for testing the simple hypothesis $H{:}\theta = \theta_0$ against the composite alternative $H'{:}\theta > \theta_0$. Draw the power curve for the test in the special case where $\theta_0 = 1$ and $n = 25$. (*Hint:* use the central limit theorem for approximation purposes.) Use level of significance $\alpha = .04$.

7. Assume that the distribution of X is $N(\theta, 1)$, where $-\infty < \theta < \infty$. Show that there does not exist a U.M.P.C.R. for testing the simple hypothesis $H{:}\theta = 0$ against the composite alternative $H'{:}\theta \neq 0$ for any level of significance α.

8. Let $X_1, \cdots, X_n$ be n independent observations on a random variable X which has a negative exponential distribution with density

$$f_X(x|\beta) = \begin{cases} e^{-(x-\beta)} & \text{if } x \in (\beta, \infty) \\ 0 & \text{if } x \leqq \beta, \end{cases}$$

where β is unknown, $-\infty < \beta < \infty$. Show that there exists a U.M.P.C.R. for testing the hypothesis $H{:}\beta = \beta_0$ against the alternative $H'{:}\beta \neq \beta_0$ with level of significance α.

12.2 The Likelihood Ratio Test

There are two methods of approaching hypothesis testing. One method is a purely rational approach in which one decides just what properties the test of hypothesis should have and then derives the test (or class of tests) which has these properties. We have already considered tests of this sort when we obtained best critical regions and uniformly most powerful critical regions. A second method of obtaining tests is based on intuitive (and possibly nonrigorous reasoning), and we deal with this method in this section. These two approaches have already been used by us in the problem of point estimation. In this problem the rational approach was to *define* the desired properties of estimates to be unbiasedness, consistency, and the property of minimum variance—and then to derive estimates which have these properties. The intuitive approach was through the use of maximum likelihood estimates.

We have already seen (in problem 7, Section 12.1) that there are cases in testing a simple hypothesis against a composite alternative in which a U.M.P.C.R. does not exist. Further, when testing a composite hypothesis H against a composite alternative H′ one might be tempted to select one of the densities f_0 in H and one of the densities f_1 in H′ and use the fundamental lemma to find a best critical region. However, this best critical region might not be independent of the choice of f_0 and f_1. In such cases we shall consider a test called the likelihood ratio test, and in cases where this test cannot be derived for practical use we shall consider tests which will have some strong appeal on intuitive grounds.

In order to introduce the likelihood ratio test, we must first present the formalism of "a density which depends on a parameter θ." Let $\mathfrak{D}$ denote the set of all joint densities of $\mathbf{X}' = (X_1, \cdots, X_n)$ in the hypotheses tested, H, and in the alternative, H′, i.e., $\mathfrak{D} = \mathrm{H} \cup \mathrm{H}'$. The set $\mathfrak{D}$ is called the *set of admissible hypotheses*. It might occur that for some positive integer k there is a subset Θ of $E^{(k)}$ which can be put into one-to-one correspondence with $\mathfrak{D}$. In such a case, the density which corresponds to $\theta \in \Theta$ will be denoted by $f_{\mathbf{X}'}(\mathbf{x}'|\theta)$, where $\theta = (\theta_1, \cdots, \theta_k)$, and one then says that "the density of $\mathbf{X}'$ depends on θ." Thus one may write

$$\mathfrak{D} = \{f_{\mathbf{X}'}(\mathbf{x}'|\theta), \theta \in \Theta\}.$$

Now let Θ_0 be a proper, nonempty subset of Θ, and let $\Theta \setminus \Theta_0$ denote the set of points in Θ which are not in Θ_0. One might wish to test the hypothesis

$$\mathrm{H}: \{f_{\mathbf{X}'}(\mathbf{x}'|\theta)|\theta \in \Theta_0\}$$

against the alternative

$$\mathrm{H}': \{f_{\mathbf{X}'}(\mathbf{x}'|\theta)|\theta \in \Theta \setminus \Theta_0\}$$

with some level of significance α. This is usually shortened by referring to the hypothesis tested as $\mathrm{H}:\theta \in \Theta_0$ and to the alternative as $\mathrm{H}':\theta \in \Theta \setminus \Theta_0$. The "dependence" of the density of $\mathbf{X}'$ on θ might be in explicit functional form, or might simply exist, or might be a combination of both.

As an example of the case where the dependence of the density of $\mathbf{X}'$ on θ is in explicit functional form, consider a random variable X whose distribution is $N(\mu, \sigma^2)$, where μ and σ^2 are unknown. Let the observable random variables be n independent observations on X, $\mathbf{X}' = (X_1, \cdots, X_n)$. Since the variance is always positive, then the set of admissible hypotheses is characterized by the subset

$$\Theta = \{(\mu, \sigma^2)|-\infty < \mu < \infty, \sigma^2 > 0\}$$

of $E^{(2)}$. One might be interested in testing the hypothesis $\mathrm{H}:\mu = \sigma^2$ against the alternative $\mathrm{H}':\mu \neq \sigma^2$. In this case both the hypothesis tested and the alternative are composite. The hypothesis Θ_0 is the line bisecting the first quadrant in the (μ, σ^2)-plane, i.e.,

$$\Theta_0 = \{(\mu, \sigma^2) | \mu = \sigma^2, \sigma^2 > 0\},$$

and the alternative $\Theta \setminus \Theta_0$ consists of all remaining points in the first two quadrants of the (μ, σ^2)-plane, i.e.,

$$\Theta \setminus \Theta_0 = \{(\mu, \sigma^2) | \mu \neq \sigma^2, \sigma^2 > 0\}.$$

Now we return to the general situation above where we considered testing the hypothesis $H: \theta \in \Theta_0$ against the alternative $\theta \in \Theta \setminus \Theta_0$ with level of significance α. Consider the following function defined over $E^{(n)}$ ·

$$\Lambda(\mathbf{x}') = \frac{\sup \{f_{\mathbf{X}'}(\mathbf{x}'|\theta) | \theta \in \Theta_0\}}{\sup \{f_{X'}(\mathbf{x}'|\theta) | \theta \in \Theta\}}.$$

(We define sup S, where S is a nonempty set of real numbers, to be a number s_0 such that $s \leqq s_0$ for every $s \in S$ and such that for every $\epsilon > 0$ there is an $s \in S$ which satisfies $s > s_0 - \epsilon$.)

Definition. *The* likelihood ratio test *is defined as follows: select as critical region $W \subset E^{(n)}$ such that for some $K \in [0, 1]$, $\Lambda(\mathbf{x}') \leqq K$ for all $\mathbf{x} \in W$ and $\Lambda(\mathbf{x}') \geqq K$ for all $\mathbf{x} \notin W$. The value of K should be the largest for which*

$$P([\mathbf{X} \in W] | \theta) \leqq \alpha \quad \textit{for all} \quad \theta \in \Theta_0.$$

We give here some intuitive reasoning behind the use of the likelihood ratio test in the case of a joint discrete distribution. For simplicity let us consider the case where

$$W = \{\mathbf{x} | \Lambda(\mathbf{x}') \leqq K\}.$$

Then the likelihood ratio test is the event

$$[\text{Reject H}] = [\mathbf{X} \in W] = [\Lambda(\mathbf{X}') \leqq K].$$

Now since $\mathbf{X}'$ has a joint discrete distribution the probability of obtaining these joint n observations is $f_{\mathbf{X}'}(\mathbf{X}'|\theta)$ when θ is true. What one is basically assuming is that whatever be the outcome $\mathbf{X}'$ the value of θ is close to or equal to that value $\hat{\theta}$ which makes the outcome $\mathbf{X}'$ most probable, i.e., an outcome with largest probability. Since Θ_0 is involved in the index set in both the numerator and denominator of $\Lambda(\mathbf{x}')$, then when the hypothesis is true the value of $\Lambda(\mathbf{X}')$ is close to one with high probability. However, if the hypothesis is not true, $f_{\mathbf{X}'}(\mathbf{X}'|\theta)$ has larger most probable values for $\theta \in \Theta \setminus \Theta_0$ than for $\theta \in \Theta_0$. Thus the denominator of $\Lambda(\mathbf{X}')$ is with large probability much larger than the numerator, and the ratio $\Lambda(\mathbf{X}')$ is closer to zero. Consequently, for small values of $\Lambda(\mathbf{X}')$ we should want to reject the hypothesis while for large values we should want to accept it. Essentially the same kind of intuitive reasoning holds for joint densities of random variables with absolutely continuous distributions.

We next consider an example. Let X be a random variable whose distribution is $N(\mu, 1)$, where μ is unknown. Let $X_1, \cdots, X_n$ be n independent observations on X, i.e., $X_1, \cdots, X_n$ are independent, and each X_i has the same distribution as X. We want to test the simple hypothesis $\mathrm{H}:\mu = \mu_0$ against the composite alternative $\mathrm{H}':\mu \neq \mu_0$ with level of significance α. There is no U.M.P.C.R. in this case (see problem 7 in the exercises of Section 12.1), and so we shall derive a likelihood ratio test. Since

$$f_{\mathbf{X}'}(\mathbf{x}'|\mu) = (2\pi)^{-n/2} \exp -\tfrac{1}{2} \sum_{i=1}^{n} (x_i - \mu)^2,$$

we have

$$\Lambda(\mathbf{x}') = \frac{(2\pi)^{-n/2} \exp -\frac{1}{2} \sum_{i=1}^{n} (x_i - \mu_0)^2}{\sup \{(2\pi)^{-n/2} \exp -\frac{1}{2} \sum_{i=1}^{n} (x_i - \mu)^2 | -\infty < \mu < \infty\}}.$$

The denominator of $\Lambda(\mathbf{x}')$ is evaluated by taking the derivative of $f_{\mathbf{X}'}(\mathbf{x}'|\mu)$ with respect to μ, equating this derivative to zero, and solving for μ. Then this value of μ is substituted into $f_{\mathbf{X}'}(\mathbf{x}'|\mu)$. The value of μ obtained by this procedure is $\bar{x}_n = (x_1 + \cdots + x_n)/n$, and

$$\begin{aligned} f_{\mathbf{X}'}(\mathbf{x}'|\bar{x}_n) &= (2\pi)^{-n/2} \exp -\tfrac{1}{2} \sum_{i=1}^{n} (x_i - \bar{x}_n)^2 \\ &= (2\pi)^{-n/2} \exp -\tfrac{1}{2} \sum_{i=1}^{n} ((x_i - \mu_0) - (\bar{x}_n - \mu_0))^2 \\ &= (2\pi)^{-n/2} \exp -\tfrac{1}{2} \left(\sum_{i=1}^{n} (x_i - \mu_0)^2 - n\,(\bar{x}_n - \mu_0)^2 \right). \end{aligned}$$

Hence

$$\Lambda(\mathbf{x}') = \exp -\tfrac{1}{2} n (\bar{x}_n - \mu_0)^2.$$

The inequality $\Lambda(\mathbf{x}') \leqq K$ is therefore equivalent to $(\bar{x}_n - \mu_0)^2 \geqq K_1$ (where K_1 is some constant) or $|\bar{x}_n - \mu_0| \geqq K_2$ (where K_2 is some constant). Thus the critical region determined by the likelihood ratio test is of the form

$$W = \{\mathbf{x} \in E^{(n)} |\ |\bar{x}_n - \mu_0| \geqq K_2\}.$$

The remaining problem, after determining the form of the critical region is called the *distributional problem* and consists of evaluating K_2 in order that

$$P([\mathbf{X} \in W]|\mu_0) = P([|\overline{X}_n - \mu_0| \geqq K_2]|\mu_0) = \alpha.$$

When $\mu = \mu_0$ the student can easily verify that $\overline{X}_n - \mu_0$ is $N(0, 1/n)$. Hence the distribution of $\sqrt{n}(\overline{X}_n - \mu_0)$ is $N(0, 1)$, and K_2 should satisfy

$$\frac{1}{\sqrt{2\pi}} \int_{-K_2\sqrt{n}}^{K_2\sqrt{n}} \exp -\frac{t^2}{2}\, dt = 1 - \alpha,$$

or

$$\frac{1}{\sqrt{2\pi}} \int_{-\infty}^{K_2\sqrt{n}} \exp -\frac{t^2}{2}\, dt = 1 - \alpha/2.$$

Depending on α and n, the value of $\sqrt{n}K_2$ and therefore of K_2 can be obtained from the table of the normal distribution. (For example, if $\alpha = .002$, then $K_2 = 3.09/\sqrt{n}$.) We remark that the test seems to be quite reasonable in that we reject the hypothesis $\mathrm{H}:\mu = \mu_0$ in favor of the alternative $\mathrm{H}':\mu \neq \mu_0$ when an unbiased, consistent, minimum variance estimate of μ differs in absolute value too much from μ_0. Thus the likelihood ratio test has led us to a reasonable test in this case.

However, there are certain pathological situations where the likelihood ratio test is not a good test. We give an example of such a situation due to Professor Charles Stein of Stanford University. In this example we have one observable random variable X with a discrete density which depends on a parameter $\theta \in \Theta = [0, 1)$. Let α and c be two constants which satisfy the inequalities

$$0 < \alpha < \tfrac{1}{2} \quad \text{and} \quad \alpha/(2 - \alpha) < c < \alpha.$$

We now define $f_X(x|\theta)$: if $\theta = 0$,

$$f_X(x|0) = \begin{cases} \alpha/2 & \text{if} \quad x = \pm 2 \\ (1 - 2\alpha)/2 & \text{if} \quad x = \pm 1 \\ \alpha & \text{if} \quad x = 0, \end{cases}$$

and if $0 < \theta < 1$,

$$f_X(x|\theta) = \begin{cases} \theta c & \text{if} \quad x = 2 \\ (1 - \theta)c & \text{if} \quad x = -2 \\ \dfrac{(1 - c)(\frac{1}{2} - \alpha)}{(1 - \alpha)} & \text{if} \quad x = \pm 1 \\ \alpha(1 - c)/(1 - \alpha) & \text{if} \quad x = 0. \end{cases}$$

We want to test the simple hypothesis $\mathrm{H}:\theta = 0$ against the composite alternative $\mathrm{H}':0 < \theta < 1$ with level of significance α. We denote

$$\Lambda(x) = \frac{f_X(x|0)}{\sup \{f_X(x|\theta)|0 \leqq \theta < 1\}}.$$

The likelihood ratio test requires a critical region W such that $\Lambda(x) \leqq K$ for all $x \in W$ and $\Lambda(x) \geqq K$ for all $x \notin W$ for some $K \in [0, 1]$. From the inequality $\alpha/(2 - \alpha) < c$ given above we obtain $\alpha < 2c - \alpha c < 2c$ or $\alpha/2 < c$. Hence $\sup \{f_X(2|\theta)|0 \leqq \theta < 1\} = c$, and $\Lambda(2) = \alpha/2c$. Similarly $\Lambda(-2) = \alpha/2c$, and we easily obtain

$$\Lambda(0) = \Lambda(1) = \Lambda(-1) = \frac{1 - \alpha}{1 - c}.$$

Again, since $\alpha/(2 - \alpha) < c$, we obtain $\alpha < 2c - \alpha c$ or $\alpha - \alpha c < 2c - 2\alpha c$, from which we obtain

$$\alpha/2c < \frac{1 - \alpha}{1 - c}.$$

If we select as critical region $W = \{2, -2\}$, then $\Lambda(x) \leqq \alpha/2c$ for all $x \in W$ and $\Lambda(x) = (1 - \alpha)/(1 - c) \geqq \alpha/2c$ for all $x \notin W$, and $P([X \in W]|H) = \alpha$. However, the power of the test is, for $0 < \theta < 1$,

$$P([X \in W]|\theta) = \theta c + (1 - \theta)c = c,$$

and $c < \alpha$. This likelihood ratio test is thus a very poor test since one could do better, i.e., could obtain a more powerful test, by simply rejecting H with probability α, no matter what value of X is observed. (The way one would do this is to fill an urn with αN red balls and $(1 - \alpha)N$ white balls. One then selects a ball at random. If the ball selected is red, reject H; if it is white, accept H.) One can do even better by doing just the opposite of what the likelihood ratio test suggests, namely, take $W = \{0\}$ as a critical region. This is indeed just the opposite of the likelihood ratio test, since $\Lambda(x) \geqq (1 - \alpha)/(1 - c)$ if $x \in W$, and $\Lambda(x) \leqq (1 - \alpha)/(1 - c)$ if $x \notin W$. Using W as a critical region we note that $P([X \in W]|\text{H}) = \alpha$, and for $0 < \theta < 1$, the power is $P([X \in W]|\theta) = \alpha(1 - c)/(1 - \alpha) > \alpha$. Thus we obtain a more powerful test if we do just the opposite of what the likelihood ratio test tells us to do.

Before closing this section we briefly summarize the essential problems of hypothesis testing. The first problem is to select some principle or principles which one would like a test to have. After using the principle (or principles) in order to derive a test, one might obtain a test in which the hypothesis is rejected when (for example) some function of $\mathbf{X}'$, say, $g(\mathbf{X}') \leqq K$, for some constant K. The problem then becomes one of determining the distribution of $g(\mathbf{X}')$ *when the hypothesis is true.* This problem is called the *distributional problem.* If the distribution function of $g(\mathbf{X}')$ is easily computable or for which tables are already in existence, then K can be determined. Thus, one problem that one always encounters in hypothesis testing is that of determining a distribution. This will be pointed out in the next two sections.

A great many times the distributional problem in the likelihood ratio test is too difficult or impossible to solve. In such a case a substitute test is used in which the distributional problem is easier to solve. Important examples of this are considered in the exercises that follow.

EXERCISES

1. Let X be one observable random variable whose distribution is binomial (n, p), where n is known and p is unknown. Let p_0 be a fixed value of p. It is desired to test the hypothesis $\text{H}: p = p_0$ against the composite alternative $\text{H}': p \neq p_0$ with level of significance α.

(a) Prove that there does not exist a U.M.P.C.R. in this case.

(b) Find the general form of the critical region of the likelihood ratio test Can you solve the distributional problem?

(c) Suppose we consider a critical region of the form

$$W = \left\{x \left| \left| \frac{x}{n} - p_0 \right| \geqq K \right.\right\},$$

i.e., the test is the event

$$[\text{Reject H}] = \left[\left|\frac{X}{n} - p_0\right| \geqq K\right].$$

Use the Laplace-DeMoivre theorem to find an approximate value of K when $\alpha = .05$.

2. Let X be a random variable whose distribution is $N(\mu, \sigma^2)$, where μ and σ^2 are unknown, $-\infty < \mu < \infty$, $\sigma^2 > 0$. Let $X_1, \cdots, X_n$ be n independent observations on X. It is desired to test the hypothesis $\text{H}:\sigma^2 = \sigma_0^2$, $-\infty < \mu < \infty$ against the alternative $\text{H}':\sigma^2 \neq \sigma_0^2$, $-\infty < \mu < \infty$, with level of significance α.

(a) Find the general form of the critical region obtained by the likelihood ratio test. Can you solve the distributional problem?

(b) Use Theorem 3 in Section 10.4 to find the distribution of

$$(n-1)s_n^2/\sigma_0^2 = \frac{1}{\sigma_0^2}\sum_{i=1}^{n}(X_i - \overline{X}_n)^2$$

when the hypothesis is true.

(c) Find the expectation of s_n^2/σ_0^2 when the hypothesis is true.

(d) Prove that $s_n^2/\sigma_0^2 \xrightarrow{P} 1$ as $n \to \infty$ when the hypothesis is true.

(e) Suppose $n = 11$, $\alpha = .05$, and suppose we take as a critical region $W = W_1 \cup W_2$, where, denoting $\bar{x}_n = (x_1 + \cdots + x_n)/n$,

$$W_1 = \left\{\mathbf{x} \in E^{(n)} \left| \frac{1}{\sigma_0^2(n-1)}\sum_{i=1}^{n}(x_i - \bar{x}_n)^2 \leqq K_L \right.\right\}$$

and

$$W_2 = \left\{\mathbf{x} \in E^{(n)} \left| \frac{1}{\sigma_0^2(n-1)}\sum_{i=1}^{n}(x_i - \bar{x}_n)^2 \geqq K_U \right.\right\}$$

Determine K_L and K_U so that

$$P([\mathbf{X} \in W_1]|H) = P([\mathbf{X} \in W_2]|H) = .025,$$

which implies that $P([\mathbf{X} \in W]|H) = .05$.

3. Let $X_1, \cdots, X_m, Y_1, \cdots, Y_n$ be $m + n$ independent random variables, where the distribution of each X_i is $N(\mu_1, \sigma_1^2)$ and the distribution of each Y_j is $N(\mu_2, \sigma_2^2)$. It is desired to test the hypothesis $\text{H}:\sigma_1^2 = \sigma_2^2$, $-\infty < \mu_1 < \infty$, $-\infty < \mu_2 < \infty$ against the alternative $\text{H}':\sigma_1^2 \neq \sigma_2^2$, $-\infty < \mu_1 < \infty$, $-\infty < \mu_2 < \infty$, with level of significance α. Let $\overline{X}_m = (X_1 + \cdots + X_m)/m$, $\overline{Y}_n = (Y_1 + \cdots + Y_n)/n$,

$$s_X^2 = \frac{1}{m-1}\sum_{i=1}^{m}(X_i - \overline{X}_m)^2, \quad s_Y^2 = \frac{1}{n-1}\sum_{i=1}^{n}(Y_i - \overline{Y}_n)^2.$$

(a) If we denote $Z_i = (X_i - \mu_1)/\sigma_1$ for $1 \leqq i \leqq m$ and $Z_{j+m} = (Y_j - \mu_2)/\sigma_2$ for $1 \leqq j \leqq n$, prove that

$$\sum_{i=1}^{m+n} Z_i^2 = m\left(\frac{\overline{X}_m - \mu_1}{\sigma_1}\right)^2 + n\left(\frac{\overline{Y}_n - \mu_2}{\sigma_2}\right)^2 + \frac{(m-1)}{\sigma_1^2} s_X^2 + \frac{(n-1)}{\sigma_2^2} s_Y^2.$$

(b) Prove that $Z_1, \cdots, Z_{m+n}$ are independent, each with an $N(0, 1)$ distribution.

(c) Use problem 6 in exercises of Section 10.4 to prove that s_X^2/s_Y^2 has an $F(m-1, n-1)$ distribution when the hypothesis is true.

(d) If $m = 11$, $n = 21$, $\alpha = .02$, we consider as a reasonable test the event

$$[\text{Reject H}] = \left[\frac{s_X^2}{s_Y^2} \leqq K_L\right] + \left[\frac{s_X^2}{s_Y^2} \geqq K_U\right],$$

where

$$P[s_X^2/s_Y^2 \leqq K_L] = P[s_X^2/s_Y^2 \geqq K_U] = .01.$$

Find the values of K_L and K_U from the tables of the F-distribution.

4. Let $X_1, \cdots, X_m, Y_1, \cdots, Y_n$ be the same as in problem 3 with the exception that $\sigma_1^2 = \sigma_2^2 = \sigma^2 > 0$. It is desired to test the hypothesis $\text{H}:\mu_1 = \mu_2, \sigma^2 > 0$ against the alternative $\text{H}':\mu_1 \neq \mu_2, \sigma^2 > 0$ with level of significance α. Let $\overline{X}_m$, $\overline{Y}_n$, s_X^2, s_Y^2 be as defined in problem 3.

(a) Prove that $U = (\overline{X}_m - \overline{Y}_n)/\sigma\sqrt{1/m + 1/n}$ has an $N(0, 1)$ distribution when H is true.

(b) (First re-read Section 6.4 and problem 7 in the exercises in Section 10.4.) Prove that $V = ((m-1)s_X^2 + (n-1)s_Y^2)/\sigma^2$ has a chi-square distribution with $m + n - 2$ degrees of freedom, no matter whether H or H′ is true.

(c) Prove that the random variables U and V are independent.

(d) Prove that the random variable

$$T_{m,n} = \frac{\overline{X}_m - \overline{Y}_n}{\sqrt{(m-1)s_X^2 + (n-1)s_Y^2}} \sqrt{\frac{mn(m+n-2)}{m+n}}$$

has a t-distribution with $m + n - 2$ degrees of freedom when the hypothesis is true.

(e) A reasonable test for the above hypothesis is the event

$$[\text{Reject H}] = [|T_{m,n}| \geqq K].$$

If $m = 7$, $n = 8$, $\alpha = .01$, determine K so that $P([\text{Reject H}]|\text{H}) = .01$.

(f) If the alternative hypothesis were $\text{H}':\mu_1 > \mu_2, \sigma^2 > 0$, it would seem reasonable to use as a test the event

$$[\text{Reject H}] = [T_{m,n} \geqq K].$$

If $m = 10$, $n = 11$, $\alpha = .025$, find K so that $P([\text{Reject H}]|\text{H}) = .025$.

(g) If the alternative hypothesis above were $\text{H}':\mu_1 < \mu_2, \sigma^2 > 0$, what would you consider as a reasonable test?

5. Let $X_1, \cdots, X_n$ be n independent observations on a random variable X which has a Poisson distribution with unknown expectation $\lambda > 0$. Let $\lambda_0 > 0$ be a fixed value of λ. We want to test the hypothesis $\text{H}:\lambda = \lambda_0$ against the alternative $\text{H}':\lambda \neq \lambda_0$ with level of significance α.

(a) Does there exist a U.M.P.C.R.?

(b) Find the general form of the critical region for the likelihood ratio test.

(c) A reasonable test would be the event

$$[\text{Reject H}] = [|\overline{X}_n - \lambda_0| \geqq K],$$

when the value of n is large. In such a case, when $\alpha = .03$ find K so that $P([\text{Reject H}]|\text{H}) = .03$. (*Hint:* Use the central limit theorem to find an approximation to K.)

12.3 The *t*-Test

In this section we derive the t-test, which is one of the more important tests in the field of statistical inference. Let X be a random variable whose distribution is $N(\mu, \sigma^2)$, where both μ and σ^2 are unknown. Let $X_1, X_2, \cdots, X_n$ be n independent observations on X, i.e., $X_1, \cdots, X_n$ are our observable random variables. The problem is to test the hypothesis $\text{H}:\mu = \mu_0$ against the alternative $\text{H}':\mu \neq \mu_0$ with level of significance α.

The first thing to notice is that the hypothesis tested and the alternative are both composite hypotheses. The set of admissible hypotheses is

$$\Theta = \{(\mu, \sigma^2)|-\infty < \mu < \infty, \sigma^2 > 0\},$$

and the hypothesis tested is

$$\Theta_0 = \{(\mu, \sigma^2)|\mu = \mu_0, \sigma^2 > 0\}.$$

We shall obtain in this case a likelihood ratio test.

The joint density of $X_1, \cdots, X_n$ is

$$f_{\mathbf{X}'}(\mathbf{x}'|\mu, \sigma^2) = (2\pi\sigma^2)^{-n/2} \exp -\frac{1}{2\sigma^2} \sum_{i=1}^{n} (x_i - \mu)^2.$$

We first evaluate the likelihood ratio

$$\Lambda(x') = \frac{\sup \{f_{\mathbf{X}'}(\mathbf{x}'|\mu_0, \sigma^2)|\sigma^2 > 0\}}{\sup \{f_{\mathbf{X}'}(\mathbf{x}'|\mu, \sigma^2)|-\infty < \mu < \infty, \sigma^2 > 0\}}$$

In order to evaluate the numerator we equate to zero the partial derivative of $f_{\mathbf{X}'}(\mathbf{x}'|\mu_0, \sigma^2)$ with respect to σ^2, solve for σ^2, and substitute this value of σ^2 into $f_{\mathbf{X}'}(\mathbf{x}'|\mu_0, \sigma^2)$. The value of σ^2 for which this density is maximum is easily verified to be

$$\sigma^2 = \frac{1}{n} \sum_{i=1}^{n} (x_i - \mu_0)^2.$$

In order to evaluate the denominator we solve jointly for μ and σ^2 in the two equations

$$\frac{\partial}{\partial\mu} f_{\mathbf{X}'}(\mathbf{x}'|\mu, \sigma^2) = 0, \qquad \frac{\partial}{\partial(\sigma^2)} f_{\mathbf{X}'}(\mathbf{x}'|\mu, \sigma^2) = 0$$

and obtain

$$\mu = \frac{1}{n}\sum_{i=1}^{n} x_i = \bar{x}_n,$$

$$\sigma^2 = \frac{1}{n}\sum_{i=1}^{n} (x_i - \bar{x}_n)^2,$$

which we then substitute into $f_{\mathbf{X}'}(\mathbf{x}'|\mu, \sigma^2)$. Thus we obtain

$$\Lambda(\mathbf{x}') = \frac{(2\pi(1/n)\sum_{i=1}^{n}(x_i - \mu_0)^2)^{-n/2}e^{-n/2}}{(2\pi(1/n)\sum_{i=1}^{n}(x_i - \bar{x}_n)^2)^{-n/2}e^{-n/2}}$$

$$= \left\{\frac{\sum_{i=1}^{n}(x_i - \bar{x}_n)^2}{\sum_{i=1}^{n}(x_i - \mu_0)^2}\right\}^{n/2}$$

The critical region is of the form

$$\{\mathbf{x}|\Lambda(\mathbf{x}') \leqq K_0\}.$$

The inequality $\Lambda(\mathbf{x}') \leqq K_0$ which determines the critical region is equivalent to the inequality

$$\frac{\sum_{i=1}^{n}(x_i - \mu_0)^2}{\sum_{i=1}^{n}(x_i - \bar{x}_n)^2} \geqq K_1,$$

where K_1 is some constant. (Actually $K_1 = (1/K_0)^{2/n}$, but we need not concern ourselves with this.) However,

$$\sum_{i=1}^{n}(x_i - \mu_0)^2 = \sum_{i=1}^{n}\{(x_i - \bar{x}_n) + (\bar{x}_n - \mu_0)\}^2$$

$$= \sum_{i=1}^{n}(x_i - \bar{x}_n)^2 + n(\bar{x}_n - \mu_0)^2.$$

Hence the inequality $\Lambda(\mathbf{x}') \leqq K_0$ is finally equivalent to

$$\frac{(\bar{x}_n - \mu_0)^2}{\sum_{i=1}^{n}(x_i - \bar{x}_n)^2} \geqq \text{(some) } K_2$$

or

$$\left|\frac{\bar{x}_n - \mu_0}{\sqrt{(n(n-1))^{-1}\sum_{i=1}^{n}(x_i - \bar{x}_n)^2}}\right| \geqq \text{(some) } K.$$

Therefore, the event [Reject H] is of the form

$$\left[\left|\frac{\sqrt{n}(\bar{X}_n - \mu_0)}{s_n}\right| \geqq K\right],$$

where

$$s_n = \sqrt{(n-1)^{-1}\sum_{i=1}^{n}(X_i - \bar{X}_n)^2}.$$

By Theorem 4 in Section 10.4, when the hypothesis is true the random variable

$$T_n = \frac{\sqrt{n}(\bar{X}_n - \mu_0)}{s_n}$$

has the t-distribution with $n - 1$ degrees of freedom. Hence K is selected from the table of the t-distribution as that number which satisfies $P[T_n \leqq K] = 1 - (\alpha/2)$. As was mentioned earlier, when n is larger than 50 the distribution of T_n is close to the $N(0, 1)$ distribution. This means that for n larger than 50 we assume that σ^2 is known and that its value is s_n^2.

EXERCISES

1. Compute the Hessian and verify that $f_{\mathbf{X}'}(\mathbf{x}'|\mu, \sigma^2)$ is a maximum at $\mu = \bar{x}_n$ and $\sigma^2 = (n - 1)s_n^2/n$.

2. Let T_n be a random variable which has a t-distribution with $n - 1$ degrees of freedom. Prove that $P[|T_n| \geqq K] = \alpha$ if and only if $P[T_n \leqq K] = 1 - (\alpha/2)$.

3. Prove that there does not exist a U.M.P.C.R. for testing H against H′ in this section.

12.4 The Analysis of Variance

The Analysis of Variance refers to a class of tests which deal with several normal populations (i.e., populations over which normally distributed random variables are defined). These tests have a great deal of practical value, especially in research work in social and agricultural sciences. This section will serve as a brief introduction to this part of mathematical statistics. However, we shall restrict ourselves to the derivation of only one test in this class of tests.

Let $X_1, X_2, \cdots, X_s$ denote s independent random variables. For each i, $1 \leqq i \leqq s$, we assume that the distribution of X_i is $N(\mu_i, \sigma^2)$, where μ_i and σ^2 are unknown. Note that the variances of all the X_i's are assumed to be unknown but equal. Let $X_{i1}, \cdots, X_{in_i}$ denote n_i independent observations on X_i, i.e., $X_{i1}, \cdots, X_{in_i}$ are assumed to be independent random variables, each having the same distribution function as X_i. The ordered set of random variables

$$\mathbf{X}' = (X_{11}, \cdots, X_{1n_1}, X_{21}, \cdots, X_{2n_2}, \cdots, X_{s1}, \cdots, X_{sn_s}),$$

are assumed to be independent. We shall denote $n = n_1 + n_2 + \cdots + n_s$. A joint density of $\mathbf{X}'$ has the form

$$f_{\mathbf{X}'}(\mathbf{x}'|\mu_1, \cdots, \mu_s, \sigma^2) = \prod_{i=1}^{s} \prod_{j=1}^{n_i} \frac{1}{\sqrt{2\pi\sigma^2}} \exp -\frac{(x_{ij} - \mu_i)^2}{2\sigma^2}$$

$$= (2\pi\sigma^2)^{-n/2} \exp -\frac{1}{2\sigma^2} \sum_{i=1}^{s} \sum_{j=1}^{n_i} (x_{ij} - \mu_i)^2.$$

The problem we are concerned with in this section is to derive a test of the composite hypothesis

$$\mathrm{H}: \mu_1 = \mu_2 = \cdots = \mu_s, \quad \sigma^2 > 0$$

against the composite alternative

$$\mathrm{H}': \text{ not all } \mu_i\text{'s are equal, } \sigma^2 > 0$$

with level of significance α. We intend to do this by finding the likelihood ratio test.

We consider the function Λ defined over $E^{(n)}$ by

$$\Lambda(\mathbf{x}') = \frac{\sup \{f_{\mathbf{X}'}(\mathbf{x}'|\mu, \mu, \cdots, \mu, \sigma^2) | -\infty < \mu < \infty, \sigma^2 > 0\}}{\sup \{f_{\mathbf{X}'}(\mathbf{x}'|\mu_1, \mu_2, \cdots, \mu_s, \sigma^2) | -\infty < \mu_i < \infty, 1 \leqq i \leqq n, \sigma^2 > 0\}}.$$

We shall use the following notation:

$$\bar{\bar{x}} = \frac{1}{n} \sum_{i=1}^{s} \sum_{j=1}^{n_i} x_{ij},$$

$$\bar{x}_i = \frac{1}{n_i} \sum_{j=1}^{n_i} x_{ij}, \qquad 1 \leqq i \leqq s.$$

In order to evaluate the numerator of $\Lambda(\mathbf{x}')$ we solve the two equations

$$\frac{\partial}{\partial \mu} f_{\mathbf{X}'}(\mathbf{x}'|\mu, \cdots, \mu, \sigma^2) = 0$$

$$\frac{\partial}{\partial (\sigma^2)} f_{\mathbf{X}'}(\mathbf{x}'|\mu, \cdots, \mu, \sigma^2) = 0$$

for μ and σ^2 and obtain

$$\mu = \bar{\bar{x}}, \qquad \sigma^2 = \frac{1}{n} \sum_{i=1}^{s} \sum_{j=1}^{n_i} (x_{ij} - \bar{\bar{x}})^2.$$

Substituting these values for μ and σ^2 in $f_{\mathbf{X}'}(\mathbf{x}'|\mu, \cdots, \mu, \sigma^2)$, we find

$$\sup \{f_{\mathbf{X}'}(\mathbf{x}'|\mu, \cdots, \mu, \sigma^2) | -\infty < \mu < \infty, \sigma^2 > 0\}$$
$$= \left(\frac{2\pi}{n} \sum_{i=1}^{s} \sum_{j=1}^{n_i} (x_{ij} - \bar{\bar{x}})^2\right)^{-n/2} e^{-n/2}.$$

In order to evaluate the denominator of $\Lambda(\mathbf{x}')$, we solve the $s + 1$ equations

$$\frac{\partial}{\partial \mu_k} f_{\mathbf{X}'}(\mathbf{x}'|\mu_1, \mu_2, \cdots, \mu_s, \sigma^2) = 0, \qquad k = 1, 2, \cdots, s,$$

$$\frac{\partial}{\partial (\sigma^2)} f_{\mathbf{X}'}(\mathbf{x}'|\mu_1, \mu_2, \cdots, \mu_s, \sigma^2) = 0$$

for $\mu_1, \mu_2, \cdots, \mu_s, \sigma^2$, and we obtain

$$\mu_k = \bar{x}_k, \qquad k = 1, 2, \cdots, s,$$

$$\sigma^2 = \frac{1}{n} \sum_{i=1}^{s} \sum_{j=1}^{n_i} (x_{ij} - \bar{x}_i)^2.$$

If we substitute these values into $f_{\mathbf{X}'}(\mathbf{x}'|\mu_1, \cdots, \mu_s, \sigma^2)$, the denominator of $\Lambda(\mathbf{x}')$ becomes

$$\left(2\pi \frac{1}{n} \sum_{i=1}^{s} \sum_{j=1}^{n_i} (x_{ij} - \bar{x}_i)^2\right)^{-n/2} e^{-n/2}.$$

Thus

$$\Lambda(\mathbf{x}') = \left\{\frac{\sum_{i=1}^{s} \sum_{j=1}^{n_i} (x_{ij} - \bar{x}_i)^2}{\sum_{i=1}^{s} \sum_{j=1}^{n_i} (x_{ij} - \bar{\bar{x}})^2}\right\}^{n/2}.$$

However,

$$\sum_{i=1}^{s} \sum_{j=1}^{n_i} (x_{ij} - \bar{\bar{x}})^2 = \sum_{i=1}^{s} \sum_{j=1}^{n_i} \{(x_{ij} - \bar{x}_i) + (\bar{x}_i - \bar{\bar{x}})\}^2$$
$$= \sum_{i=1}^{s} \sum_{j=1}^{n_i} (x_{ij} - \bar{x}_i)^2 + \sum_{i=1}^{s} n_i(\bar{x}_i - \bar{\bar{x}})^2,$$

and so we obtain, by using this identity,

$$\Lambda(\mathbf{x}') = \left\{1 + \frac{\sum_{i=1}^{s} n_i(\bar{x}_i - \bar{\bar{x}})^2}{\sum_{i=1}^{s} \sum_{j=1}^{n_i} (x_{ij} - \bar{x}_i)^2}\right\}^{-n/2}.$$

Consequently, an inequality of the form $\Lambda(\mathbf{x}') \leqq K$ is equivalent to an inequality of the form $\mathfrak{F}(\mathbf{x}') \geqq C$, where

$$\mathfrak{F}(\mathbf{x}') = \frac{(s - 1)^{-1} \sum_{i=1}^{s} n_i(\bar{x}_i - \bar{\bar{x}})^2}{(n - s)^{-1} \sum_{i=1}^{s} \sum_{j=1}^{n_i} (x_{ij} - \bar{x}_i)^2}.$$

Thus the likelihood ratio test is to reject the hypothesis when the event $[\mathfrak{F}(\mathbf{X}') \geqq C]$ occurs.

The problem remains to determine the value of C in order that

$$P([\mathfrak{F}(\mathbf{X}') \geqq C]|\mathrm{H}) = \alpha.$$

It is at this point that the "distributional problem" arises, namely, the problem of deriving the distribution of $\mathfrak{F}(\mathbf{X}')$ when the hypothesis H is true. Let us therefore denote $Y_{ij} = (X_{ij} - \mu_i)/\sigma$. When the hypothesis H is true, it is easy to verify that

$$\mathfrak{F}(\mathbf{X}') = \mathfrak{F}(\mathbf{Y}')$$

where $\mathbf{Y}'$ denotes the random variables

$$Y_{11}, \cdots, Y_{1n_1}, Y_{21}, \cdots, Y_{2n_2}, \cdots, Y_{s1}, \cdots, Y_{sn_s}.$$

Thus our problem reduces to finding the distribution of $\mathfrak{F}(\mathbf{Y}')$. The reader can easily verify that the random variables $\mathbf{Y}'$ are independent and that each has an $N(0, 1)$ distribution. Let us denote

$$\bar{Y}_i = \frac{1}{n_i} \sum_{j=1}^{n_i} Y_{ij}, \qquad 1 \leqq i \leqq n,$$

and

$$\overline{\overline{Y}} = \frac{1}{n}\sum_{i=1}^{s}\sum_{j=1}^{n_i} Y_{ij}.$$

Then we may write

$$\sum_{i=1}^{s}\sum_{j=1}^{n_i} Y_{ij}^2 = \sum_{i=1}^{s}\sum_{j=1}^{n_i} ((Y_{ij} - \overline{Y}_{i}) + \overline{Y}_{i})^2$$

$$= \sum_{i=1}^{s}\sum_{j=1}^{n_i} (Y_{ij} - \overline{Y}_{i})^2 + \sum_{i=1}^{s} n_i\overline{Y}_{i\cdot}^2.$$

But

$$\sum_{i=1}^{s} n_i\overline{Y}_i^2 = \sum_{i=1}^{s} n_i((\overline{Y}_i - \overline{\overline{Y}}) + \overline{\overline{Y}})^2$$

$$= \sum_{i=1}^{s} n_i(\overline{Y}_i - \overline{\overline{Y}})^2 + n\overline{\overline{Y}}^2.$$

Thus

$$\sum_{i=1}^{s}\sum_{j=1}^{n_i} Y_{ij}^2 = \sum_{i=1}^{s}\sum_{j=1}^{n_i} (Y_{ij} - \overline{Y}_{i})^2 + \sum_{i=1}^{s} n_i(\overline{Y}_i - \overline{\overline{Y}})^2 + n\overline{\overline{Y}}^2,$$

which may be written as

$$\mathbf{Y}'\mathbf{Y} = \mathbf{Y}'A\mathbf{Y} + \mathbf{Y}'B\mathbf{Y} + \mathbf{Y}'C\mathbf{Y},$$

a sum of three quadratic forms. The rank of the quadratic form $\sum_{j=1}^{n_i} (Y_{ij} - \overline{Y}_{i})^2$ can easily be computed as follows. Note that

$$\sum_{j=1}^{n_i} (Y_{ij} - \overline{Y}_{i})^2 = \sum_{j=1}^{n_i} Y_{ij}^2 - n\overline{Y}_{i\cdot}^2.$$

Hence the matrix of this quadratic form is

$$D = \begin{pmatrix} 1 - \frac{1}{n} & -\frac{1}{n} & -\frac{1}{n} & \cdots & -\frac{1}{n} \\ -\frac{1}{n} & 1 - \frac{1}{n} & -\frac{1}{n} & \cdots & -\frac{1}{n} \\ -\frac{1}{n} & -\frac{1}{n} & 1 - \frac{1}{n} & \cdots & -\frac{1}{n} \\ \vdots & \vdots & \vdots & & \\ -\frac{1}{n} & -\frac{1}{n} & -\frac{1}{n} & \cdots & 1 - \frac{1}{n} \end{pmatrix}.$$

The columns are obviously linearly dependent, since their sum is **0**, and hence rank $D \leqq n_i - 1$. If one then subtracts the first column from each of the remaining columns, the resulting matrix (with the same rank as D) is

$$\left(\begin{array}{c|c} 1-\dfrac{1}{n} & F \\ \hline E & I \end{array}\right),$$

where

$$E = \begin{pmatrix} -\dfrac{1}{n} \\ \cdot \\ \cdot \\ \cdot \\ -\dfrac{1}{n} \end{pmatrix}, \quad F = (-1 - 1 \cdots -1),$$

and I is the $(n-1) \times (n-1)$ identity matrix. This establishes that rank $D = n_i - 1$. Since, for different values of i the quadratic form $\sum_{j=1}^{n_i} (Y_{ij} - \overline{Y}_i)^2$ involves different random variables, it follows that the rank of $\mathbf{Y}'A\mathbf{Y}$ or rank A is $\sum_{i=1}^{s} (n_i - 1) = n - s$. The rank of $\mathbf{Y}'C\mathbf{Y}$ or of C is easy to compute, since all entries in C are $1/n$. Hence rank $C = 1$. It remains to compute rank B. Since $I = A + B + C$, it follows from Theorem 61 in Chapter 9 that $n \leqq n - s + \text{rank } B + 1$, or rank $B \geqq s - 1$. We next prove that equality holds, but in order to do so, we need a lemma.

1. Lemma. *Suppose* $Q(\mathbf{x}') = L_1^2 + \cdots + L_p^2$ *is a quadratic form which is the sum of squares of* p *linear forms,* $L_1, \cdots, L_p$*, where* $L_i = \sum_{j=1}^{n} a_{ij}x_j$*, and* $p \leqq n$*. Assume that* $L_1, \cdots, L_p$ *are linearly dependent, i.e., there exist constants* $c_1, \cdots, c_p$*, not all zeros, such that* $c_1L_1 + \cdots + c_pL_p = 0$ *identically in* $x_1, \cdots, x_n$*. Then* rank $Q(\mathbf{x}') \leqq p - 1$.

Proof. Let

$$L = \begin{pmatrix} L_1 \\ \cdot \\ \cdot \\ \cdot \\ L_p \end{pmatrix} = A\mathbf{x},$$

where

$$A = \begin{pmatrix} a_{11} & \cdots & a_{1n} \\ \cdot & & \cdot \\ \cdot & & \cdot \\ \cdot & & \cdot \\ a_{p1} & \cdots & a_{pn} \end{pmatrix}.$$

Linear dependence of $L_1, \cdots, L_p$ implies that the p rows of A are linearly dependent. Thus, rank $A \leqq p - 1$. But $Q(\mathbf{x}') = \mathbf{x}'A'A\mathbf{x}$. Hence

$$\text{rank } Q(\mathbf{x}') = \text{rank } A'A \leqq \min \{\text{rank } A', \text{rank } A\} = \text{rank } A \leqq p - 1,$$

which proves the lemma.

Now

$$\mathbf{Y}'B\mathbf{Y} = \sum_{i=1}^{s} n_i(\overline{Y}_i - \overline{\overline{Y}})^2 = \sum_{i=1}^{s} L_i^2,$$

where

$$L_i = \sqrt{n_i}(\overline{Y}_i - \overline{\overline{Y}}), \quad i = 1, 2, \cdots, s.$$

These s linear forms are linearly dependent, since

$$\sum_{i=1}^{s} \sqrt{n_i} L_i = \sum_{i=1}^{s} n_i(\overline{Y}_i - \overline{\overline{Y}}) = \sum_{i=1}^{s} n_i \overline{Y}_i - n\overline{\overline{Y}} = 0.$$

Hence, by Lemma 1, rank $B \leqq s - 1$. Before stating Lemma 1 we proved rank $B \geqq s - 1$, and combining these two results we obtain rank $B = s - 1$.

We now note that in the sum of quadratic forms

$$\mathbf{Y}'\mathbf{Y} = \mathbf{Y}'A\mathbf{Y} + \mathbf{Y}'B\mathbf{Y} + \mathbf{Y}'C\mathbf{Y}$$

the conditions of Cochran's theorem are satisfied. Consequently the random variables $\mathbf{Y}'A\mathbf{Y}$, $\mathbf{Y}'B\mathbf{Y}$, and $\mathbf{Y}'C\mathbf{Y}$ are independent, and each has a chi-square distribution with $n - s$, $s - 1$, and 1 degrees of freedom, respectively. By the definition of the F-distribution, the random variable

$$\mathfrak{F}(\mathbf{Y}') = \frac{(s - 1)^{-1}\,\mathbf{Y}'B\mathbf{Y}}{(n - s)^{-1}\,\mathbf{Y}'A\mathbf{Y}}$$

has the F-distribution with $(s - 1, n - s)$ degrees of freedom. Therefore, when the hypothesis is true, the distribution of $\mathfrak{F}(\mathbf{X}')$ is the F-distribution with $(s - 1, n - s)$ degrees of freedom. The value of C for which $P([\mathfrak{F}(\mathbf{X}') \geqq C]|\mathrm{H}) = \alpha$ is denoted by $F_{1-\alpha}(s - 1, n - s)$. The test then is to reject the hypothesis H whenever the event $[\mathfrak{F}(\mathbf{X}') \geqq F_{1-\alpha}(s - 1, n - s)]$ occurs.

EXERCISES

1. Prove: If the hypothesis H is true, then

$$E\text{ (numerator of }\mathfrak{F}(\mathbf{X}')) = E\text{ (denominator of }\mathfrak{F}(\mathbf{X}')) = \sigma^2.$$

2. Prove: If the hypothesis H is not true, then

$$E\text{ (denominator of }\mathfrak{F}(\mathbf{X}')) = \sigma^2,$$

but

$$E\text{ (numerator of }\mathfrak{F}(\mathbf{X}')) = \sigma^2 + (s - 1)^{-1} \sum_{i=1}^{s} n_i(\mu_i - \bar{\mu})^2 > \sigma^2$$

where $\bar{\mu} = (\mu_1 + \cdots + \mu_s)/s$.

3. Prove: If the hypothesis H is true, then $\mathfrak{F}(\mathbf{X}') \xrightarrow{P} 1$ as $\min \{n_i\} \to \infty$.

4. Prove: If the hypothesis H is not true, then $\mathfrak{F}(\mathbf{X}') \xrightarrow{P} M > 1$ as $\min \{n_i\} \to \infty$, where

$$M = 1 + (s-1)^{-1} \sum_{i=1}^{s} n_i(\mu_i - \bar{\mu})^2/\sigma^2.$$

5. Prove: If the hypothesis H is true, then $\mathfrak{F}(\mathbf{X}') = \mathfrak{F}(\mathbf{Y}')$.

CHAPTER 13

Confidence Intervals

13.1 The Neyman Theory of Confidence Intervals

The problem of estimation has already been considered from the point of view of point estimates. Although point estimates are quite useful they still leave something to be desired. For one thing, and we shall go into this in more detail later, a point estimate in the overwhelming majority of situations actually equals the unknown value of the parameter being estimated with either an extremely small probability or zero probability. Instead, it is more satisfying or rewarding to observe a "random interval" which will contain the true value of this unknown constant with probability close to one. Such a random interval is called a confidence interval. There are several theories and approaches to the problem of confidence intervals. The method presented in this chapter is due to J. Neyman and was first given a complete treatment in his memoir "Outline of a theory of statistical estimation based on the classical theory of probability" in the *Philosophical Transactions of the Royal Society of London* (**236**, No. 767) in 1937.

Let us consider the case where we take n independent observations $X_1, \cdots, X_n$ on a random variable X whose distribution is $N(\mu, 1)$. The value of μ is assumed to be unknown, and it is desired to estimate μ after observing $X_1, \cdots, X_n$. We know already that $\overline{X}_n$ does give us an unbiased, consistent and minimum variance estimate of μ. However, the probability that $\overline{X}_n$ equals μ is, as we now show, zero. Certainly

$$[\overline{X}_n = \mu] \subset [\mu - \epsilon/2\sqrt{n} \leqq \overline{X}_n \leqq \mu + \epsilon/2\sqrt{n}]$$

for every $\epsilon > 0$. Since $\sqrt{n}(\overline{X}_n - \mu)$ has an $N(0, 1)$ distribution, we obtain

$$\begin{aligned} P[\overline{X}_n = \mu] &\leqq P[\mu - \epsilon/2\sqrt{n} \leqq \overline{X}_n \leqq \mu + \epsilon/2\sqrt{n}] \\ &= P[-\epsilon/2 \leqq \sqrt{n}(\overline{X}_n - \mu) \leqq \epsilon/2] \\ &= \frac{1}{\sqrt{2\pi}} \int_{-\epsilon/2}^{\epsilon/2} \exp -\frac{t^2}{2}\, dt \leqq \frac{\epsilon}{\sqrt{2\pi}}. \end{aligned}$$

Hence $P[\overline{X}_n = \mu] < \epsilon$ for every $\epsilon > 0$ which implies that $P[\overline{X}_n = \mu] = 0$.

However, we do know that although $\overline{X}_n$ never equals μ with probability one, it is "near" μ, and we could possibly get a better idea of the true value of μ if only we could "broaden" this estimate. Let us illustrate what is meant by "broadening" the estimate. Instead of considering just the random variable $\overline{X}_n$, let us consider the two random variables

$$\underline{\mu}(\mathbf{X}') = \overline{X}_n - 1.96/\sqrt{n}$$

and

$$\bar{\mu}(\mathbf{X}') = \overline{X}_n + 1.96/\sqrt{n}.$$

Clearly $\underline{\mu}(\mathbf{X}')$ and $\bar{\mu}(\mathbf{X}')$ are functions of $X_1, \cdots, X_n$. Let us compute the probability of the event

$$[\underline{\mu}(\mathbf{X}') \leqq \mu \leqq \bar{\mu}(\mathbf{X}')] = [\underline{\mu}(\mathbf{X}') \leqq \mu] \cap [\bar{\mu}(\mathbf{X}') \geqq \mu]$$

when μ is the true expectation of X. We obtain

$$\begin{aligned} P([\underline{\mu}(\mathbf{X}') \leqq \mu \leqq \bar{\mu}(\mathbf{X}')]|\mu) \\ &= P([\overline{X}_n - 1.96/\sqrt{n} \leqq \mu \leqq \overline{X}_n + 1.96/\sqrt{n}]|\mu) \\ &= P([-1.96 \leqq \sqrt{n}(\overline{X}_n - \mu) \leqq 1.96]|\mu). \end{aligned}$$

Since $\sqrt{n}(\overline{X}_n - \mu)$ has an $N(0, 1)$ distribution, we use Table I to discover that the above probability is equal to .95. What this means is this: **if,** whenever we observe $X_1, \cdots, X_n$ and compute $\underline{\mu}(\mathbf{X}') = \overline{X}_n - 1.96/\sqrt{n}$ and $\bar{\mu}(\mathbf{X}') = \overline{X}_n + 1.96/\sqrt{n}$ and assert that $\underline{\mu}(\mathbf{X}') \leqq \mu \leqq \bar{\mu}(\mathbf{X}')$ *whatever the value of* μ *might be,* **then** we shall in the long run be making a correct assertion about the value of μ approximately 95% of the time, *regardless of the change in the value of* μ *from experiment to experiment.*

We are now able to formulate the general problem of confidence intervals. Let $X_1, X_2, \cdots, X_n$ denote n observable random variables defined over some fundamental probability set Ω which is associated with a sigma-field of events $\mathcal{A}$. These random variables are not necessarily assumed to be independent, but they are assumed to have either a joint discrete distribution or a joint absolutely continuous distribution. Whichever one it does have, it has a joint density

$$f_{X_1, \cdots, X_n}(x_1, \cdots, x_n|\theta_1, \cdots, \theta_k)$$

which we assume depends on k unknown parameters $\theta_1, \cdots, \theta_k$. The problem is to make an assertion about the value of θ_1 from an interval point of view after having observed $X_1, \cdots, X_n$, whatever the values might be of the remaining parameters $\theta_2, \cdots, \theta_k$. That is to say: we must find two functions, $\underline{\theta}_1$ and $\bar{\theta}_1$, defined over $E^{(n)}$ or a subset of $E^{(n)}$ so that upon observing $X_1, \cdots, X_n$ we may evaluate $\underline{\theta}_1(\mathbf{X})$ and $\bar{\theta}_1(\mathbf{X})$ and then assert that $\underline{\theta}_1(\mathbf{X}) \leqq \theta_1 \leqq \bar{\theta}_1(\mathbf{X})$.

Before giving the definition of these two functions we give two definitions. As in Section 12.2 let Θ denote a subset of $E^{(k)}$ which is the set of all possible k-tuples $(\theta_1, \theta_2, \cdots, \theta_k)$ for which the joint density

$$f_{X_1, \ldots, X_n}(x_1, \cdots, x_n|\theta_1, \cdots, \theta_k)$$

exists or is defined. We shall denote Θ_1 as the set of all first coordinates of points in Θ, or

$$\Theta_1 = \{\theta_1| \text{ for some } \theta_2, \cdots, \theta_k, (\theta_1, \theta_2, \cdots, \theta_k) \in \Theta\}.$$

Also, in what follows we shall deal with what is called the *sample space* of $\mathbf{X}$. The *sample space* of $\mathbf{X}$, denoted by $\mathbf{X}(\Omega)$, is defined to be the union of the ranges of $\mathbf{X}$ for all $(\theta_1, \cdots, \theta_k) \in \Theta$, i.e.

$$\mathbf{X}(\Omega) = \{\mathbf{x} \in E^{(n)}| \text{ for some } \omega \in \Omega \text{ and some } (\theta_1, \cdots, \theta_k) \in \Theta, \mathbf{X}(\omega) = \mathbf{x}\}.$$

Thus the sample space of $\mathbf{X}$ is a subset of $E^{(n)}$. We now state a formal definition of a confidence interval.

Definition. *A pair of functions, $\underline{\theta}_1$ and $\bar{\theta}_1$ defined over the sample space $\mathbf{X}(\Omega)$ of $X_1, \cdots, X_n$ is said to be a $100\beta\%$ confidence interval if the following two conditions are satisfied:*

(*a*) *for every $\mathbf{x} \in \mathbf{X}(\Omega)$, $\underline{\theta}_1(\mathbf{x}) \leqq \bar{\theta}_1(\mathbf{x})$ and $[\underline{\theta}_1(\mathbf{x}), \bar{\theta}_1(\mathbf{x})] \subset \Theta_1$, and*

(*b*) *for every $\theta_1 \in \Theta_1$, $[\underline{\theta}_1(\mathbf{X}) \leqq \theta_1 \leqq \bar{\theta}_1(\mathbf{X})] \in \mathcal{A}$ and*

$$P([\underline{\theta}_1(\mathbf{X}) \leqq \theta_1 \leqq \bar{\theta}_1(\mathbf{X})]|\theta_1, \cdots, \theta_k) = \beta,$$

this equation holding identically in $(\theta_1, \cdots, \theta_k) \in \Theta$.

The first thing to point out about the pair of functions $\underline{\theta}_1$ and $\bar{\theta}_1$ is that we do not require $\underline{\theta}_1(\mathbf{X})$ and $\bar{\theta}_1(\mathbf{X})$ to be random variables, although in practice they usually are. The first requirement in part (b) of the definition is not strong enough to imply that $\underline{\theta}_1(\mathbf{X})$ and $\bar{\theta}_1(\mathbf{X})$ are random variables. The second thing to notice is that although a confidence interval usually refers to an interval of numbers whose endpoints are random, in the formal definition given above and in the treatment pursued in this chapter the word confidence interval only refers to the pair of functions which satisfy the above definition and which ultimately determine the endpoints of an interval. (It should be clear, then, that we are misusing the term interval in the expression "confidence interval" as defined here.) The number β in the above definition is called the *confidence coefficient* of the confidence interval $\underline{\theta}_1$, $\bar{\theta}_1$. In practice, values taken for β are quite large, e.g., .90, .95, .99, and .995 are typical values. Notice also that the equality in part (b) of the definition is supposed to hold identically in $\theta_1, \cdots, \theta_k$. The operational meaning of this is as follows: *If one observes $\mathbf{X}'$ a very large number* *of times, and if the values of $\theta_1, \cdots, \theta_k$ are possibly different at each time $\mathbf{X}'$ is observed, and if each time one observes $\mathbf{X}'$ one computes $\underline{\theta}_1(\mathbf{X})$ and $\bar{\theta}_1(\mathbf{X})$ and states that the value of θ_1 at that time is included between the two values of these two functions, then about $100\beta\%$ of these assertions are correct.*

In the example given at the beginning of this section, $\underline{\mu}$ and $\bar{\mu}$ are easily verified to satisfy the conditions given in the definition, and hence we may call $\underline{\mu}, \bar{\mu}$ a 95% confidence interval of μ.

EXERCISES

1. Prove: If X_n is one observable random variable whose distribution is binomial, $B(n, p)$, and if p is rational, then there is a value of n such that $P[X_n/n = p] > 0$, but if p is irrational, then $P[X_n/n = p] = 0$ for all n.

2. Verify that the functions $\underline{\mu}, \bar{\mu}$ defined in the example discussed at the beginning of this section satisfy the definition of a 95% confidence interval.

3. Let $X_1, \cdots, X_n$ be as in problem 2 in Section 12.2. Let $\underline{\sigma}^2(\mathbf{X}) = s_n^2/K_U$ and $\bar{\sigma}^2(\mathbf{X}) = s_n^2/K_L$, where n, K_U, and K_L are as in part (e) of that problem. Prove that $\underline{\sigma}^2, \bar{\sigma}^2$ is a 95% confidence interval of σ^2.

4. In many practical situations, requirement (b) in the definition of a $100\beta\%$ confidence interval is relaxed in that approximate equality is allowed. We shall call the resulting pair of functions an *approximate* $100\beta\%$ *confidence interval*. Now suppose that $X_1, \cdots, X_n$ are n independent observations on a random variable X which has a Poisson distribution with expectation $\lambda > 0$. It is assumed that λ is unknown and that n is fairly large, and the problem is to find an approximate 98% confidence interval of λ. This is accomplished as follows.

(a) Use the central limit theorem to find a value of K so that the following equality is approximately true:

$$P\left(\left[-K \leqq \left(\sum_{i=1}^{n} X_i - n\lambda\right) \Big/ \sqrt{n\lambda} \leqq K\right] \Big| \lambda\right) = 0.98.$$

(b) Prove that the pair of functions $\underline{\lambda}, \bar{\lambda}$ is an approximate 98% confidence interval of λ, where

$$\underline{\lambda}(\mathbf{X}) = \bar{X}_n + K^2/2n - \sqrt{\bar{X}_n K^2/n + K^4/4n^2},$$
$$\bar{\lambda}(\mathbf{X}) = \bar{X}_n + K^2/2n + \sqrt{\bar{X}_n K^2/n + K^4/4n^2},$$

and where K is as determined in part (a).

5. Let X be one observable random variable whose distribution is binomial $B(n, p)$, where n is known and p is unknown. Use the Laplace-DeMoivre theorem to find an approximate 96% confidence interval for p. (*Hint:* See problem 1 in Section 12.2.)

6. Verify and make more precise the operational interpretation given in this section of requirement (b) in the definition of a $100\beta\%$ confidence interval by using Bernoulli's theorem.

13.2 The Relation between Confidence Intervals and Tests of Hypotheses

In the last section we gave a definition of confidence interval and an operational interpretation of this definition. In this section we display the connection between the problem of finding a confidence interval for θ_1 and the problem of testing the hypothesis $\mathrm{H}:\theta_1 = \theta_1^0$ against the alternative $\mathrm{H}':\theta_1 \neq \theta_1^0$ for all $\theta_1^0 \in \Theta_1$. More precisely, we shall show that if a $100\beta\%$ confidence interval exists for θ_1, then for each $\theta_1^0 \in \Theta_1$ there exists a critical region $W(\theta_1^0)$ for testing the hypothesis $\mathrm{H}:\theta_1 = \theta_1^0$ against the alternative $\mathrm{H}':\theta_1 \neq \theta_1^0$ with level of significance $1 - \beta$, i.e.,

$$P([\mathbf{X} \in W(\theta_1^0)]|\theta_1^0, \theta_2, \cdots, \theta_k) = 1 - \beta$$

identically in $\theta_1^0, \theta_2, \cdots, \theta_k$.

First let us ask ourselves: if we are able to find a $100\beta\%$ confidence interval for θ_1, what additional properties would we like to see satisfied (i.e., in addition to the ones given in the definition in Section 13.1)? For one thing, we should desire that the probability of the $100\beta\%$ confidence interval covering an incorrect value of θ_1 be small, i.e., if θ_1' is the true value of θ_1, and if $\theta_1'' \neq \theta_1'$, we should want

$$P([\underline{\theta}_1(\mathbf{X}) \leqq \theta_1'' \leqq \bar{\theta}_1(\mathbf{X})]|\theta_1', \theta_2, \cdots, \theta_k)$$

to be small. This first additional property is not an accurately stated property; however, it will have to remain that way.

We might hope for a second additional property. For this we formulate what we mean by a uniformly best $100\beta\%$ confidence interval. Suppose we not only succeed in finding one confidence interval $\underline{\theta}_1$, $\bar{\theta}_1$, but also others. We shall say that $\underline{\theta}_1$, $\bar{\theta}_1$ is a uniformly best $100\beta\%$ confidence interval if for every $\theta_1^0 \in \Theta_1$ and $\theta_1' \in \Theta_1$ and every $100\beta\%$ confidence interval $\underline{\varphi}_1$, $\bar{\varphi}_1$ of θ_1 we have

$$P([\underline{\theta}_1(\mathbf{X}) \leqq \theta_1^0 \leqq \bar{\theta}_1(\mathbf{X})]|\theta_1', \theta_2, \cdots, \theta_k) \leqq P([\underline{\varphi}_1(\mathbf{X}) \leqq \theta_1^0 \leqq \bar{\varphi}_1(\mathbf{X})]|\theta_1', \theta_2, \cdots, \theta_k)$$

identically in $\theta_1^0, \theta_1', \theta_2, \cdots, \theta_k$. However desirable these two additional properties appear, our first problem is always to find a pair of functions which satisfies the definition given in Section 13.1.

Let us suppose that a confidence interval $\underline{\theta}_1$, $\bar{\theta}_1$ does exist which satisfies the definition given in Section 13.1. Then for every $\theta_1 \in \Theta_1$ we define a subset $A(\theta_1)$ of $\mathbf{X}(\Omega)$ as follows:

$$A(\theta_1) = \{\mathbf{x} \in \mathbf{X}(\Omega)|\underline{\theta}_1(\mathbf{x}') \leqq \theta_1 \leqq \bar{\theta}_1(\mathbf{x}')\}.$$

The set $A(\theta_1) \subset \mathbf{X}(\Omega)$ is called the *acceptance region* for θ_1. The best explanation for giving this name to $A(\theta_1)$ is the following lemma.

1. Lemma. *For every* $\theta_1 \in \Theta_1$,

$$[\mathbf{X} \in A(\theta_1)] = [\underline{\theta}_1(\mathbf{X}) \leqq \theta_1 \leqq \bar{\theta}_1(\mathbf{X})] \in \mathcal{A}.$$

Proof. If $\omega \in [\mathbf{X} \in A(\theta_1)]$, then $\mathbf{X}(\omega) \in A(\theta_1)$. By the definition of $A(\theta_1)$, this implies that $\underline{\theta}_1(\mathbf{X}(\omega)) \leqq \theta_1 \leqq \bar{\theta}_1(\mathbf{X}(\omega))$. Hence $\omega \in [\underline{\theta}_1(\mathbf{X}) \leqq \theta_1 \leqq \bar{\theta}_1(\mathbf{X})]$. If we reverse the order of the steps of the argument just given we accomplish a proof of inclusion in the other direction, thus establishing the lemma.

Because of Lemma 1, requirement (b) in the definition of confidence interval can be recast in terms of the family of acceptance regions $\{A(\theta_1), \theta_1 \in \Theta_1\}$ as follows:

(b′) *For every* $\theta_1 \in \Theta_1$, $[\mathbf{X} \in A(\theta_1)] \in \mathcal{A}$ *and* $P([\mathbf{X} \in A(\theta_1)]|\theta_1, \cdots, \theta_k) = \beta$ *for all* $(\theta_1, \cdots, \theta_k) \in \Theta$.

We denote the complement of $A(\theta_1)$ in $\mathbf{X}(\Omega)$ by $\mathbf{X}(\Omega) \setminus A(\theta_1)$, i.e., we define

$$\mathbf{X}(\Omega)\setminus A(\theta_1) = \{\mathbf{x} \in \mathbf{X}(\Omega)|\mathbf{x} \notin A(\theta_1)\}.$$

Thus, requirement (b′) can be rewritten as:

(b″) *For every* $\theta_1^0 \in \Theta_1$, $[\mathbf{X} \in \mathbf{X}(\Omega) \setminus A(\theta_1^0)] \in \mathcal{A}$ *and*

$$P([\mathbf{X} \in \mathbf{X}(\Omega) \setminus A(\theta_1^0)]|\theta_1^0, \theta_2, \cdots, \theta_k) = 1 - \beta$$

for every $(\theta_1^0, \theta_2, \cdots, \theta_k) \in \Theta$.

In requirement (b″) the probability $1 - \beta$ is quite small, somewhat on the order of a level of significance in hypothesis testing. Now it so happens that, upon close inspection of (b″), $\mathbf{X}(\Omega) \setminus A(\theta_1)$ is nothing other than a critical region for testing the hypothesis $\mathrm{H}: \theta_1 = \theta_1^0$ against the alternative $\mathrm{H}': \theta_1 \neq \theta_1^0$ with level of significance $1 - \beta$. The first additional property we wanted for confidence intervals, restated in terms of the acceptance regions $A(\theta_1)$, simply states that we want the probability

$$P([\mathbf{X} \in A(\theta_1^0)]|\theta_1', \theta_2, \cdots, \theta_k)$$

to be small when $\theta_1' \neq \theta_1^0$. This can then be restated to say that

$$P([\mathbf{X} \in \mathbf{X}(\Omega) \setminus A(\theta_1^0)]|\theta_1', \theta_2, \cdots, \theta_k)$$

be large for $\theta_1' \neq \theta_1^0$, which says that if $\theta_1 = \theta_1'$, then we want to reject the hypothesis that $\theta_1 = \theta_1^0$ with high probability. In other words, we want a powerful test. We add parenthetically that in case $k = 1$, $X(\Omega) \setminus A(\theta_1^0)$ is a critical region for testing a simple hypothesis against a composite alternative; if $k > 1$, then it is a critical region for testing a composite hypothesis against a composite alternative. Thus we have proved:

2. Theorem. *If a* $100\beta\%$ *confidence interval exists for* θ_1, *then for every* $\theta_1^0 \in \Theta_1$ *there exists a critical region for testing the hypothesis* $\mathrm{H}: \theta_1 = \theta_1^0$ *against* $\mathrm{H}': \theta_1 \neq \theta_1^0$ *with level of significance* $1 - \beta$.

Now this is *not* to say that if a $100\beta\%$ confidence interval $\underline{\theta}_1$, $\bar{\theta}_1$ of θ_1 exists, and if we can find a critical region $W(\theta_1^0)$ for testing the hypothesis $\text{H}:\theta_1 = \theta_1^0$ against the alternative $\text{H}':\theta_1 \neq \theta_1^0$ with level of significance $1 - \beta$ for every $\theta_1^0 \in \Theta_1$, then the family of complements of the critical regions is the family of acceptance regions for some $100\beta\%$ confidence interval. What it does mean is this: if one is looking for a $100\beta\%$ confidence interval, one searches through the tests for θ_1 to see which of these will be such that the complements of the critical regions are acceptance regions. In order that this family of complements of critical regions be a family of acceptance regions it must satisfy certain conditions which are given in the next section. Also, the general procedure for finding the confidence interval, once one knows that one has a family of acceptance regions, is given in the next section. However, it sometimes happens that once one finds what he hopes is the family of acceptance regions, the confidence interval falls into his lap.

In order to illustrate this last remark, let us consider one of the most important confidence intervals in mathematical statistics. Let $X_1, \cdots, X_n$ be n independent observations on a random variable X whose distribution is $N(\mu, \sigma^2)$. The constants μ, σ^2, where $-\infty < \mu < \infty$, $\sigma^2 > 0$, are both unknown, and it is desired to find a $100\beta\%$ confidence interval for μ. Accordingly, we look for a test of the composite hypothesis $\text{H}:\mu = \mu_0$ against the alternative $\text{H}':\mu \neq \mu_0$ with level of significance $1 - \beta$ for every $\mu_0 \in (-\infty, +\infty)$. We found such a test in Section 12.3, the critical region being

$$\left\{\mathbf{x} \,\middle|\, \left|\frac{\sqrt{n}(\bar{x}_n - \mu_0)}{s_n}\right| \geqq K\right\},$$

where $\bar{x}_n = (x_1 + \cdots + x_n)/n$. The constant K is selected now in order to satisfy

$$P[T_n \leqq K] = 1 - \frac{1-\beta}{2} = \frac{1+\beta}{2},$$

where T_n has a t-distribution with $n - 1$ degrees of freedom. The complement of the above critical region is

$$C(\mu_0) = \left\{\mathbf{x} \,\middle|\, \left|\frac{\sqrt{n}(\bar{x}_n - \mu_0)}{s_n}\right| \leqq K\right\}.$$

Thus

$$\begin{aligned}[\mathbf{X} \in C(\mu)] &= [-K \leqq \sqrt{n}(\bar{X}_n - \mu)/s_n \leqq K] \\ &= [\bar{X}_n - Ks_n/\sqrt{n} \leqq \mu \leqq \bar{X}_n + Ks_n/\sqrt{n}],\end{aligned}$$

and

$$P([\mathbf{X} \in C(\mu)] | \mu, \sigma^2) = \beta$$

for all values of μ and σ^2. If we define $\underline{\mu}$, $\bar{\mu}$ by

$$\underline{\mu}(\mathbf{X}) = \overline{X}_n - Ks_n/\sqrt{n}, \qquad \bar{\mu}(\mathbf{X}) = \overline{X}_n + Ks_n/\sqrt{n},$$

then it is easy to verify that they satisfy the definition of a $100\beta\%$ confidence interval.

Let us now investigate what the second additional property discussed earlier in this section becomes when discussed in terms of acceptance regions and tests of hypotheses. We shall only consider the case when $k = 1$. Let us suppose that $\underline{\theta}_1$, $\bar{\theta}_1$ is a uniformly best $100\beta\%$ confidence interval of θ_1, and let $\underline{\varphi}_1$, $\bar{\varphi}_1$ be any other $100\beta\%$ confidence interval of θ_1. Let $\{A(\theta_1), \theta_1 \in \Theta_1\}$ denote the family of acceptance regions determined by $\underline{\theta}_1$, $\bar{\theta}_1$, and let $\{B(\theta_1), \theta_1 \in \Theta_1\}$ be the family of acceptance regions determined by $\underline{\varphi}_1$, $\bar{\varphi}_1$. Then the condition that $\underline{\theta}_1$, $\bar{\theta}_1$ be uniformly best is that

$$P([\mathbf{X} \in A(\theta_1^0)]|\theta_1') \leqq P([\mathbf{X} \in B(\theta_1^0)]|\theta_1')$$

for each θ_1^0 and every θ_1'. In terms of the complements of acceptance regions, i.e., critical regions, this condition becomes

$$P([\mathbf{X} \in \mathbf{X}(\Omega) \setminus A(\theta_1^0)]|\theta_1') \geqq P([\mathbf{X} \in \mathbf{X}(\Omega) \setminus B(\theta_1^0)]|\theta_1')$$

for each θ_1^0 and every θ_1'. Now suppose that $X(\Omega) \setminus A(\theta_1^0)$ is a U.M.P.C.R. for testing the hypothesis $\mathrm{H}:\theta_1 = \theta_1^0$ against $\mathrm{H}':\theta_1 \neq \theta_1^0$ with level of significance $1 - \beta$. Thus we have proved:

3. Theorem. *If the family of complements of the acceptance regions of a* $100\beta\%$ *confidence interval* $\underline{\theta}_1$, $\bar{\theta}_1$ *of* θ_1 *are U.M.P.C.R.'s then the pair* $\underline{\theta}_1$, $\bar{\theta}_1$ *is a uniformly best* $100\beta\%$ *confidence interval.*

As an example of a uniformly best confidence interval, let us consider n independent observations $X_1, \cdots, X_n$ on a random variable X with a discrete distribution, whose density is

$$f_X(x|N) = 1/N, \qquad x = 1, 2, \cdots, N,$$

where N is an unknown positive integer. The problem is to find a $100\beta\%$ confidence interval $\underline{N}$, $\overline{N}$ of N. Accordingly, we look for a test of hypothesis $\mathrm{H}:N = N_0$ against the alternative $\mathrm{H}':N \neq N_0$ with level of significance $1 - \beta$. In this case the range $\mathbf{X}(\Omega)$ is the set of all points $\mathbf{x}' = (x_1, \cdots, x_n)$ where each x_i is a positive integer, regardless of the value of N. In Section 12.1 we found that there exists a U.M.P.C.R. for this test, namely,

$$\mathbf{X}(\Omega) \setminus A(N_0) = \{\mathbf{x}| \max_{1 \leqq i \leqq n} \{x_i\} \leqq N_0(1 - \beta)^{1/n}\} \cup \{\mathbf{x}| \max_{1 \leqq i \leqq n} \{x_i\} > N_0\}.$$

Hence, by the DeMorgan formula,

$$\begin{aligned} A(N) &= \{\mathbf{x}|N(1 - \beta)^{1/n} < \max_{1 \leqq i \leqq n}\{x_i\} \leqq N\} \\ &= \{\mathbf{x}| \max_{1 \leqq i \leqq n} \{x_i\} \leqq N < (\max_{1 \leqq i \leqq n} \{x_i\})/(1 - \beta)^{1/n}\}. \end{aligned}$$

We define $\underline{N}$, $\overline{N}$ over $\mathbf{X}(\Omega)$ by

$$\underline{N}(\mathbf{x}) = \max_{1 \leqq i \leqq n} \{x_i\},$$

$$\overline{N}(\mathbf{x}) = \max_{1 \leqq i \leqq n} \{x_i\}/(1 - \beta)^{1/n} - 1.$$

One can easily verify that $\underline{N}$, $\overline{N}$ is a $100\beta\%$ confidence interval. Thus we have, by Theorem 3, that $\underline{N}$, $\overline{N}$ is a uniformly best $100\beta\%$ confidence interval of N.

EXERCISES

1. Let $X_1, \cdots, X_n$ be n independent observations on a random variable X which has an absolutely continuous distribution with a density

$$f_X(x|\theta) = \begin{cases} (1/\theta)e^{-x/\theta} & \text{if } x > 0 \\ 0 & \text{if } x \leqq 0, \end{cases}$$

where $\theta \in (0, \infty)$ is unknown. Find an approximate 95% confidence interval for θ.

2. Let $X_1, \cdots, X_n$ be n independent observations on X which has an absolutely continuous distribution with a density

$$f_X(x|\theta) = \begin{cases} (1/\theta)(1 - x)^{(1/\theta)-1} & \text{if } x \in (0, 1) \\ 0 & \text{if } x \leqq 0 \text{ or } x \geqq 1, \end{cases}$$

where θ is unknown and $\Theta = (0, 1)$. Find an approximate 95% confidence interval for θ.

3. In a sequence of Bernoulli trials where the probability of success is $1/\theta$, $\theta > 1$ being unknown, one continues to observe the sequence of outcomes until the nth success has occurred, and then he stops. Assume that n is large. For suitably chosen random variables on these observations find an approximate 98% confidence interval of θ. (*Hint:* consider the Pascal distribution.)

4. Let $X_1, \cdots, X_n$ be n independent observations on X, which has an absolutely continuous distribution with density

$$f_X(x|\theta) = \begin{cases} 1/\theta & \text{if } 0 < x < \theta \\ 0 & \text{if } x \leqq 0 \text{ or } x \geqq \theta, \end{cases}$$

where $\theta > 0$ is unknown. Show that for any $\beta \in (0, 1)$ there exists a uniformly best $100\beta\%$ confidence interval for θ, and find it.

5. Let $X_1, \cdots, X_n$ be n independent observations on a random variable X which has a negative exponential distribution with density

$$f_X(x/\theta) = \begin{cases} e^{-(x-\theta)} & \text{if } x > \theta \\ 0 & \text{if } x \leqq \theta, \end{cases}$$

where $\theta \in (-\infty, \infty)$ is unknown. Prove that for any $\beta \in (0, 1)$ there exists a uniformly best $100\beta\%$ confidence interval for θ.

13.3 Necessary and Sufficient Conditions for the Existence of Confidence Intervals

In the previous section it was shown that if a confidence interval exists for the value of some parameter, then the problem of finding it becomes one of finding a test of hypothesis. However, if a confidence interval does exist, it does not necessarily follow that a test of hypothesis for that parameter yields this particular confidence interval or any other confidence interval. The family of complements of critical regions obtained from testing all possible values of the parameter must satisfy certain conditions and from these conditions we are able to obtain the confidence interval directly. In this section we obtain necessary and sufficient conditions that a family of subsets $\{A(\theta_1), \theta_1 \in \Theta_1\}$ of $E^{(n)}$ be a family of acceptance regions for some confidence interval $\underline{\theta}_1, \bar{\theta}_1$.

We shall assume $\mathbf{X}' = (X_1, \cdots, X_n)$ to satisfy the same general conditions in this section as in the previous two sections.

1. Theorem. *If $\underline{\theta}_1, \bar{\theta}_1$, is a $100\beta\%$ confidence interval of θ_1 with acceptance regions $\{A(\theta_1), \theta_1 \in \Theta_1\}$, then*

(i) for every $\theta_1 \in \Theta_1$, $[\mathbf{X} \in A(\theta_1)] \in \mathfrak{A}$, and

$$P([\mathbf{X} \in A(\theta_1)]|\theta_1, \cdots, \theta_k) = \beta$$

for all $(\theta_1, \cdots, \theta_k) \in \Theta$, and

(ii) for every $\mathbf{x} \in \mathbf{X}(\Omega)$, the set

$$S(\mathbf{x}) = \{\theta_1 | \mathbf{x} \in A(\theta_1)\}$$

is a nonempty, bounded, closed interval, and $S(\mathbf{x}) \subset \Theta_1$.

Proof. Part (i) is an immediate consequence of Lemma 1 in Section 13.2 and the definition of confidence interval (see (b′) in Section 13.2). In order to prove (ii) we first prove that $S(\mathbf{x})$ is nonempty. Let $\mathbf{x} \in \mathbf{X}(\Omega)$. Then by requirement (a) in the definition of confidence interval, $\underline{\theta}_1(\mathbf{x}) \leqq \bar{\theta}_1(\mathbf{x})$. Select as θ_1 any number in the closed interval $[\underline{\theta}_1(\mathbf{x}), \bar{\theta}_1(\mathbf{x})]$. By requirement (a) of the definition of confidence interval, $\theta_1 \in \Theta_1$. Since $\underline{\theta}_1(\mathbf{x}) \leqq \theta_1 \leqq \bar{\theta}_1(\mathbf{x})$, then by the definition of acceptance region, $\mathbf{x} \in A(\theta_1)$, and this proves that $S(\mathbf{x})$ is nonempty. However, by the very definition of $S(\mathbf{x})$ and of acceptance region,

$$S(\mathbf{x}) = \{\theta_1 | \underline{\theta}_1(\mathbf{x}) \leqq \theta_1 \leqq \bar{\theta}_1(\mathbf{x})\} = [\underline{\theta}_1(\mathbf{x}), \bar{\theta}_1(\mathbf{x})],$$

which proves the assertion of the theorem.

The two necessary conditions in the theorem just proved are also sufficient. This converse is proved in the next theorem.

2. Theorem. *Let* $\{A(\theta_1), \theta_1 \in \Theta_1\}$ *be a family of subsets of* $E^{(n)}$ *which satisfy conditions* (i) *and* (ii) *in Theorem* 1. *Then there exists a* $100\beta\%$ *confidence interval* $\underline{\theta}_1, \bar{\theta}_1$ *of* θ_1 *whose acceptance regions are this family of sets.*

Proof. Let us define two functions $\underline{\theta}_1, \bar{\theta}_1$ over $\mathbf{X}(\Omega)$ as follows: for every $\mathbf{x} \in \mathbf{X}(\Omega)$,

$$\underline{\theta}_1(\mathbf{x}) = \min S(\mathbf{x}),$$

and

$$\bar{\theta}_1(\mathbf{x}) = \max S(\mathbf{x}),$$

where $S(\mathbf{x})$ is as defined in Theorem 1. By condition (ii) of our hypothesis, $S(\mathbf{x})$ is a nonempty, closed interval, and thus $\underline{\theta}_1, \bar{\theta}_1$ are well defined above. Also, since

$$[\underline{\theta}_1(\mathbf{x}), \bar{\theta}_1(\mathbf{x})] = S(\mathbf{x}) \subset \Theta_1,$$

we have verified requirement (a) in the definition of confidence interval. In order to verify requirement (b) of the definition we need to prove that

$$\{\mathbf{x}|\mathbf{x} \in A(\theta_1)\} = \{\mathbf{x}|\underline{\theta}_1(\mathbf{x}) \leqq \theta_1 \leqq \bar{\theta}_1(\mathbf{x})\}.$$

Let $\mathbf{x}^0 \in \{\mathbf{x}|\underline{\theta}_1(\mathbf{x}) \leqq \theta_1 \leqq \bar{\theta}_1(\mathbf{x})\}$. Then $\underline{\theta}_1(\mathbf{x}^0) \leqq \theta_1 \leqq \bar{\theta}_1(\mathbf{x}^0)$. Since $S(\mathbf{x}^0)$ is a closed interval, this implies that $\mathbf{x}^0 \in A(\theta_1)$ or $\mathbf{x}^0 \in \{\mathbf{x}|\mathbf{x} \in A(\theta_1)\}$. On the other hand, if $\mathbf{x}^0 \in \{\mathbf{x}|\mathbf{x} \in A(\theta_1)\}$, i.e., $\mathbf{x}^0 \in A(\theta_1)$, then $\theta_1 \in S(\mathbf{x}^0)$. Then by the definition above of $\underline{\theta}_1, \bar{\theta}_1$ it follows that $\underline{\theta}_1(\mathbf{x}^0) \leqq \theta_1 \leqq \bar{\theta}_1(\mathbf{x}^0)$. Thus, $\mathbf{x}^0 \in \{\mathbf{x}|\underline{\theta}_1(\mathbf{x}) \leqq \theta_1 \leqq \bar{\theta}_1(\mathbf{x})\}$, and the theorem is proved.

Theorems 1 and 2 together give necessary and sufficient conditions for the existence of a $100\beta\%$ confidence interval of θ_1. We saw in Section 13.2 that if, for every $\theta_1^0 \in \Theta_1$, a critical region exists for testing the hypothesis $\mathrm{H}: \theta_1 = \theta_1^0$ against the alternative $\mathrm{H}': \theta_1 \neq \theta_1^0$ with level of significance $1 - \beta$, then the family of complements of the critical regions always satisfies requirement (i) in Theorem 1. Thus, after obtaining a test, we need only verify that condition (ii) holds. Actually in the examples of the preceding two sections we did verify condition (ii), because it just occurs that in seeking the pair of functions we simultaneously verified condition (ii).

We close this section with an example in which condition (i) in Theorems 1 and 2 is satisfied but where condition (ii) is not satisfied. Let X be a random variable with a $N(\mu, 1)$ distribution, where μ is unknown. Let $X_1, \cdots, X_n$ be n independent observations on X. For each value of μ, let $A(\mu)$ be defined by

$$A(\mu) = \{\mathbf{x}|\sqrt{n}(\bar{x}_n - \mu) \notin (2.5, 3.0)\}.$$

Since $\sqrt{n}(\bar{X}_n - \mu)$ has a $N(0, 1)$ distribution for every value of μ, then

$$\begin{aligned} P([\mathbf{X} \in A(\mu)]|\mu) &= P([\sqrt{n}(\bar{X}_n - \mu) \notin (2.5, 3.0)]|\mu) \\ &= P([\sqrt{n}(\bar{X}_n - \mu) \leqq 2.5]|\mu) + P([\sqrt{n}(\bar{X}_n - \mu) \geqq 3.0]|\mu). \end{aligned}$$

Using Table I at the end of this book we obtain

$$P([\mathbf{X} \in A(\mu)]|\mu) = .9938 + .0013 = .9951$$

for all values of μ. However, the family of sets $\{A(\mu), \{A(\mu), -\infty < \mu < \infty\}$ does not form a family of acceptance regions for a 99.51% confidence interval for the unknown parameter μ, since, for every $\mathbf{x} \in E^{(n)}$,

$$S(\mathbf{x}) = \{\mu|\mathbf{x} \in A(\mu)\} = (-\infty, \bar{x}_n - 3.0/\sqrt{n}] \cup [\bar{x}_n - 2.5/\sqrt{n}, \infty),$$

which is the union of two disjoint closed intervals, and thus condition (ii) of Theorems 1 and 2 is violated.

EXERCISE

1. In the last example given in this section, verify the assertion that

$$S(\mathbf{x}) = (-\infty, \bar{x}_n - 3.0/\sqrt{n}] \cup [\bar{x}_n - 2.5/\sqrt{n}, \infty).$$

Suggested Reading

The following two books are strongly recommended to the student during the time he is studying out of this book:

[1] J. Neyman, "First Course in Probability and Statistics," Henry Holt, New York, 1950.

[2] J. Neyman, "Lectures and Conferences on Mathematical Statistics and Probability," The Graduate School, U. S. Department of Agriculture, Washington, D. C., 1952.

Two good introductions to probability theory are:

[3] William Feller, "An Introduction to Probability Theory and Its Applications," Vol. I, 2 ed., Wiley, New York, 1957.

[4] Emanuel Parzen, "Modern Probability Theory and Its Applications," Wiley, New York, 1960.

The following two books are designed for advanced undergraduates and beginning graduate students. In these two books there is less emphasis on probability theory and more emphasis on statistical inference than in this book. Also, a wider range of topics is covered.

[5] H. D. Brunk, "An Introduction to Mathematical Statistics," Ginn, Boston, 1960.

[6] Robert V. Hogg and Allen T. Craig, "Introduction to Mathematical Statistics," Macmillan, New York, 1960.

An excellent book for advanced study in probability theory is:

[7] M. Loève, "Probability Theory," 2nd ed., Van Nostrand, Princeton, New Jersey, 1960.

An excellent book for advanced study in statistical inference is:

[8] E. L. Lehmann, "Testing Statistical Hypotheses," Wiley, New York, 1959.

TABLE I

Normal Distribution

$$F(x) = \int_{-\infty}^{x} \frac{1}{\sqrt{2\pi}} \exp -\frac{t^2}{2} \, dt$$

x	.00	.01	.02	.03	.04	.05	.06	.07	.08	.09
.0	.5000	.5040	.5080	.5120	.5160	.5199	.5239	.5279	.5319	.5359
.1	.5398	.5438	.5478	.5517	.5557	.5596	.5636	.5675	.5714	.5753
.2	.5793	.5832	.5871	.5910	.5948	.5987	.6026	.6064	.6103	.6141
.3	.6179	.6217	.6255	.6293	.6331	.6368	.6406	.6443	.6480	.6517
.4	.6554	.6591	.6628	.6664	.6700	.6736	.6772	.6808	.6844	.6879
.5	.6915	.6950	.6985	.7019	.7054	.7088	.7123	.7157	.7190	.7224
.6	.7257	.7291	.7324	.7357	.7389	.7422	.7454	.7486	.7517	.7549
.7	.7580	.7611	.7642	.7673	.7704	.7734	.7764	.7794	.7823	.7852
.8	.7881	.7910	.7939	.7967	.7995	.8023	.8051	.8078	.8106	.8133
.9	.8159	.8186	.8212	.8238	.8264	.8289	.8315	.8340	.8365	.8389
1.0	.8413	.8438	.8461	.8485	.8508	.8531	.8554	.8577	.8599	.8621
1.1	.8643	.8665	.8686	.8708	.8729	.8749	.8770	.8790	.8810	.8830
1.2	.8849	.8869	.8888	.8907	.8925	.8944	.8962	.8980	.8997	.9015
1.3	.9032	.9049	.9066	.9082	.9099	.9115	.9131	.9147	.9162	.9177
1.4	.9192	.9207	.9222	.9236	.9251	.9265	.9279	.9292	.9306	.9319
1.5	.9332	.9345	.9357	.9370	.9382	.9394	.9406	.9418	.9429	.9441
1.6	.9452	.9463	.9474	.9484	.9495	.9505	.9515	.9525	.9535	.9545
1.7	.9554	.9564	.9573	.9582	.9591	.9599	.9608	.9616	.9625	.9633
1.8	.9641	.9649	.9656	.9664	.9671	.9678	.9686	.9693	.9699	.9706
1.9	.9713	.9719	.9726	.9732	.9738	.9744	.9750	.9756	.9761	.9767
2.0	.9772	.9778	.9783	.9788	.9793	.9798	.9803	.9808	.9812	.9817
2.1	.9821	.9826	.9830	.9834	.9838	.9842	.9846	.9850	.9854	.9857
2.2	.9861	.9864	.9868	.9871	.9875	.9878	.9881	.9884	.9887	.9890
2.3	.9893	.9896	.9898	.9901	.9904	.9906	.9909	.9911	.9913	.9916
2.4	.9918	.9920	.9922	.9925	.9927	.9929	.9931	.9932	.9934	.9936
2.5	.9938	.9940	.9941	.9943	.9945	.9946	.9948	.9949	.9951	.9952
2.6	.9953	.9955	.9956	.9957	.9959	.9960	.9961	.9962	.9963	.9964
2.7	.9965	.9966	.9967	.9968	.9969	.9970	.9971	.9972	.9973	.9974
2.8	.9974	.9975	.9976	.9977	.9977	.9978	.9979	.9979	.9980	.9981
2.9	.9981	.9982	.9982	.9983	.9984	.9984	.9985	.9985	.9986	.9986
3.0	.9987	.9987	.9987	.9988	.9988	.9989	.9989	.9989	.9990	.9990
3.1	.9990	.9991	.9991	.9991	.9992	.9992	.9992	.9992	.9993	.9993
3.2	.9993	.9993	.9994	.9994	.9994	.9994	.9994	.9995	.9995	.9995
3.3	.9995	.9995	.9995	.9996	.9996	.9996	.9996	.9996	.9996	.9997
3.4	.9997	.9997	.9997	.9997	.9997	.9997	.9997	.9997	.9997	.9998

x	1.282	1.645	1.960	2.326	2.576	3.090	3.291	3.891	4.417
$F(x)$	.90	.95	.975	.99	.995	.999	.9995	.99995	.999995
$2[1 - F(x)]$	.20	.10	.05	.02	.01	.002	.001	.0001	.00001

TABLE II

Chi-Square Distribution

$$F(u) = \int_0^u \frac{x^{(n-2)/2} e^{-x/2}\, dx}{2^{n/2}\,\Gamma(n/2)}$$

n \ F	.005	.010	.025	.050	.100	.250	.500	.750	.900	.950	.975	.990	.995
1	$.0^4393$	$.0^3157$	$.0^3982$	$.0^2393$	.0158	.102	.455	1.32	2.71	3.84	5.02	6.63	7.88
2	.0100	.0201	.0506	.103	.211	.575	1.39	2.77	4.61	5.99	7.38	9.21	10.6
3	.0717	.115	.216	.352	.584	1.21	2.37	4.11	6.25	7.81	9.35	11.3	12.8
4	.207	.297	.484	.711	1.06	1.92	3.36	5.39	7.78	9.49	11.1	13.3	14.9
5	.412	.554	.831	1.15	1.61	2.67	4.35	6.63	9.24	11.1	12.8	15.1	16.7
6	.676	.872	1.24	1.64	2.20	3.45	5.35	7.84	10.6	12.6	14.4	16.8	18.5
7	.989	1.24	1.69	2.17	2.83	4.25	6.35	9.04	12.0	14.1	16.0	18.5	20.3
8	1.34	1.65	2.18	2.73	3.49	5.07	7.34	10.2	13.4	15.5	17.5	20.1	22.0
9	1.73	2.09	2.70	3.33	4.17	5.90	8.34	11.4	14.7	16.9	19.0	21.7	23.6
10	2.16	2.56	3.25	3.94	4.87	6.74	9.34	12.5	16.0	18.3	20.5	23.2	25.2
11	2.60	3.05	3.82	4.57	5.58	7.58	10.3	13.7	17.3	19.7	21.9	24.7	26.8
12	3.07	3.57	4.40	5.23	6.30	8.44	11.3	14.8	18.5	21.0	23.3	26.2	28.3
13	3.57	4.11	5.01	5.89	7.04	9.30	12.3	16.0	19.8	22.4	24.7	27.7	29.8
14	4.07	4.66	5.63	6.57	7.79	10.2	13.3	17.1	21.1	23.7	26.1	29.1	31.3
15	4.60	5.23	6.26	7.26	8.55	11.0	14.3	18.2	22.3	25.0	27.5	30.6	32.8
16	5.14	5.81	6.91	7.96	9.31	11.9	15.3	19.4	23.5	26.3	28.8	32.0	34.3
17	5.70	6.41	7.56	8.67	10.1	12.8	16.3	20.5	24.8	27.6	30.2	33.4	35.7
18	6.26	7.01	8.23	9.39	10.9	13.7	17.3	21.6	26.0	28.9	31.5	34.8	37.2
19	6.84	7.63	8.91	10.1	11.7	14.6	18.3	22.7	27.2	30.1	32.9	36.2	38.6
20	7.43	8.26	9.59	10.9	12.4	15.5	19.3	23.8	28.4	31.4	34.2	37.6	40.0
21	8.03	8.90	10.3	11.6	13.2	16.3	20.3	24.9	29.6	32.7	35.5	38.9	41.4
22	8.64	9.54	11.0	12.3	14.0	17.2	21.3	26.0	30.8	33.9	36.8	40.3	42.8
23	9.26	10.2	11.7	13.1	14.8	18.1	22.3	27.1	32.0	35.2	38.1	41.6	44.2
24	9.89	10.9	12.4	13.8	15.7	19.0	23.3	28.2	33.2	36.4	39.4	43.0	45.6
25	10.5	11.5	13.1	14.6	16.5	19.9	24.3	29.3	34.4	37.7	40.6	44.3	46.9
26	11.2	12.2	13.8	15.4	17.3	20.8	25.3	30.4	35.6	38.9	41.9	45.6	48.3
27	11.8	12.9	14.6	16.2	18.1	21.7	26.3	31.5	36.7	40.1	43.2	47.0	49.6
28	12.5	13.6	15.3	16.9	18.9	22.7	27.3	32.6	37.9	41.3	44.5	48.3	51.0
29	13.1	14.3	16.0	17.7	19.8	23.6	28.3	33.7	39.1	42.6	45.7	49.6	52.3
30	13.8	15.0	16.8	18.5	20.6	24.5	29.3	34.8	40.3	43.8	47.0	50.9	53.7

Reproduced by permission of the *Biometrika* Trustees from *Biometrika*, Vol. 32 (1941), and abridged by A. M. Mood in "Introduction to the Theory of Statistics," McGraw-Hill, New York, 1950.

TABLE III

F-Distribution

m degrees of freedom in numerator; *n* in denominator

$$G(F) = \int_0^F \frac{[(m+n-2)/2]!\,m^{m/2}n^{n/2}x^{(m-2)/2}(n+mx)^{-(m+n)/2}\,dx}{[(m-2)/2]!\,[(n-2)/2]!}$$

G	n \ m	1	2	3	4	5	6	7	8	9	10	12	15	20	30	60	120	∞
.90		39.9	49.5	53.6	55.8	57.2	58.2	58.9	59.4	59.9	60.2	60.7	61.2	61.7	62.3	62.8	63.1	63.3
.95		161	200	216	225	230	234	237	239	241	242	244	246	248	250	252	253	254
.975	1	648	800	864	900	922	937	948	957	963	969	977	985	993	1000	1010	1010	1020
.99		4050	5000	5400	5620	5760	5860	5930	5980	6020	6060	6110	6160	6210	6260	6310	6340	6370
.995		16,200	20,000	21,600	22,500	23,100	23,400	23,700	23,900	24,100	24,200	24,400	24,600	24,800	25,000	25,200	25,400	25,500
.90		8.53	9.00	9.16	9.24	9.29	9.33	9.35	9.37	9.38	9.39	9.41	9.42	9.44	9.46	9.47	9.48	9.49
.95		18.5	19.0	19.2	19.2	19.3	19.3	19.4	19.4	19.4	19.4	19.4	19.4	19.5	19.5	19.5	19.5	19.5
.975	2	38.5	39.0	39.2	39.2	39.3	39.3	39.4	39.4	39.4	39.4	39.4	39.4	39.4	39.5	39.5	39.5	39.5
.99		98.5	99.0	99.2	99.2	99.3	99.3	99.4	99.4	99.4	99.4	99.4	99.4	99.4	99.5	99.5	99.5	99.5
.995		199	199	199	199	199	199	199	199	199	199	199	199	199	199	199	199	199
.90		5.54	5.46	5.39	5.34	5.31	5.28	5.27	5.25	5.24	5.23	5.22	5.20	5.18	5.17	5.15	5.14	5.1
.95		10.1	9.55	9.28	9.12	9.01	8.94	8.89	8.85	8.81	8.79	8.74	8.70	8.66	8.62	8.57	8.55	8.53
.975	3	17.4	16.0	15.4	15.1	14.9	14.7	14.6	14.5	14.5	14.4	14.3	14.3	14.2	14.1	14.0	13.9	13.9
.99		34.1	30.8	29.5	28.7	28.2	27.9	27.7	27.5	27.3	27.2	27.1	26.9	26.7	26.5	26.3	26.2	26.1
.995		55.6	49.8	47.5	46.2	45.4	44.8	44.4	44.1	43.9	43.7	43.4	43.1	42.8	42.5	42.1	42.0	41.8
.90		4.54	4.32	4.19	4.11	4.05	4.01	3.98	3.95	3.93	3.92	3.90	3.87	3.84	3.82	3.79	3.78	3.76
.95		7.71	6.94	6.59	6.39	6.26	6.16	6.09	6.04	6.00	5.96	5.91	5.86	5.80	5.75	5.69	5.66	5.63
.975	4	12.2	10.6	9.98	9.60	9.36	9.20	9.07	8.98	8.90	8.84	8.75	8.66	8.56	8.46	8.36	8.31	8.26
.99		21.2	18.0	16.7	16.0	15.5	15.2	15.0	14.8	14.7	14.5	14.4	14.2	14.0	13.8	13.7	13.6	13.5
.995		31.3	26.3	24.3	23.2	22.5	22.0	21.6	21.4	21.1	21.0	20.7	20.4	20.2	19.9	19.6	19.5	19.3
.90		4.06	3.78	3.62	3.52	3.45	3.40	3.37	3.34	3.32	3.30	3.27	3.24	3.21	3.17	3.14	3.12	3.11
.95		6.61	5.79	5.41	5.19	5.05	4.95	4.88	4.82	4.77	4.74	4.68	4.62	4.56	4.50	4.43	4.40	4.37
.975	5	10.0	8.43	7.76	7.39	7.15	6.98	6.85	6.76	6.68	6.62	6.52	6.43	6.33	6.23	6.12	6.07	6.02
.99		16.3	13.3	12.1	11.4	11.0	10.7	10.5	10.3	10.2	10.1	9.89	9.72	9.55	9.38	9.20	9.11	9.02
.995		22.8	18.3	16.5	15.6	14.9	14.5	14.2	14.0	13.8	13.6	13.4	13.1	12.9	12.7	12.4	12.3	12.1
.90		3.78	3.46	3.29	3.18	3.11	3.05	3.01	2.98	2.96	2.94	2.90	2.87	2.84	2.80	2.76	2.74	2.72
.95		5.99	5.14	4.76	4.53	4.39	4.28	4.21	4.15	4.10	4.06	4.00	3.94	3.87	3.81	3.74	3.70	3.67
.975	6	8.81	7.26	6.60	6.23	5.99	5.82	5.70	5.60	5.52	5.46	5.37	5.27	5.17	5.07	4.96	4.90	4.85
.99		13.7	10.9	9.78	9.15	8.75	8.47	8.26	8.10	7.98	7.87	7.72	7.56	7.40	7.23	7.06	6.97	6.88
.995		18.6	14.5	12.9	12.0	11.5	11.1	10.8	10.6	10.4	10.2	10.0	9.81	9.59	9.36	9.12	9.00	8.88
.90		3.59	3.26	3.07	2.96	2.88	2.83	2.78	2.75	2.72	2.70	2.67	2.63	2.59	2.56	2.51	2.49	2.47
.95		5.59	4.74	4.35	4.12	3.97	3.87	3.79	3.73	3.68	3.64	3.57	3.51	3.44	3.38	3.30	3.27	3.23
.975	7	8.07	6.54	5.89	5.52	5.29	5.12	4.99	4.90	4.82	4.76	4.67	4.57	4.47	4.36	4.25	4.20	4.14
.99		12.2	9.55	8.45	7.85	7.46	7.19	6.99	6.84	6.72	6.62	6.47	6.31	6.16	5.99	5.82	5.74	5.65
.995		16.2	12.4	10.9	10.1	9.52	9.16	8.89	8.68	8.51	8.38	8.18	7.97	7.75	7.53	7.31	7.19	7.08
.90		3.46	3.11	2.92	2.81	2.73	2.67	2.62	2.59	2.56	2.54	2.50	2.46	2.42	2.38	2.34	2.31	2.29
.95		5.32	4.46	4.07	3.84	3.69	3.58	3.50	3.44	3.39	3.35	3.28	3.22	3.15	3.08	3.01	2.97	2.93
.975	8	7.57	6.06	5.42	5.05	4.82	4.65	4.53	4.43	4.36	4.30	4.20	4.10	4.00	3.89	3.78	3.73	3.67
.99		11.3	8.65	7.59	7.01	6.63	6.37	6.18	6.03	5.91	5.81	5.67	5.52	5.36	5.20	5.03	4.95	4.86
.995		14.7	11.0	9.60	8.81	8.30	7.95	7.69	7.50	7.34	7.21	7.01	6.81	6.61	6.40	6.18	6.06	5.95

.90		3.36	3.01	2.81	2.69	2.61	2.55	2.51	2.47	2.44	2.42	2.38	2.34	2.30	2.25	2.21	2.18	2.16
.95		5.12	4.26	3.86	3.63	3.48	3.37	3.29	3.23	3.18	3.14	3.07	3.01	2.94	2.86	2.79	2.75	2.71
.975	9	7.21	5.71	5.08	4.72	4.48	4.32	4.20	4.10	4.03	3.96	3.87	3.77	3.67	3.56	3.45	3.39	3.33
.99		10.6	8.02	6.99	6.42	6.06	5.80	5.61	5.47	5.35	5.26	5.11	4.96	4.81	4.65	4.48	4.40	4.31
.995		13.6	10.1	8.72	7.96	7.47	7.13	6.88	6.69	6.54	6.42	6.23	6.03	5.83	5.62	5.41	5.30	5.19
.90		3.29	2.92	2.73	2.61	2.52	2.46	2.41	2.38	2.35	2.32	2.28	2.24	2.20	2.15	2.11	2.08	2.06
.95		4.96	4.10	3.71	3.48	3.33	3.22	3.14	3.07	3.02	2.98	2.91	2.84	2.77	2.70	2.62	2.58	2.54
.975	10	6.94	5.46	4.83	4.47	4.24	4.07	3.95	3.85	3.78	3.72	3.62	3.52	3.42	3.31	3.20	3.14	3.08
.99		10.0	7.56	6.55	5.99	5.64	5.39	5.20	5.06	4.94	4.85	4.71	4.56	4.41	4.25	4.08	4.00	3.91
.995		12.8	9.43	8.08	7.34	6.87	6.54	6.30	6.12	5.97	5.85	5.66	5.47	5.27	5.07	4.86	4.75	4.64
.90		3.18	2.81	2.61	2.48	2.39	2.33	2.28	2.24	2.21	2.19	2.15	2.10	2.06	2.01	1.96	1.93	1.90
.95		4.75	3.89	3.49	3.26	3.11	3.00	2.91	2.85	2.80	2.75	2.69	2.62	2.54	2.47	2.38	2.34	2.30
.975	12	6.55	5.10	4.47	4.12	3.89	3.73	3.61	3.51	3.44	3.37	3.28	3.18	3.07	2.96	2.85	2.79	2.72
.99		9.33	6.93	5.95	5.41	5.06	4.82	4.64	4.50	4.39	4.30	4.16	4.01	3.86	3.70	3.54	3.45	3.36
.995		11.8	8.51	7.23	6.52	6.07	5.76	5.52	5.35	5.20	5.09	4.91	4.72	4.53	4.33	4.12	4.01	3.90
.90		3.07	2.70	2.49	2.36	2.27	2.21	2.16	2.12	2.09	2.06	2.02	1.97	1.92	1.87	1.82	1.79	1.76
.95		4.54	3.68	3.29	3.06	2.90	2.79	2.71	2.64	2.59	2.54	2.48	2.40	2.33	2.25	2.16	2.11	2.07
.975	15	6.20	4.77	4.15	3.80	3.58	3.41	3.29	3.20	3.12	3.06	2.96	2.86	2.76	2.64	2.52	2.46	2.40
.99		8.68	6.36	5.42	4.89	4.56	4.32	4.14	4.00	3.89	3.80	3.67	3.52	3.37	3.21	3.05	2.96	2.87
.995		10.8	7.70	6.48	5.80	5.37	5.07	4.85	4.67	4.54	4.42	4.25	4.07	3.88	3.69	3.48	3.37	3.26
.90		2.97	2.59	2.38	2.25	2.16	2.09	2.04	2.00	1.96	1.94	1.89	1.84	1.79	1.74	1.68	1.64	1.61
.95		4.35	3.49	3.10	2.87	2.71	2.60	2.51	2.45	2.39	2.35	2.28	2.20	2.12	2.04	1.95	1.90	1.84
.975	20	5.87	4.46	3.86	3.51	3.29	3.13	3.01	2.91	2.84	2.77	2.68	2.57	2.46	2.35	2.22	2.16	2.09
.99		8.10	5.85	4.94	4.43	4.10	3.87	3.70	3.56	3.46	3.37	3.23	3.09	2.94	2.78	2.61	2.52	2.42
.995		9.94	6.99	5.82	5.17	4.76	4.47	4.26	4.09	3.96	3.85	3.68	3.50	3.32	3.12	2.92	2.81	2.69
.90		2.88	2.49	2.28	2.14	2.05	1.98	1.93	1.88	1.85	1.82	1.77	1.72	1.67	1.61	1.54	1.50	1.46
.95		4.17	3.32	2.92	2.69	2.53	2.42	2.33	2.27	2.21	2.16	2.09	2.01	1.93	1.84	1.74	1.68	1.62
.975	30	5.57	4.18	3.59	3.25	3.03	2.87	2.75	2.65	2.57	2.51	2.41	2.31	2.20	2.07	1.94	1.87	1.79
.99		7.56	5.39	4.51	4.02	3.70	3.47	3.30	3.17	3.07	2.98	2.84	2.70	2.55	2.39	2.21	2.11	2.01
.995		9.18	6.35	5.24	4.62	4.23	3.95	3.74	3.58	3.45	3.34	3.18	3.01	2.82	2.63	2.42	2.30	2.18
.90		2.79	2.39	2.18	2.04	1.95	1.87	1.82	1.77	1.74	1.71	1.66	1.60	1.54	1.48	1.40	1.35	1.29
.95		4.00	3.15	2.76	2.53	2.37	2.25	2.17	2.10	2.04	1.99	1.92	1.84	1.75	1.65	1.53	1.47	1.39
.975	60	5.29	3.93	3.34	3.01	2.79	2.63	2.51	2.41	2.33	2.27	2.17	2.06	1.94	1.82	1.67	1.58	1.48
.99		7.08	4.98	4.13	3.65	3.34	3.12	2.95	2.82	2.72	2.63	2.50	2.35	2.20	2.03	1.84	1.73	1.60
.995		8.49	5.80	4.73	4.14	3.76	3.49	3.29	3.13	3.01	2.90	2.74	2.57	2.39	2.19	1.96	1.83	1.69
.90		2.75	2.35	2.13	1.99	1.90	1.82	1.77	1.72	1.68	1.65	1.60	1.54	1.48	1.41	1.32	1.26	1.19
.95		3.92	3.07	2.68	2.45	2.29	2.18	2.09	2.02	1.96	1.91	1.83	1.75	1.66	1.55	1.43	1.35	1.25
.975	120	5.15	3.80	3.23	2.89	2.67	2.52	2.39	2.30	2.22	2.16	2.05	1.94	1.82	1.69	1.53	1.43	1.31
.99		6.85	4.79	3.95	3.48	3.17	2.96	2.79	2.66	2.56	2.47	2.34	2.19	2.03	1.86	1.66	1.53	1.38
.995		8.18	5.54	4.50	3.92	3.55	3.28	3.09	2.93	2.81	2.71	2.54	2.37	2.19	1.98	1.75	1.61	1.43
.90		2.71	2.30	2.08	1.94	1.85	1.77	1.72	1.67	1.63	1.60	1.55	1.49	1.42	1.34	1.24	1.17	1.00
.95		3.84	3.00	2.60	2.37	2.21	2.10	2.01	1.94	1.88	1.83	1.75	1.67	1.57	1.46	1.32	1.22	1.00
.975	∞	5.02	3.69	3.12	2.79	2.57	2.41	2.29	2.19	2.11	2.05	1.94	1.83	1.71	1.57	1.39	1.27	1.00
.99		6.63	4.61	3.78	3.32	3.02	2.80	2.64	2.51	2.41	2.32	2.18	2.04	1.88	1.70	1.47	1.32	1.00
.995		7.88	5.30	4.28	3.72	3.35	3.09	2.90	2.74	2.62	2.52	2.36	2.19	2.00	1.79	1.53	1.36	1.00

Reproduced by permission of the *Biometrika* Trustees from *Biometrika*, Vol. 33 (1943), and abridged by A. M. Mood in "Introduction to the Theory of Statistics," McGraw-Hill, New York, 1950.

TABLE IV

"Student's" Distribution

$$F(t) = \int_{-\infty}^{t} \frac{((n-1)/2)!}{((n-2)/2)!\sqrt{\pi n}(1 + (x^2/n))^{(n+1)/2}} dx$$

n \ F	.75	.90	.95	.975	.99	.995	.9995
1	1.000	3.078	6.314	12.706	31.821	63.657	636.619
2	.816	1.886	2.920	4.303	6.965	9.925	31.598
3	.765	1.638	2.353	3.182	4.541	5.841	12.941
4	.741	1.533	2.132	2.776	3.747	4.604	8.610
5	.727	1.476	2.015	2.571	3.365	4.032	6.859
6	.718	1.440	1.943	2.447	3.143	3.707	5.959
7	.711	1.415	1.895	2.365	2.998	3.499	5.405
8	.706	1.397	1.860	2.306	2.896	3.355	5.041
9	.703	1.383	1.833	2.262	2.821	3.250	4.781
10	.700	1.372	1.812	2.228	2.764	3.169	4.587
11	.697	1.363	1.796	2.201	2.718	3.106	4.437
12	.695	1.356	1.782	2.179	2.681	3.055	4.318
13	.694	1.350	1.771	2.160	2.650	3.012	4.221
14	.692	1.345	1.761	2.145	2.624	2.977	4.140
15	.691	1.341	1.753	2.131	2.602	2.947	4.073
16	.690	1.337	1.746	2.120	2.583	2.921	4.015
17	.689	1.333	1.740	2.110	2.567	2.898	3.965
18	.688	1.330	1.734	2.101	2.552	2.878	3.922
19	.688	1.328	1.729	2.093	2.539	2.861	3.883
20	.687	1.325	1.725	2.086	2.528	2.845	3.850
21	.686	1.323	1.721	2.080	2.518	2.831	3.819
22	.686	1.321	1.717	2.074	2.508	2.819	3.792
23	.685	1.319	1.714	2.069	2.500	2.807	3.767
24	.685	1.318	1.711	2.064	2.492	2.797	3.745
25	.684	1.316	1.708	2.060	2.485	2.787	3.725
26	.684	1.315	1.706	2.056	2.479	2.779	3.707
27	.684	1.314	1.703	2.052	2.473	2.771	3.690
28	.683	1.313	1.701	2.048	2.467	2.763	3.674
29	.683	1.311	1.699	2.045	2.462	2.756	3.659
30	.683	1.310	1.697	2.042	2.457	2.750	3.646
40	.681	1.303	1.684	2.021	2.423	2.704	3.551
60	.679	1.296	1.671	2.000	2.390	2.660	3.460
120	.677	1.289	1.658	1.980	2.358	2.617	3.373
∞	.674	1.282	1.645	1.960	2.326	2.576	3.291

This table is abridged by A. M. Mood in "Introduction to the Theory of Statistics," McGraw-Hill, New York, 1950, from Table III of Fisher and Yates, "Statistical Tables for Biological, Agricultural, and Medical Research," Oliver and Boyd, Edinburgh, and used here by permission of the authors and publishers.

Index